TRUE COLOURS

HAIR COLOURING FOR THE CURIOUS AND THE CAUTIOUS

MILLY AHLQUIST
MARK CONSTANTINE

A Note on the Henna Ink

This book has been printed using a specially created henna ink.

Lush worked with printer Dayfold Ltd and ink manufacturer PMS to incorporate Henna into a four colour set of lithographic inks with the aim to print this book.

After many trials, the chemists at the ink manufacturer, with the help from Lush Buyer Pendle Hill, ground the henna down to the finest possible grade and created a high pigment four colour set made up of 20% henna. Dayfold adapted the chemistry on the printing press and after several attempts they finally achieved a printed result using the henna ink.

First published in Great Britain by Lush 2022

Printed in the UK by Dayfold Ltd,
27 Black Moor Road, Verwood, Dorset,
BH31 6BE , United Kingdom

A catalogue record for this book is available on request from the British Library.

PLU 212351

ISBN 978-1-7397576-9-4

Contents

Why your hairdresser should ask about your heritage, not your holiday…

1

Early one morning in the cold post-festive disappointment of January 2019, a text pings on my work phone. It's Lush co-founder and CEO Mark Constantine. "Looking for a friend to help re-write my *Herbal Hair Colouring* book," it reads. "Interested?"

My response is instant: "Yes, please!"

Mark's *Herbal Hair Colouring* is something of a holy grail amongst Lush staff. First published in 1978, he wrote the book as a young trichologist after he was commissioned by The Herb Society to inform people about the alternatives available to synthetic oxidative dyes. These were made with aromatic amines, materials originally derived from coal tar, which were having nasty effects in mice at the time. Vehemently against animal testing in cosmetics, Mark used the book to record all his knowledge about plants that have been used to colour the hair for thousands of years including his favourite, henna, and recipes that a health-conscious hair dyer could use at home. Work with him for any reasonable amount of time and he is sure to tout the benefits of henna over synthetic hair dyes to you.

"I first got into henna in my early twenties," he confides. "And it was partially because I was into herbs and partially because I have had a morbid fear of chemicals since I was a child. It started when I went to the cinema with my mum. In those days, they used to show three films at the cinema: an A film, which was the big attraction; a B film, which was low budget; and a newsreel. My mum and I watched a B film called *Devil's Bait*. It was about a rat-catcher who leaves some of his poison behind in a bakery, where it is accidentally baked into bread. It really frightened me. I couldn't believe that something as wholesome as bread could have rat poison in it.

"So, after that, I didn't trust chemicals. When my mum used to perm her hair, I'd hide at the other side of the house. That fear never left me. It was what fuelled my preference for herbal cosmetics and partly what fuelled my environmentalism too; I didn't like the thought of unnecessary chemicals infiltrating our bodies and water systems."

I'm not much of a hair dyer myself but it's easy to see that the hair colourant industry today is big business, despite the scare in the 1970s. In 2019, the global hair colour market was valued at about $30.3 billion, and that's predicted to increase to $42 billion by 2025.[1] In the UK alone, 36% of adults used at least one type of at-home hair colourant in 2019, and that's not counting those who go to the salon.[2] Such is the value we place on the colour of the stuff growing out of our heads.

If the Covid-19 pandemic has taught me anything, it's that we are more attached to our hair today than ever. Deprived of professional help during local lockdowns, salons have since been inundated with customers to correct the dodgy dye jobs and wonky fringes that didn't *quite* come out like Daisy Edgar-Jones' of *Normal People* fame. You can take away our Christmas but taking away our hairdressers is another matter.

Hair is not only important to our identity as individuals, but our identity as humans. Millions of years ago when our ancestors were little more than primates, body hair protected our skin from scorching temperatures. When we swapped four legs for two, it dwindled to improve our sweating ability as we chased down prey over the savannah. Over tens of thousands of years since, our unique head hair developed to protect our brains from the sun and our necks from the cold. It's helped us to adapt to different climates, taking a very unique shape and colour handed down and honed over generations.

I admit, in the course of researching and writing this book, I have gone from hair novice to hair enthusiast. "Did you know you have the rarest colouring in the world?" I announce to a red-haired, blue-eyed colleague who is innocently making a spot of tea. "Isn't it amazing that he has all the hair follicles he will ever have?" I coo over a friend's newborn.

Before we even look at why and how we change our hair colour, we need to get to grips with our natural hair, whether coily, curly or straight, dark, blonde, grey, or even red. And that doesn't start with a salon appointment. Instead, it starts with a trip back in time to where one of our very first, very hairy ancestors began to walk on two legs. Whether curly or straight, black or blonde, whether you choose to colour it or not, your hair has been integral to human evolution.

Shedding fur: the origins of modern human hair

In 1967, zoologist Desmond Morris published his controversial tome, *The Naked Ape*. This sexually explicit and entertaining look into humans' more basic behaviors argued that we are fundamentally not very different from apes, and outraged some religious quarters. "Viewing man as a risen ape rather than a fallen angel had caused offence," wrote Morris decades later, recounting a run-in with a particularly upset bishop. But despite the criticisms the book has come in for over the last 50 years, Morris hit the nail on the head with his self-penned term for modern humans.

"There are one hundred and ninety-three living species of monkeys and apes," writes Morris. "One hundred and ninety-two of them are covered with hair. The exception is a naked ape self-named *Homo sapiens*. This unusual and highly successful species spends a great deal of time examining his higher motives and an equal amount of time studiously ignoring his fundamental ones. He is proud that he has the biggest brain of all the primates, but attempts to conceal the fact that he also has the biggest penis, preferring to accord this honour falsely to the mighty gorilla."[3]

Genitals aside, the closest living relatives to modern humans today are indeed very hairy: chimpanzees and bonobos. In fact, we share around 96% of our DNA with these primates[4] and millions of years ago, we shared a common ancestor.[5]

Our mysterious common ancestor lived in a much greener Africa than we know now.[6] This ancient great ape was pale-skinned and covered in thick hair, which helped to regulate temperature and provide protection from the strong ultraviolet rays of the African sun.[7] It walked on all fours and had opposable feet made for life in the trees, living in tight-knit family groups, safe from predators.[8]

But, as tectonics formed the East African Rift Valley, the climate and terrain changed. The savannahs expanded and woodland was replaced by dry open grasslands, punctuated by lakes in rock basins. Desmond Morris describes the next chapter for our species particularly well:

"The ancestral apes were forced to do one of two things: either they had to cling on to what was left of their old forest homes, or, in an almost biblical sense, they had to face expulsion from the Garden. The ancestors of the chimpanzees, gorillas, gibbons and orangs stayed put, and their numbers have been slowly dwindling ever since. The ancestors of the only other surviving ape – the naked ape – struck out, left the forests, and threw themselves into competition with the already efficiently adapted ground-dwellers."[9]

One of the most obvious physical differences between us today is body hair, or lack of it. So just why did our very ancient ancestors lose that thick covering of hair?

The quirky 'Aquatic Ape' theory of the 1970s is one of my personal favourites. This hypothesis suggested that after ancient pre-humans (known as hominins) diverged from ancestral chimpanzees and bonobos, they spent a lot of time swimming in lakes to hunt for fish. According to this theory, hominin body hair thinned accordingly to make them more streamlined. Perhaps it's fitting that the hypothesis sounds like a low-budget horror title, as the idea has been widely panned by critics, based on what we know about formidable water parasites and waterside predators at the time. (Similarly, it's mammals that live solely in water that have shed their body hair, rather than land mammals dipping in and out.) [10]

Another theory is that hominins began making and wearing clothes of some sort, leaving body hair unnecessary. This was initially debunked by archaeological finds that dated needles (which could be used to sew skins) to within the last 40,000 years, when we know human hair loss vastly predates that.[11]

Most modern anthropologists agree that walking upright was key to human evolution, which then led to the subsequent changes to our body hair.[12] One of the first hominins we know definitely had some bipedal promise was Lucy, the 3.2 million-year-old *Australopithecus afarensis* (affectionately named by an anthropologist with a penchant for The Beatles).[13] Species of *Australopithecus* lived between four million and one million years ago and they all share key tree-climbing features - short legs and long arms - but also had some of the key skeletal changes in the pelvis, knees and feet that indicate adaptation to walking. Lucy's particular brand of *Australopithecus*, for example, had large, flat feet to help with balance.[14] These would have made her that little bit less agile in the trees than her ape ancestors: a trade off that came with better mobility on foot.

So why did hominins like Lucy begin to walk on two legs rather than on their feet and their knuckles? Most theories lead us back to climate change. Lucy's ancestors would have lived on a fruit-based diet, but, by her lifetime, the drier climate was making fruit scarcer and more seasonal. Lucy probably had to cover more ground to find fruit and also forage for roots and plants to supplement her diet. Walking on two legs sacrificed a fair amount of speed compared to four legs, and so keeping the adaptations that allowed her to escape predators and reach safety in the trees would also have been important.[15]

Lucy might also have had another trick up her sleeve: better heat dumping. This required less body hair. While fur or hair provides protection against the sun for less active mammals (thick fur traps short-wave radiation and disperses it as long-wave radiation before the skin has a chance to overheat), it limits the time an animal can spend in the heat before needing to find shade.[16] Being able to forage during the heat of day would have significantly reduced run-ins with predators, and so this may have been when humans began to develop more eccrine sweat glands and lose some of their body hair.

At some point, humans dropped the tree-climbing act. I mean, I'm a reasonable tree climber (my dad thought it was character-building) but

The *Australopithecus afarensis* species could seek refuge in the trees but showed some of the key skeletal changes that came with adaptation to walking.

I'm no Tarzan. This was probably when we got a taste for meat, initially scavenged by foraging but increasingly enjoyed fresh from hunting. Meat and exercise fuelled our brains, which began to increase in size.[17] Human species descended from *Australopithecus* like Lucy show the adaptations for running over walking: shorter toes, elongated tendons and narrow waists.[18] The size of our hair follicles dwindled, the fibres became puny and our sweat glands changed to support this change in behavior.[19]

Humans have three types of sweat glands: eccrine, apocrine and the recently identified but poorly understood apoeccrine gland.[20] Eccrine glands get most of the attention. They are located close to the surface of the skin and are responsible for the watery sweat we excrete in extreme heat or exercise. This sweat uses the heat of your body for the energy necessary to change itself into a vapour, and this clever process cools you down. Humans have around 10 times more eccrine glands than chimpanzees.[21]

Apocrine glands are the sexy pheromone-producing ones, normally attached to a hair follicle in the breasts, scalp, face, genitals and armpits.[22] Together, the sebaceous gland (an oil-producing duct attached to the hair follicle) and apocrine glands produce an appetising blend of lipids, proteins and steroids that's more viscous than sweat from the eccrine gland,[23] but still waterier than apocrine sweat in other mammals.[24] While our large number of eccrine glands have assumed most of the cooling work, this dream team also helps to keep our skin functioning in sweaty conditions.

Sebum produced from the sebaceous gland is remarkably versatile. At lower temperatures, it repels rain on naked skin, but at higher temperatures takes on surfactant qualities that stops eccrine sweat from being evaporated too quickly before it can lower the body temperature.[25] Every drop of sweat lost is a step closer to dehydration for a long-distance hunter so they really did sweat the small stuff.

Bipedalism, loss of body hair, and increased sweat capacity were key to our hunting success before we began to fashion weapons. We may not have been built for speed, but we were built for marathons. Loss of thick body hair and those handy glands enabled ancient humans to tire their prey into heat exhaustion by pursuing them over long distances in the heat of the day and not giving them the opportunity to rest and cool down.[26] I'm astonished to learn that a well-rested Usain Bolt could not outrun the average African quadruped in a short sprint[27] but a physically fit human could beat a horse in a marathon on a sweltering hot day.[28]

How? Well, hoofed mammals like horses and camels mostly rely on their apocrine glands to lower their body temperature in high temperatures or during exercise.[29] As the animal's coat provides protection from ultraviolet rays and incoming heat,[30] beneath it, the sweat evaporation cools the skin and is then dispersed through the fur. This stops being effective when the fur or hair becomes saturated and the site of sweat evaporation moves away from the skin.[31] Horses and dogs are two of the few mammals capable of prolonged running but not in excessively hot conditions.[32]

In 2001, David Attenborough's *Life Of Mammals* gave an incredible example of human running endurance when it followed a group of persistence hunters in one of the few regions it is still practised: central Kalahari, Southern Africa. Aged 38, hunter Karoha Langwane eventually dispatched a much faster species of antelope called a kudu after eight hours of pursuit, tracking and catching up with the animal as it was forced to rest and find shade to lower its body temperature.[33]

Of course, sweat was no good if we were routinely burned to a crisp. Ancient hunters needed to be able to not only deal with the heat of the African sun but also its ultraviolet light. Sebum has been shown to have some basic protective qualities against ultraviolet light, but, by 1.2 million years ago *Homo sapiens* appear to have gained some serious skin pigmentation to deal with sun exposure.[34] The dark pigment found within our skin, eumelanin, is an excellent natural sunscreen, able to dissipate nearly 100 percent of the absorbed energy from sunlight radiation into heat in less than a thousandth of a billionth of a second[35] - impressive stuff.

Celebrated anthropologist and paleobiologist Professor Nina Jablonski believes she has the answer to why we gained dark skin as we lost our body hair, and it's related to a little B vitamin called folate. She explains, "Folate is essential for the production, modification, and repair of DNA, but breaks down easily in the presence of various wavelengths of ultraviolet light. Ultraviolet rays and ultraviolet B-rays especially [short-wavelength rays that cause sunburn] are extremely damaging to cells, and all life on earth has evolved to protect itself from this damage."

Homo sapiens also had to protect their unusually large brains from lethal overheating. To do so, the dark hair they retained on their heads became tightly coiled and springy to deflect heat and provide a buffer of cool air around the skull.[36] This type of coily hair texture is still common across the African continent today.

Africa: home of the curl

They say curly hair holds more secrets - and they're right. It may be the prototype for our species, but we still have a lot to learn about curly and coily hair types.

I email Professor Jablonski to see if she can shed a little light into why. She's open about the lack of research into hair biology amongst African populations, musing, "At present we still know relatively little..." but says she can tell me a few facts for certain. "There is no 'one type' of African hair. There is considerable variation in hair texture among people in Africa, for instance, in variety in the degree of hair curl. There are some trends in texture, but these are hard to interpret against the backdrop of climate because people have moved around so much in the last few thousand years."

We know a little more about skin and hair colour. African populations have varying shades of dark skin and hair, thanks to a little gene called MC1R. This gene gives instructions to specialised cells in the skin called melanocytes to produce a dark pigment called eumelanin in the skin, hair and eyes. Unlike Europeans (who have picked up more faulty versions of this gene), it works like clockwork in most African people, suggesting dark colouring is under strong natural selection in Africa.[37] Based on what we know about eumelanin's protective qualities against ultraviolet light this makes perfect sense.

But hair texture variation within Africa is more complex, controlled by a range of genes and environmental pressures that we haven't deciphered yet.[38] This has led to a range of textures, from a wide distribution of very coily, springy hair in the hottest, equatorial regions (commonly referred to as Afro hair although this is also a style), to tightly coiled hair in West African people like the Mandinka, and looser curls in North African people like the Ashanti.[39]

Recent migrations (evolutionarily speaking) have also influenced skin colour and hair texture distribution across the region, particularly in urban hotspots. One prime example that Professor Jablonski points me to is the migration of the Bantu-language speaking people. Originally from western central Africa, Bantu people are both connected by approximately 500 closely related languages[40] and widely acknowledged with bringing agriculture to hunter-gatherers in southern Africa. However, it looks as if they also brought the genes for darker skin and Afro-textured hair too,[41] as they widely replaced but also had children with the lighter skinned, looser-haired hunter-gatherer populations in the south.[42]

Go forward thousands of years and the prevalence of very curly and coily hair in areas like the Caribbean and America, is a result of the Trans-Atlantic Slave Trade, not natural migration. It is estimated that about 12 million enslaved Africans were transported under horrific conditions primarily by the Europeans to work on sugar and cotton plantations in America and the Caribbean between the 16th and 19th century,[43] and this has had an immeasurable impact on the dispersion of coily Black hair and attitudes towards it.[44]

Modern humans had many ambitious but failed excursions out of Africa before they actually flew the nest, leaving behind part of a 210,000-year-old skull in Greece[45] and 100,000-year-old teeth in China for modern archaeologists to find.[46] These pioneering groups are not thought to have passed their genes down to humans today. Incredibly, however, some of the first modern humans to leave Africa between 75,000 and 50,000 years ago managed to trek all the way to Oceania (a region that includes Australasia, Melanesia, Micronesia and Polynesia), while their relatives were mucking about in Asia and Europe.[47]

We don't know what drove that small group of superhumans to make such an epic journey, but it was the earliest of the migrations that have characterised human behavior for thousands of years. Hunters would follow herds, foragers would move with the seasons; we lived a nomadic life that very few of us do nowadays. I probably speak for a lot of homeowners when I say that my mortgage will certainly keep me tethered to a certain spot for the rest of my life.

The Ancient Oceanians, however, were an entirely different kettle of fish. What's of particular interest to us is that, despite being over 10,000 kilometres apart, the descendants of these explorers (the Indigenous Australian, Polynesian and Melanesian populations) share a similar coily hair texture to central African populations.[48] WWhether this is a relic from their African ancestors or a re-evolved form of heat protection is up for debate.

Even more strikingly, although they have the darkest skin of individuals outside of Africa, 5 to 10% of indigenous people in Oceania also have blonde hair - the highest percentage outside of Europe.[49] Once we thought some blonde gene-carrying Europeans must have arrived much earlier than expected, but recent research has suggested that's not the case. Instead blonde hair appears to be due to an independent gene mutation that was selected for in this dark-skinned population, who were isolated for approximately 50,000 years until the British turned up in 1788 and generally began ruining their lives.[50] Was blonde hair the attraction, or was the slightly lighter skin that comes along for the ride the appealing factor? It would be interesting to know.

The Ancient Oceanians may have shunned other Homo sapien company for 50,000 years, but there is evidence that they got up close and personal with another now extinct species of human: *Homo denisova*. Specimens of this mysterious species have only been found in Siberia and Central Asia so far[51] yet they somehow contributed up to 5% of their DNA to Oceanian populations.[52]

I'm learning that a little inter-species sex between humans wasn't that unusual. Over a Skype call, Molecular Biologist Dr Jarek Bryk explains our ancestors were pretty open-minded when it came to hook ups. "Throughout evolution, humans had sex whenever they could with any other species of human that were around the world," he says, bluntly. "We met some Neanderthals in Europe, we had sex with them; we met some Denisovans in East Asia, we had sex with them. Everywhere we look at human populations, it's the same story. And we now know there are parts of our DNA that do not match either of these genomes, so there must be some other sex going on with populations we don't know about yet."

That will give the critics of Morris's *Naked Ape* something to look forward to.

In the thick of it: adapting to Asia

The *Homo sapien* settlement of the world was the ultimate experiment in human adaptation to different environments. Seriously, geneticists get really excited about it.

Dr Bryk explains, "We are incredibly uniform if you look at humans on a DNA level. The commonly given figure is that only around 0.1% of the genomes [complete DNA sequence] of two randomly chosen people are different. But obviously someone who lives in equatorial Africa has very different living conditions than someone who lives in a cold, mountainous terrain, and our physiology and bodies have adapted. Spread a small, uniform group of humans around the globe, give them 50,000 years to evolve, and by analysing different variants, we can shine a spotlight on where these various populations are very, very different."

'Variants' is a general term for tiny genetic changes in your DNA that can add up to have a big impact over time. Darwin famously coined the term 'natural selection' to mean that animals carrying useful genetic variants (let's say a white-haired rabbit in the Arctic) have a better chance of surviving and passing on these useful traits to their offspring.[53] Let's be honest, a brown-haired rabbit in the same scenario is more likely to get eaten than get lucky.

Skin colour aside, straighter hair texture is one of the biggest changes in the appearance of the humans who left Africa and settled in Asia and Europe tens of thousands of years ago. I spend days reading countless scientific papers in search of what exactly triggered this change only for the penny to finally drop: we don't actually have the answers yet.

Hair biologist Dr Gillian Westgate, whose papers on the evolution of curly hair I have been scouring, kindly agrees to a phone call. "We don't really know what all the genes involved in the curly to straight hair transition are," she admits. "We've ended up with a really diverse load of hair types all over the world, but we've not got enough pieces of the jigsaw to put it together yet. But, I would think that, because the climate was cooler, the necessity to have this close, cropped, short hair for keeping the brain cool became less needed."

Scientists get really enthusiastic about this topic. That's because hair texture amongst East Asian and Indigenous American populations is practically fixed as thick, long, dark and straight with little deviation. The reason is a small but mighty genetic change that took hold in human populations somewhere between the Middle East and East Asia.[54]

To anyone less than geographically competent like myself, Asia and America sound pretty far apart. So, I was interested to read that the first modern human settlers in North America actually reached the continent from Siberia, probably travelling by boat and also across a now flooded land bridge 15,000 years ago.[55] It means that East Asian and Indigenous American populations are closely related and share lots of common gene variants. One of the most exciting is a mutation known as EDAR370A (if you want to get very technical, this refers to a change in the 370th amino acid inside the coding part of the EDAR gene.)[56]

A tiny change in one of the estimated 20,000 to 25,000 genes we carry[57] might seem miniscule. Yet I'm informed by Dr Bryk that it's a bit of a big deal for two reasons. One: EDAR370A is only found in very low levels in Europeans and not at all in African populations, although nearly all East Asian and Indigenous American people carry it. Clearly it's very closely linked to this region specifically.[58] Two: it has a number of associated features, including increased number of sweat glands, increased density of mammary glands in breasts, a change in tooth shape, and, significantly for us, thick, straight hair.[59]

Dr Bryk enthuses, "EDAR is one of the very few genes that allows us to go from the differences in frequencies of alleles [variations in the gene] all the way down to how it affects physical traits, like appearance, and potentially evolution. There are very, very few cases like that in humans where we as scientists are able to do that." Forced to take his word for it, I am nevertheless impressed.

He further explains that the wide-ranging associated traits of EDAR370A make it hard to date or place. If, as some scientists believe, the mutation evolved in China, it may have been that increased sweat glands were handy in a potentially more humid climate.[60] Alternatively, it could have been tooth shape that was under selection because people used them as tools.[61] Either of these suggestions would mean that thick straight hair was a coincidence: a by-product of a different trait that became useful.[62]

Dr Bryk has studied both theories. "One of the interesting possibilities is that hair type was under some sort of sexual selection," he explains. "The Asian hair structure could have been more attractive to mates during the human colonisation of that part of the world. Therefore, people who had the Asian hair structure could simply have had more offspring because they were perceived to be more attractive. But my bet is on various glands being under natural selection personally, because that's easier to imagine."

We could also have breastfeeding in Beringia to thank. During the Last Glacial Maximum (an icy era broadly defined from 27 to 18 thousand years ago),[63] Beringia may have been a sort of ancient holiday hot spot situated between Siberia and Alaska. (Okay, hot might be pushing it a bit, but it was possibly not as cold as much of the northern hemisphere, which was in the grip of a bitter ice age.) [64] Desperate to escape the encroaching ice, settlers of Siberia found sanctuary in this drier climate, and remained isolated there for several thousand years.[65]

If the mutation did originate here, it was probably triggered by a lack of sunlight. Newborn babies need vitamin D for a healthy immune system and this is produced in the skin when it's exposed to ultraviolet light. But with sunlight at high latitudes in short supply, a gene mutation that increased the density of mammary glands in the breasts to provide more fat and vitamin D to a breastfed baby would certainly be favourable.[66] If so, when the ice finally thawed, and the Siberians either paddled or trekked their way over to Alaska and Canada (and also headed back into Siberia), they would have carried it with them.[67] (Disclaimer: Beringia began flooding approximately 11,000 years ago and is now underwater.)

Why or wherever the mutation occurred, statistical geneticist Dr Kaustubh Adhikari says the selection pressures on these people were incredibly strong. "EDAR is a poster child for the kind of things that we work on because it's a gene that affects a lot of phenotypes [physical traits], and it's a nice example of a very strong selection. There must have been a very strong selection pressure that drove EDAR370A to be

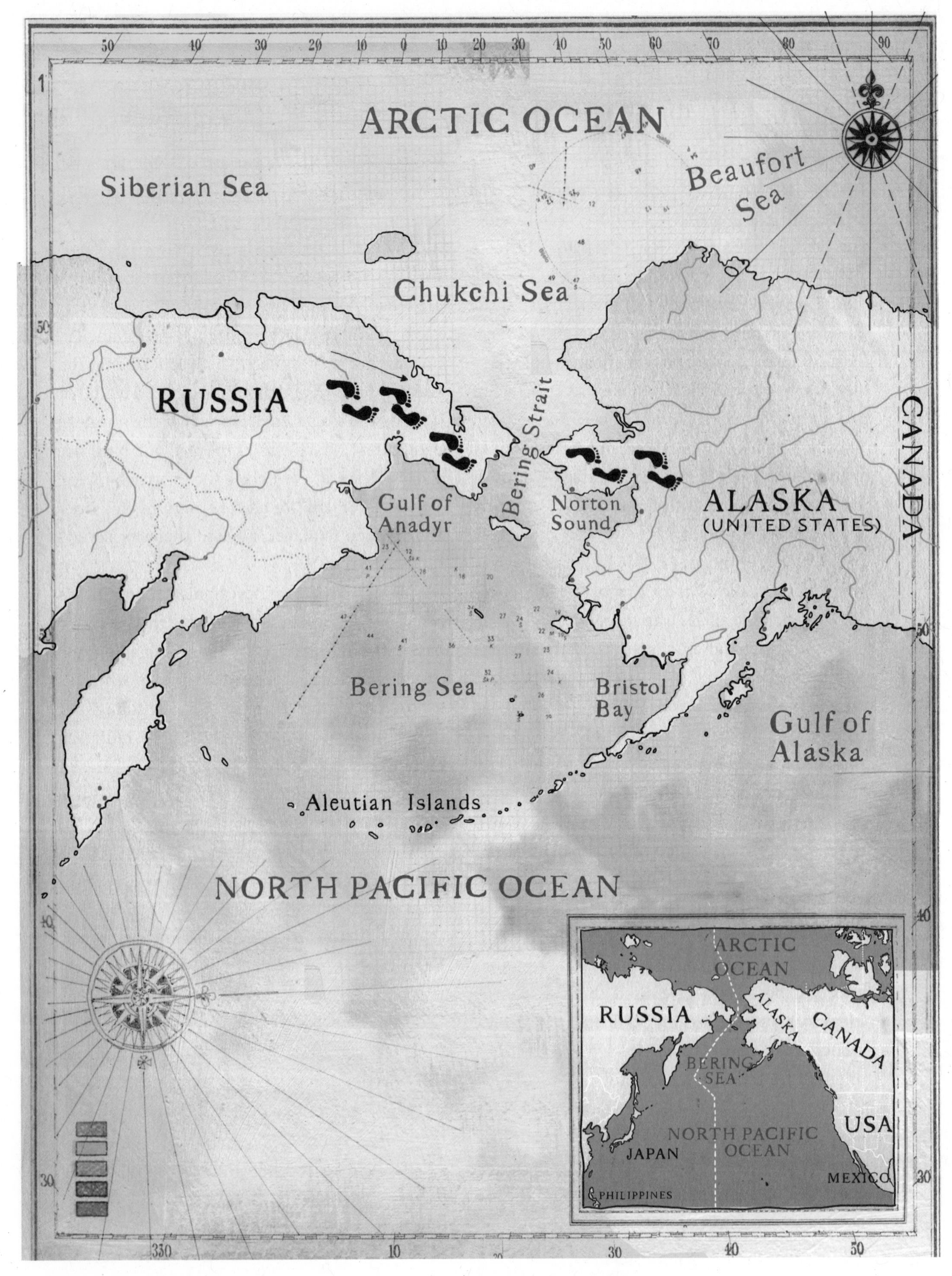

Beringia: an ancient hot(ish) spot that Homo sapiens crossed to reach North America.

almost fixed in East Asia by the time these people migrated to the Americas. If those people had high variability, then when they moved back to lower latitudes that are closer to the sun, like Mexico, the selection pressure on EDAR would have vanished."

An explosion of colour: what on earth happened in Europe?

Once our explanation for Europe was simple. Humans successfully moved out of those toasty, dark skin-favouring environments about 50,000 years ago[68] and then into chilly light-poor ones; natural selection pressures on dark skin relaxed and so hair and eye colour, which are influenced by the same genes, followed suit.[69] Now, however, we know that as early as 6,000 years ago some hunter-gatherers in Europe still had dark skin and hair but startling blue eyes. So, this discovery neatly derails that theory.

We know that lighter skin became more beneficial and evolutionarily advantageous than dark skin in light-poor northern regions first, separately in Asia and Europe. This is probably when a range of lighter hair and eye colours followed suit. "There definitely has to be positive selection for light skin," says Dr Adhikari, who has done a lot of work on the topic, "and we believe that this happened when people started to move into northern latitudes in Asia and Europe. There's a strong correlation between the particular genetic variant that is causing lighter skin and sunlight."

Professor Jablonski believes the female need to compensate for less sunlight was key. This is based on previous work showing that women across the world tend to have paler skin than men. "Women of reproductive age need to be able to direct vitamin D and calcium toward their developing foetus and newborn while breastfeeding," she argues. "This is in order to ensure normal development of the skeleton (and all the other many parts of the body that depend on vitamin D and calcium). Lighter skin helps to insure this and so skin continued to lighten in northwestern European populations up through recent history as the result of minor mutations becoming favoured in populations living under low ultraviolet light."

The dark-skinned hunter-gatherers who live in very northern regions today are seemingly at odds with her theory, but Professor Jablonski has taken these people into consideration too. "Living at this latitude has only been possible because the Inuit-Yupik-Unangan language-speaking people subsist largely on a diet that is rich in vitamin D," she explains. "It is interesting that, with natural selection's pressure towards lighter skin apparently relaxed because of their diet, these populations have evolved darker skin to protect themselves from the high levels of UVA that reflect on them from snow, ice and open water."[70]

So, light skin first became beneficial in light-poor northern regions, probably because vitamin D is so essential for healthy human growth. But a meaty vitamin D-rich diet could just have compensated for the lack of sunlight in these regions.[71]

Do gentlemen prefer blondes?

Research has given me some interesting trivia to try out on the blondies in my life, namely my mother. She tries hard to look attentive as I spiel them off over a cuppa.

Fun Fact One: Only about 2% of the world's population is naturally blonde[72] and your chances of being one of them are higher if you have northern European heritage.[73] In fact, in a recent analysis of seven European studies on hair colour (Denmark, Estonia, Iceland, Great Britain, France,

Germany and The Netherlands), The Netherlands, Germany, Estonia and Denmark were found to have the highest number of blondes and blonde gene carriers.[74] This fits with what we know about blonde hair circulating around northern Europe before it was carried down south.

Fun Fact Two: Women and children are more likely to be fair-haired than men. In fact, many children are notably fairer than adults, but their hair darkens naturally during puberty due to the influx of hormones that affect texture and pigmentation.[75] Blonde-haired girls, however, are more likely to remain fair after puberty than boys, and women are also more likely to have fairer shades of brown hair too.[76]

Fun Fact Three: Blondes have more genetic variants, but most of them are pretty weak. In fact, genetics researcher at the University of Edinburgh Professor Ian Jackson worked on research that uncovered 200 variants for blonde hair in Britain alone, but each only increased your probability of being blonde by a few percent.

"The interesting question is how are those genes influencing the colour of the hair?" asks Professor Jackson. "One suggestion is that the thickness itself might have a very subtle influence on our perception of the colour. Each of these genes is only contributing a very small amount to colour, and it doesn't take very much to push you from light brown to blonde, maybe just a slight difference in hair thickness. So that's one way the texture of the hair may affect the perception of the colour."

So was blonde hair simply a natural byproduct of selection for lighter skin in the northern hemisphere? There's another, more controversial theory that draws open derision from Mark when we discuss it. It suggests that the emergence of lighter hair and eye colours was driven by European men, who were in the unique position of being able to be picky about who they coupled up with. Hear me out. In hotter regions like southern Africa, childrearing women could gather a large amount of food by foraging, and were not as reliant on men to provide for them during pregnancy or breast-feeding.[77] These communities would typically be polygamous because women were able to feed and raise bigger families. Male reproductive success, consequently, depended on physically competing against rival males.[78]

But, so goes the argument, the balance of sexual power between men and women shifted as humans migrated away from the Equator towards northern Europe, where the land did not offer as much opportunity for foraging. All of the burden of providing shifted to men, who had to hunt over longer distances the further north they settled. Their chances of dying from injury increased dramatically, and only the most able hunter was able to provide for more than one family. Polygamy rates declined,[79] and European women suddenly faced competition for a mate.[80]

If true, this would have been a very unusual dynamic in the animal kingdom. That's because female choice typically governs evolution. They're the ones who put the energy into pregnancy or egg-laying, and then feed and rear their young, so they are pretty picky about who they chose as a father for their little darlings. However *Homo sapien* society is unusual in that women's reproduction has been strictly controlled by men for millenia. While in much of the animal kingdom female choice does determine mating outcomes, we have been an overwhelmingly patriarchal society for tens of thousands of years - longer according to some anthropologists.[81] No one knows exactly how men came out on top, though there are plenty of intriguing theories.[82] Many modern women may decide who they have children with but that hasn't been the case in the past.

I think that gives this theory of female

competition some credence though Mark doesn't agree. "No. Women who make a mistake lose a breeding cycle or even the chance to reproduce at all, so they don't waste their time. Would women be less discerning with their choice if there were less men? No. They would be just as picky." He launches into numerous birding examples of male ineptitude compared to the ruthless and discerning behavior of the females. "Amongst Red-winged Blackbirds, the female will not bother with a mocking bird, but the male will. He doesn't have as effective faculties as her, or he doesn't use them. It's not why are women better, it's why did they become better? The females that made a mistake didn't pass on their genes. It's natural selection."

Interesting. I hadn't thought about this before but a quick dip into some research informs me that women are generally believed to have better cognitive abilities than men, especially when it comes to hearing and smelling.[84] And it is true that my partner is able to sleep through any amount of noise while a gnat could land on my daughter's window and I'd hear it.

Female choice and human patriarchy is a conundrum I get stuck into in Chapter 3, so I quickly distract Mark with some eye colour theory. Another hypothesis posits that blue-eyed women were initially preferred by blue-eyed men because it increased paternal confidence. Blue eyes are recessive, meaning that blue-eyed parents are highly likely to have a blue-eyed child that fathers would recognise as their own.[85] (Cue Mark spitting out his tea. "I really don't rate men that highly.") After musing on the fact that I have blue eyes, so does my partner and our daughter, I interrogate colleagues around the office to see if there could be any truth to this theory. It's inconclusive.

Professor Jablonski, however, argues that blue eyes were a "genetic accident" rather than the result of sexual selection. This could be more up Mark's street. "Eye colour is regulated by a much smaller complement of genes than skin colour," she explains. "When the absence of melanin - resulting in blue eye colour - appeared in ancient western European populations, it was not selected against because ultraviolet levels were so low and highly seasonal. People living under stronger ultraviolet rays need melanin in their irises to help protect their eyes against damage, and this is why most of the world's people have dark eyes."

Tall, dark and handsome: Cheddar Man

To find out more, I travel up to the Natural History Museum in London to meet Ancient DNA specialist Dr Selina Brace. This turns out to be a fascinating trip. Not only is Dr Brace's office behind the giant sloth in the behind-the-scenes section of the museum ("This is where we keep the dead things!"), but she's going to introduce me to a distant relative.

Dr Brace is exactly the kind of person I want to be working at the Natural History Museum: quirky, intelligent, and an enthusiastic collector of stuffed animals. These are on display in her office. "My students get me one for each project we do," she explains. "Though..." she picks up a one-eyed dodo, "this one I just wanted."

I'm talking to Dr Brace because she was one of a team to extract genetic material from a British hunter-gatherer known as Cheddar Man, who died in Cheddar Gorge, Somerset, 10,000 years ago. This information was used by Dutch twins and famous sculptors of early humans Adrie and Alfons Kennis to construct a bust, unveiled in a 2018 Channel 4 programme, which I have dutifully watched.[86] When the programme revealed that this ancient Brit very probably had blue eyes, dark skin and dark hair, they received racist backlash. Cheddar Man's skin tone also varied remarkably in pictures printed in the newspapers.

Dr Brace shows me the reports on her laptop. "The newspapers were all given one hour to photograph the bust. The photographs were therefore taken on the same day, at the same time and in the same lighting conditions. That the skin tone of the bust varies so considerably across photographs, one must assume some artificial artistic licence with whether the tone was lightened or darkened," she says.

Despite the response in the press, Dr Brace says that scientists in the field were not shocked by Cheddar Man's colouring. "All of the individuals sequenced from Central Europe during this time period and just prior to it have the same genetic signature of dark skin pigmentation and blue eyes. That was the standard, as far as we can tell, although it's a very unusual combination today."

She admits it's difficult to reach a conclusion about why lighter eye colour might have spread more quickly than paler skin and hair. "Why the blue eyes? I don't know. It could have been a form of selective adaptation. I've heard some theories that blue eyes might help reflect light from the snow. However, if most people had dark eyes, and if someone rocked up with really blue eyes, that's going to be quite unusual and probably kind of sexy. So, one could see how that might allow blue eyes to spread." Looking into the piercing blue eyes of the Cheddar Man's replica on proud display in the Human Evolution gallery, I have to admit he was struck down in his prime.

How did they decide on his wavy hair texture? I ask Dr Brace. "That was a bit of artistic license," she confesses. "We suggested it be modelled it on my colleague, Tom."

Going against the grain: what's wheat got to do with European hair colour?

The Middle East, 10,000 BC. In a region ranging from the southern Levant to the Zagros Mountains in Iran, northern Iraq and southeastern Turkey, a gradual change in human behaviour is sowing the seeds of seismic change for the entire species.[87] Plants, once foraged, are being domesticated.[88] Animals like prehistoric goats and boar are not simply being hunted, but herded and bred for desirable characteristics like increased body fat and submissiveness.[89] Across the world, similar practices are beginning to independently develop - notably with pigs in China and llamas in America.[90] Over the next several thousand years, agriculture and animal domestication spread to Europe.[91] Farming has arrived and it is to have big consequences for people, the planet, and even human appearance.

Human life changed dramatically with this change of lifestyle. As only a few of the thousands of species that we hunted and gathered were suitable for farming, our diets changed, and not really for the better. We went from living seasonally and nomadically, relying on our intimate knowledge of animal behaviours and plant cycles, to focusing all our efforts on a select few crops and species.

"Even today, with all our advanced technologies, more than 90 percent of the calories that feed humanity comes from the handful of plants that our ancestors domesticated between 9500 and 3500 BC," writes Dr Yuval Noah Harari, author of *Sapiens*.[92] The historian also argues very chillingly that rather than humans cultivating wheat, the plant actually domesticated us: tying us down to back-breaking labour to increase its yields, protect it from herbivores and drought. For wheat, having an entire species of ape dedicated to its survival was a stroke of evolutionary brilliance. For us, it was a trap.[93] PPersonally, I haven't looked at a loaf of bread in the same way since.

But why did humans fall into the farming trap when the benefits were certainly dubious, compared to the versatile hunter-gatherer lifestyle? "It has always been very difficult to ascertain the mechanism by which that change occurred," says Dr Brace. "Farming was probably the biggest change in modern human behaviour. People, certainly in the beginning, weren't particularly good at it either, which affected their health; we know this from looking at the unhealthy state of some of their bones from this time. So why did people switch to such a different lifestyle which had such massive knock-on effects?"

Dr Harari argues it was a classic case of quantity over quality. While nomadic hunter-gatherers roamed large expanses of land and had versatile, fairly healthy diets, farming could sustain larger numbers of people on a more basic, less nutritious diet. Women had more children, weaned them earlier to get back to work in the fields, and then fell pregnant again more quickly. (Many women do not menstruate while they are breastfeeding young children. It's nature's contraceptive - though not a reliable one I should point out.) The farmers had numbers on their side, and once the population increased there was no going back.[94]

The migration of farmers and the farming lifestyle into Europe was the start of the end for the hunter-gatherers like Cheddar Man. Suddenly the land they hunted on was cultivated and animals they preyed on were driven off or domesticated. Whether the hunter-gatherers feared, fought or tolerated this new dark-eyed, pale-skinned crowd is anybody's guess, but their way of life became unsustainable and eventually disappeared as the farming bug spread.[95] It's this population replacement that's part of the key to our paler skin and hair in these regions. "People don't suddenly evolve different skin pigmentation and different eye colours," Dr Brace stresses. "It's about the migrations of people with those variants: lighter skin pigmentation and different colour eyes."

One of the latest hunter-gatherers we have found so far lived in Denmark. Professor in Evolutionary Genomics at the University of Copenhagen Hannes Schroeder led a team who casually sequenced the entire genome of a 5,700-year-old woman from a piece of chewed birch.[96] He admits it was a bit of a surprise to find that 'Lola' shared Cheddar Man's hunter-gatherer genetic footprint, dark skin and hair and blue eyes, considering the influx of farming at the time.

"What's interesting about Lola is that she dates so late," he says. "It's not surprising to find these western hunter-gatherers genetically 10,000 years ago like Cheddar Man, but Lola dates to about 6,000 years ago when you have farming coming into Europe, and yet she doesn't carry any farming ancestry."

Over the phone, Professor Schroeder ponders aloud why Lola's farming neighbours might have developed paler skin when she hadn't. "On the one hand, populations are moving into light-poor environments and humans need sunlight for life," he muses. "Given that we do not have much light in Denmark, having lighter skin and also blue eye colour will help absorb more light. One would assume that as populations move into northern Europe, they would slowly adapt to these light-poor conditions, but then we also have hunter-gatherer populations in Greenland and the Arctic, who have darker skin tones and they moved into that region 5,000 or 6,000 years ago from Russia.

"Perhaps the most important factor is the changes to our diet in the last 5,000 to 6,000 years. Hunter-gatherers living in the northern latitudes had sources of game that maybe gave them enough nutrients so that they didn't need light skin. That may have changed as we adopted a more settled lifestyle and a simpler and less varied diet, relying on crops. With that then came the lack of nutrients which meant that we had to get them from somewhere else."

It seems vitamin D deficiency has a lot to answer for.

Got milk? How dairy brought the genes for lighter skin into Europe

The ability to digest milk past childhood has also been linked to the development of paler skin in Europe. Most of the world don't get on well with dairy. That's because once we begin eating solid foods, the production of an enzyme known as lactase, which helps us to digest milk, usually peters out.

In fact, an estimated 68% of the adult global population are unable to effectively digest milk sugars, reaching heights of up 66% in Northern Africa, 64% in Asia (rising to 70% in the Middle East), and 47% in Eastern Europe, Russia and former Soviet Republics. Head down to northern, southern and western Europe and the intolerance rates instead rest at around 28%.[97] As milk is a source of vitamin D, and populations in those light-poor regions of northern Europe commonly do continue to produce lactase, it was once thought to have originated there. Evidence also suggests that by 7,000 BC, dairy farming was emerging in the European steppe.[98]

Now, however, the dairy-digesting genes are believed to have been brought into these regions of northern Europe from Northwest Hungary and Southwest Slovakia with cattle farming.[99] People who continue to produce this enzyme are known as lactase persistent, or lactose tolerant.

There's just one problem: none of the farmers sequenced during this period appear to have that particular variant. In fact, it doesn't appear to become prominent until the Bronze Age: the period after farming has been established.

"That's caused much head-scratching," Dr Brace admits. "We don't of course sample the entire population. So, it could have been present, just at very low frequency and it just took time to increase. We see some evidence of the lactase persistence genes in the Bronze Age peoples, but selection for these genes looks to be ongoing across Europe and the most rapid increase in frequency was probably between 1,500 and 4,000 years ago."

These drastic population turnovers had a big impact on the European population. Today, the supposed average European is roughly the same parts Yamnaya and Anatolian farmer with a smaller dollop of African hunter-gatherer, but you'll find more hunter-gatherer DNA in Eastern Europe and more farming genes in Spain and Italy.[100] With the farming populations, came the genes for lighter skin, hair and eye colours, the big dietary changes that made them useful, and perhaps just a tiny element of men having a little more power in the mating dynamics? Hopefully Mark skims this bit.

Farming had a big role in restricting our nomadic lifestyles and tethering humans to a specific area. Many governments implement strict immigration laws to do the trick today. But Dr Brace has some wisdom to share with me. "If evolution has taught us anything, it's that you shouldn't be afraid of change. You shouldn't be afraid of different people because our shared past is multiple waves of migrations of peoples coming and going throughout our history."

Mark wholeheartedly agrees. "We've forgotten how key freedom of movement is to all animals, including us. We've been educated out of understanding that we are free."

Seeing red: an Englishman, an Irishman and a Scotsman walk into a bar...

Red hair is the rarest colour in the world, occurring naturally in only 1 to 2% of the global population.[101] But despite its prestige, redheads have had a pretty rough time in history. In fact, not so long ago, it was argued that we inherited the genes for red hair from interbreeding with Neanderthals.[102] (Charming - although, to be fair, Neanderthals get an unnecessarily bad rap.) This conclusion was based on DNA extracted from two sets of Neanderthal remains found in northwest Spain that had not been found in modern humans.

Evolutionary and population genomics researcher and Neanderthal enthusiast Professor Michael Dannemann explains we can discount this theory, at least temporarily. "We now know that one of these individuals is not a Neanderthal," he explains. "It was initially falsely classified. So suddenly this variant that people said doesn't exist in modern humans does exist in humans because it was a human bone."

Dr Dannemann and colleagues have since conducted extensive sweeps of existing Neanderthal genomes and found no evidence of the gene variants that we know contribute to red hair in modern humans.[103] "While we cannot exclude the theory that some Neanderthals had red hair, we do not have evidence that the kind of variant that would lead to red hair in modern humans is very prevalent in Neanderthals. It's unlikely that they might have given this particular trait to us," he explains. However, he concedes, "But so many things we think we know about Neanderthal DNA come from studying its effects in us - *Homo sapiens*. It remains unclear whether the same effects would also be observed in a Neanderthal."

Red hair very often comes hand in hand with pale skin and both are strongly related to changes to the MC1R gene, which, as discussed, controls production of dark-coloured eumelanin in the skin and hair.[104] If, like me, you're a little pasty, you've inherited variants that make the MC1R gene less effective at producing dark pigment. This gives me an advantage in not-so-sunny England (not to mention my five-year stint in Wales).

Red hair, however, is still a very recessive trait. Even if both parents carry those specific variants there is only a 25% chance that their child will have red hair.[105] So redheads are super rare - but may also pop up unexpectedly when two unsuspecting gene carriers have a child. Thanks to this misunderstood genetic fluke, such new parents may find themselves the butt of jokes regarding the milkman.

Recent work by Professor Jackson and colleagues has found that red hair is not only related to variants in the MC1R gene, but that other genes can be involved too. In 2018, he was involved in the largest genetic study of hair colour to date based on data taken from the UK Biobank: a unique database containing information on the genetic material of half a million people in Britain.[106] "What we are learning is that interactions between genes can be just as important as the actions of the genes themselves," he explains. "Some of the variants of MC1R are what we call highly penetrant, which means you are very likely to have red hair if you have them. Others are very weak, and you need other genes interacting with them to cause red hair."

Red hair is not believed to have originated in Britain,[107] yet it is often associated with Scotland and Ireland - a link that Professor Jackson's team could confirm, at least for the former. They not only found the highest number of British redheads in Scotland, but also that a higher proportion of women had red hair compared to men.[108]

This may just support Professor Jablonski's argument that women around the world have fairer skin to improve their synthesis of vitamin D during pregnancy and breastfeeding. Redheads normally have very fair skin, thanks to reduced levels of dark eumelanin in their skin and higher levels of reddish-yellow pheomelanin - setting them up for reproductive success in less sunny regions. Unfortunately, it also means that redheads are prone to skin cancer later in life because they are very vulnerable to ultraviolet skin damage after prolonged sun exposure.[109]

"Surely the increased odds of skin cancer must have meant red hair would be selected against, not for?" I ask.

But Professor Jackson explains, "Natural selection almost only acts on reproductive age individuals. So, if you develop skin cancer after you've had children, then there's no selection. So, I guess that's one angle. The other is that if skin cancer was being selected against, then you'd have to say well the vitamin D selection is stronger, so it overcomes that disadvantage."

A little concerning. I make a mental note to tell my red-haired friends to not be stingy with the sunscreen. I also ask what I fear is a very basic question: "why do I have pale skin but dark blue eyes and darkish brown hair? "

"Ah," professor Jackson concedes. "That is a very good question." Phew. "Well, in my view, hair colour is a byproduct of selection of skin colour. The colour in your skin is made by the pigment cells, and then transferred to the skin cells and it's the same process for the hair. So, selection for pale skin results in red hair or blonde hair in some circumstances. However, while there's a lot of overlap between hair and skin colour genes, there are some that are specific to the skin. The interesting genes I think are those ones that don't overlap. What's that telling us about how skin is pigmented versus hair?"

Before I became a mum, I was very critical of my body. I didn't like this bit, or that bit. I still have days like that but going through pregnancy, having my daughter, and now being pregnant with my second, has made me more appreciative of how amazing the female body is. This Alice-In-Wonderland-esque trip down the human evolution rabbit hole has had a similar effect on my view of head hair. I'm bloody fascinated by the stuff now: its colours, its textures, its purpose. This brain covering we treat as an accessory is a relic of the massive changes our species have been through.

What we do to change our natural hair is a whole other chapter (Chapters 3 to 5, in fact). But, one look at the booming hair industry, and it's clear that hair is just as key to our identity as humans now as it was millions of years ago when we stepped out on two legs and left our furry ancestors behind.

Extraordinary human head hair

2

London, 1973. Young, self-confessed nerd Mark Constantine is about to swap a potentially dazzling hairdressing career with the Ginger Group of Hairdressers for the geeky pursuits of trichology: the study of the scalp and hair. After years of blood, sweat and shampoo, it's a bold leap into the unknown.

Ok, it wasn't quite like that.

Mark is definitely a nerd but he confesses he was never star pupil at the salon. "I wasn't much of a hairdresser," he admits, "but I was academically very good, which is bizarre considering I left school without any qualifications. But I'm nerdy and that nerdiness always comes out. I read a lot, and I like to self-educate. I think that's why my boss suggested trichology to me instead. Of course, the other thing that you do if you're a nerdy hairdresser, is you become a colourist, but I never liked hair dyes even before all the research came out in the 1970s."

Mark's nerdiness turned out to be lucky, considering what was to come next. His boss fired the resident head trichologist and also his second in command, promoting his very junior member of staff - Mark - to head of trichology. "I'd only just started studying it," Mark groans, "it was horrific. I was so stressed. I mean someone just asked me recently, if the business with Covid-19 this year was the most stressed I've ever felt, but no, that comes close!"

Mark spent his day to day with a qualified trichologist, and split his time between the salon floor in Knightsbridge and the Hair and Scalp Hospital in Brixton, working furiously at night to prepare for his exams. It was, he says, a big education in a short period of time, but he reflects fondly on one place in particular. "Brixton was just a real pleasure. I learned so much stuff every minute of every day, and that's where the final exams were. If I hadn't been in Brixton, I wouldn't have been anywhere near as good."

His training involved learning about and treating hair and scalp diseases, and serving clientele including Vogue editor Anna Wintour. "In those days, when you went to an expensive hairdressing salon, the hairdresser, the trichologist and the stylist would come over to talk to you about what you wanted to achieve. When I worked for The Ginger Group, the chief stylist would drift by and if he didn't like the look of a client's hair, would go to reception and shake his head. Then someone else would come over and say, 'Oh, I'm terribly sorry but so-and-so is busy today, so you'll be seen by someone else.' So the colour and styling of your hair was discussed with the stylist and then the condition of your hair would be discussed with the trichologist. That was me. And I would take you away, and perhaps treat your hair if it needed it. It was my job to get your hair in the right condition for the stylist.

"Invariably the kind of work I would pick up would be a model who needed to look great but whose hair looked shit. You had to get an effect. You had to get their hair in a good state. Then one of the secrets we had were treatment creams. You would get someone in and apply a scalp oil and then ladle an entire treatment over their hair and then steam that in. And then shampoo and condition it again. The combination of those things would get the condition back into the hair so the stylist could make it look good again." Lush's very own pre-shampoo hair treatments were inspired by Mark's experiences and work in this salon.

But, tired of London life after only a year, he moved with wife and future Lush co-founder Mo Constantine to Bournemouth, Dorset, and persuaded Poole-based hairdresser Marc Young that he needed a trichologist. Part of the role required him to adopt the name of Matthew so as not to be confused with the big boss - a sacrifice for which Mark still bears a small grudge - but it was here that he finished his qualifications and became an associate member of the Institute of Trichologists.

But, despite Mark's efforts, a career in trichology wasn't for him. "I think this is why specialists play a lot of golf," says Mark sagely. "There were only so many conditions to diagnose and only so many treatments I could offer and I got bored."

Yet trichology offered Mark a springboard into product formulation and a different kind of cosmetics. "The best thing I learned was all about the microbiome of the skin and the scalp and the importance of not fucking that over," he reflects " I also understood how much people were damaging their scalps with products that were too strong. So, my speciality would be to stop people from hurting their skin and instead get the scalp in balance. A healthier scalp will produce healthier hair."

As Mark has, on numerous occasions, told me off for tackling outbreaks with harsh cleansing regimes - "Stop punishing your skin!" - this is familiar territory. But it's also the ethos that inspired his development of gentle, naturally-derived products using minimal synthetics, and attracted like-minded co-conspirators who we know as the co-founders of Lush. And, I have to admit, that taking his advice did help my forehead recover in the end.

The recent research I am uncovering is also igniting Mark's nerdiness once more. He reads a draft of this chapter and calls me to tell me I am missing something very obvious. "Freckles!" he declares, with the air of a man presenting me with a fine dish. "I really think you need to explain those if you're looking at hair pigmentation. And besides I've always been curious about them."

I might not have Mark's trichology background but I do share his nerdiness. And I have to admit that the more I delve into the mechanisms behind our colouring, the deeper I could go. Human hair is extraordinary. Melanin is extraordinary. And so, as it turns out, are freckles.

Human hair: a mammalian inheritance

Chimpanzees aren't that hairy.

No, really. Take another look. All great apes including orangutans and gorillas are actually barer than smaller primates, but our closest relatives are especially so.[1] In fact, we even share the same number of hair follicles all over our bodies as chimps (about five million)[2] although the thickness of the hairs in both species is dramatically different.[3] We also beat them on scalp hair follicle density.[4]

Our body hair might not exactly provide us with a thick protective coat any more, but our evolutionary instinct to cyclically produce, then replace, hair fibres is just as strong. In fact, the only other organ that adult humans regularly shed then regrow is the uterus lining of menstruating people.[5]

Yet cycles of hair growth are familiar

territory in the animal kingdom. Birds routinely replace worn-out feathers with new ones, grow colourful plumage for breeding season and then duller feathers for camouflage.[6] Mammals collectively shed their fur to adapt to warmer and colder seasons. Many grow heavier coats in winter and shed them in preparation for summer - at the cost of disgruntled pet owners' sofas. This enables them to adapt to temperature changes and cleanse their coats of parasites.[7] Some mammals, like the Arctic hare, have even evolved to grow fur that is a different colour depending on the season, which enables them to camouflage themselves in snow or vegetation.[8]

A lack of body hair means us 'naked apes' depend heavily on the very old family of complex pigments that inhabit our skin for protection: melanin.[9] It's the substance that forms colour in our skin, hair, and eyes, but is believed to have had thousands of evolutionary purposes,[10] from facilitating the removal of heavy metals from our bodies,[11] to wound healing and triggering immune responses in plants.[12] Melanin-producing organelles called melanosomes have even been found in fossils dated over 300 million years ago, though experts believe it's far older.[13]

Blast off: kickstarting the pigmentation process

Pigmentation of the skin, hair and eyes starts before we are even born, when cells known as melanoblasts form in the first few weeks of embryonic development. These migrate through the body to the skin where they form specialised cells capable of producing pigment called melanocytes. By 12-13 weeks the majority of melanocytes are localised in the surface of the skin and by 18 weeks they can also be found in the hair follicle (more on that later).[14] (That's bell pepper week if, like me, you Googled what fruit your baby was every week without fail.) As we grow, melanocytes increase in number to cover the expanding surface of the skin.[15]

A number of melanoblasts also form what are known as melanocyte stem cells, and set up home in a handy little bulge at the side of the hair follicle. These cells are capable of creating more melanocytes to make pigment in future hair cycles.[16] In some conditions, they also donate colour to the skin as well. Given the high number of melanocytes found in the skin, biologists are sure that its outer layer - the epidermis - has its own bank of melanocyte stem cells too. We just haven't found it yet.[17]

Melanocytes could be considered employees of the month. Not only do they produce two types of pigment, dark eumelanin and the rarer yellowish pheomelanin,[18] but they also act as baggage handlers, packing them into little pigment suitcases called melanosomes and passing them over to the surface skin cells known as keratinocytes.

Like real holdalls, melanosomes come in different shapes and sizes. This affects the strength of the pigment they carry.[19] Once they've entered the keratinocytes, they act like tiny sunshades, migrating over the top of the nucleus to shield that DNA control centre from ultraviolet light.[20] Gradually the melanosome packaging disintegrates and the melanin disperses throughout the skin cell.[21] Just one melanocyte can transfer melanin to as many as 30 to 50 keratinocytes, all to keep our skin constantly supplied with fresh pigment.[22]

The size and functionality of your melanocytes determines your skin colour. If you have dark skin, the keratinocytes in your skin are regularly fed with large melanosomes that provide a protective barrier against UV light. If, like me, you have pale skin, well, the melanosomes are weedier and less pigmented, meaning you don't

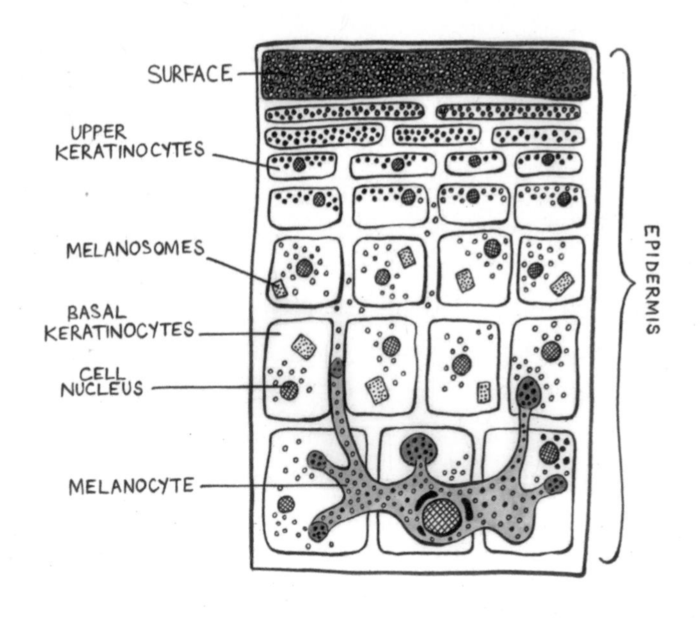

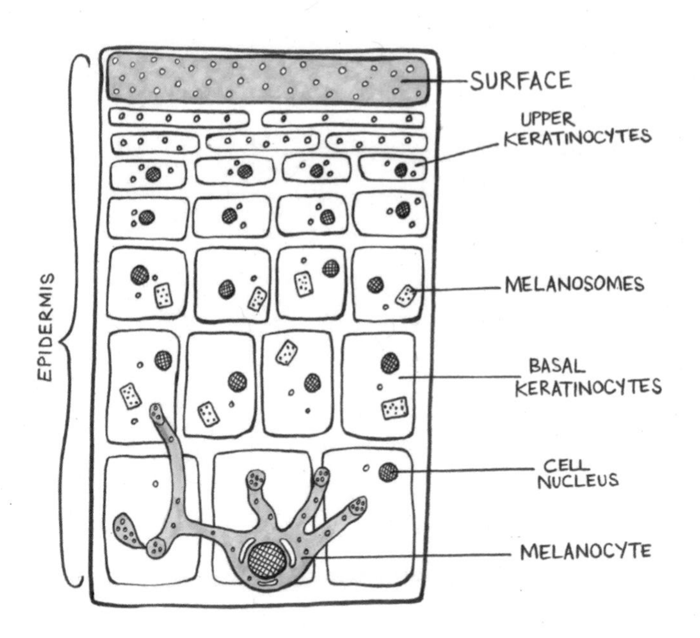

Melanocytes give pigment-filled melanosomes to the skin cells, which then migrate towards the surface. The melanocytes in light skin produce weaker melanosomes that result in paler skin.

receive the same level of UV protection. It's also been suggested that the melanosomes in pale skin tend to form clusters, leading to less protection, and that they degrade as they get closer to the surface of the skin. In fact, dark skin is not only less susceptible to UVR damage but also appears to be more efficient at removing the damaged skin cells that could become cancerous.[23]

Let's say I pop down to the beach for a sunbathe. It's hot, I've got a nice book, perhaps even some childcare. Outwardly, I may be relaxed, but my skin is anything but. The protective cells in exposed areas are calling for backup and rallying the troops. Within minutes of UVR exposure, the melanin in my skin begins to oxidise. A few hours later, an initial tanning response begins, followed by a second phase of tanning a few days later. During this, my melanocytes get busy producing more melanosomes, while existing melanin may also be transferred to the upper layers of my skin.[24] Unfortunately, one study estimated that this 'delayed tanning response' only corresponds to protection equivalent to SPF 3.[25] That's so low it's not even available in shops. Evidently a tan is not a reliable form of sun protection compared to existing skin pigmentation and a generous layer of SPF 50.

Melanocytes are also responsible for creating freckles: those lovely pigmented spots you'll often find in pale skin and redheads. These typically appear in childhood after exposure to the sun.[26] Now I like my own freckles, but I really adore my sister's. She was freckly to the point of impossibility as a child, and I remember her ephelides (scientific name for freckles) charming the locals abroad. She was also once memorably asked by a fascinated neighbour's daughter if they could 'join the dots on her face'.

On the downside, freckles are a key indicator of susceptibility to sun damage and may even form in response to UV harm at a young age.[27] Why? Well, the exact mechanism of freckling remains a mystery but it appears that pale-skinned, freckled folk have some melanocytes that still fire on all cylinders, creating darker, more effective pigment,[28] while the others around them have been downgraded over thousands of years of selection for lighter skin. These large melanocytes churn out pigment in sun-sensitive children exposed to UV light, explaining why freckles tend to appear at a young age.[29]

It may also be that the melanocyte stem cells in freckled individuals are sending a higher number of melanocytes to the same spot in the skin, or creating stronger ones. As our melanocyte stem cells deplete as we age, that would also explain why freckles tend to fade as we get older.[30]

One of the key areas that we see melanocytes hard at work is in our hair.

The root of hair colour

Meet the human hair follicle. Every single one is formed during the very early stages of foetus development in pregnancy,[31] and their first job is to cover unborn babies with lanugo hair. This hair is often fine and downy, and binds a protective, creamy biofilm known as the vernix caseosa to the skin. Some babies are even born with this hair - my daughter had lovely furry shoulders and a very fetching dark fringe that I'd style into a little combover for photos. However, it is ultimately replaced by vellus hair (fine and wispy strands that cover most of our body) and terminal hair (the thicker hairs found on our scalp, eyebrows and eyelashes).[32]

During puberty, human hair becomes more gendered. This is unusual for mammals but not unheard of. One of the most iconic examples is the lion, with males sporting spectacular manes to intimidate rivals and impress females.[33] The males in species like coyotes and white-tailed deers have also been found to have thicker hair than the females.[34] Sex hormones are to blame. In humans, they replace the vellus hairs under the arms and around the genitals with darker terminal hairs, and give men hairier bodies and faces than women.[35]

There are an average of 100,000 hair follicles on the human scalp,[36] and from these grow a range of remarkably different shapes and textures. In fact, we used to attribute hair shape solely to the shape of our follicles. If you have straight hair, your follicle is a bit 'straight up, straight down', while curly and coily hairs have a hooked base. I speak to hair biologist Dr Gillian Westgate and she explains that hair shape is not quite that simple. "Clearly the shape of the follicle is much less curled than the final fibre curl in some cases," she says, "And all the people who've done work on curly hair follicles have also found that there's an

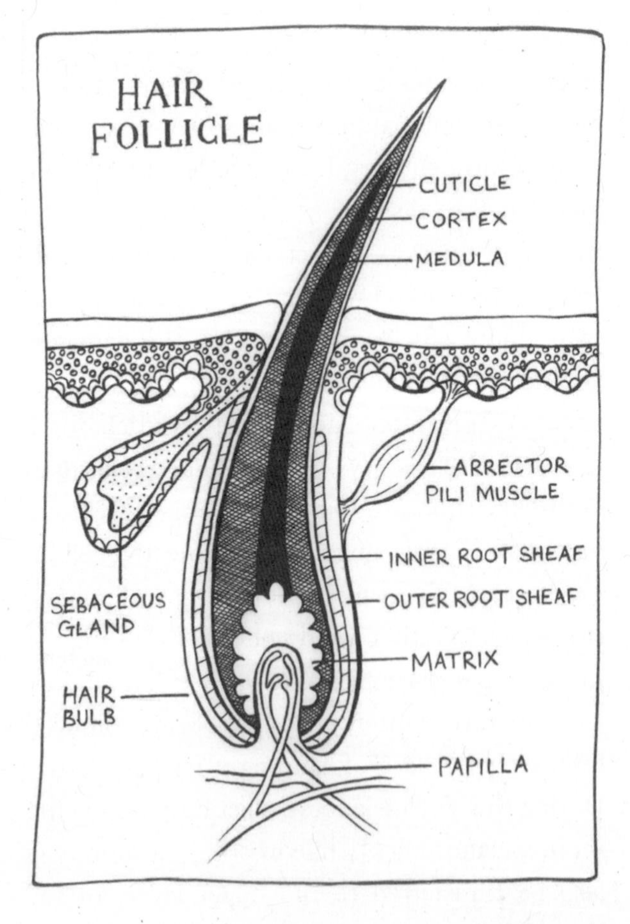

There are an average of 100,000 hair follicles on your scalp and each one is a complex mini organ.

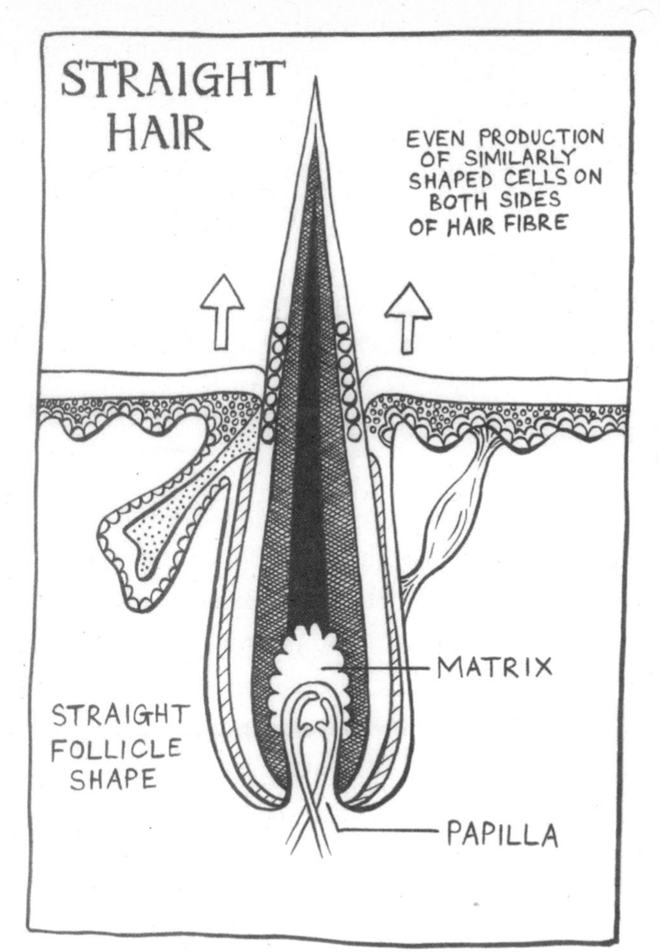

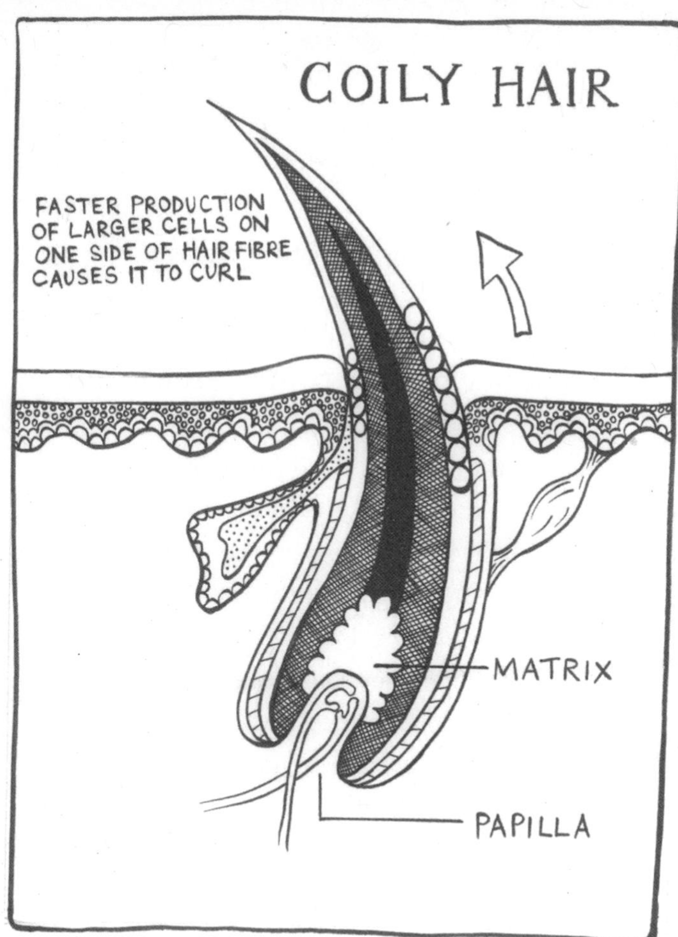

As well as follicle shape, the size, form and production rate of cells inform the curl of the hair fibre.

asymmetry in the proteins that are produced and the timings of their production."

Straight hair fibres are made of large round cells that are produced symmetrically in the follicle. Curly and coily hair fibres have smaller, more irregularly-shaped cells on the concave side of the fibre. These are produced more slowly than the large cells on the outside of the curl, putting pressure on the fibre to curve.[37] Hair shape and follicle density also appear to be linked, with evidence suggesting that people with lighter and finer hair have a higher number of scalp follicles than curly or thick-haired folks.[38] This is probably to provide them with adequate scalp protection.

The injection of melanin into the hair fibre follows a similar Deliveroo-style process to the skin. Stem cells in the hair bulb cook up melanocytes that specialise in pigment delivery. These create melanosomes and transfer them to the keratinocytes in the forming hair fibre.[39]

There's a few key differences to this order-in service, however. Hair melanocytes are larger than their cousins in the skin. They produce bigger melanosomes, have fewer cells to pass them to (around five each, rather than the 30 to 50 their skin cousins cater to), and the melanosomes don't really degrade much. All of this means your hair usually looks more strongly pigmented than your skin, and explains why someone with paler skin can have dark hair.[40]

Melanocyte stem cells in the hair follicle do something even more amazing though. If they receive an SOS from the skin - let's say you've cut yourself or been sunburned - they divert nearby melanocytes from the hair follicle to the damaged area. This creates an area of protective pigmentation to shield the wounded skin from UV light. Isn't that incredible? Your body prioritises the integrity of the skin over the hair, which is why you may notice the hairs near the damaged area appear to lose their pigment.[41]

On the same wavelength: the science of hair colour and shine

Known in the science world as 'colorimetry' or 'chromatics', the colours we see all around us are tricks of light determined by the wavelengths we see on what is known as the electromagnetic radiation. Basically, colour is an illusion. As I have a few gaps in my knowledge here, having spent most of my science lessons fending off bunsen burner attacks from the less enthusiastic students, I'm calling on the services of chemist and science teacher Andrew Browning.

The joys of learning before lockdown means I am able to visit Andrew's house, receive a homemade flapjack from his wife, Jo, (also a teacher), and experience what it's like to have both parents as academics (Andrew's son, who momentarily escapes revision for a snack, is about to sit his GCSEs - or so he thinks). So here I am, all geared up for a science lesson once more. My driving instructor had two years to perform a miracle; Andrew has an hour.

Thankfully, I'm in the hands of a seasoned pro and I'm quickly reminded that our perception of colour is determined by the different wavelengths of light that reflect back from, or are absorbed by, an object. Black absorbs all light, whereas white reflects it all. So, the exact shade of, let's say, brown hair you see depends on exactly how much eumelanin is absorbing light in each and every fibre on your head.

Buoyed by my science lesson, I dive into melanin differences within the hair fibres. Turns out that if you're a brunette, like me, you have a large number of big dark eumelanin melanosomes packed into your hair fibre. These are the pigments that would get picked first in a PE lesson: they're stacked and hardworking, absorbing a majority of the light, which in turn gives the impression of brown or black. Unsurprisingly, dark hair fibres do not contain much yellow pheomelanin (the melanin ratio of someone with black hair is approximately 99% eumelanin and a tiny 1% pheomelanin).[42]

Neither, however, do blonde hair fibres. In fact, only redheads have hair that contains high levels of pheomelanin (about 33%). Blonde hair is also primarily composed of eumelanin (between 82%[43] to 95% according to different studies).[44] However, these melanosomes aren't quite up to scratch, they're a bit weedy and don't really work together well.[45] Because of that, they reflect more light, and we see a lighter colour.

Colour also has a big impact on how shiny your hair looks. Melanin is housed in the middle column of three key layers in the hair fibre, known as the cortex. It surrounds an inner column called the medulla (absent in finer hair, and often thought to be a bit pointless) and is surrounded by a protective outer layer called the cuticle. "Light hitting a hair can do one of two things," explains Andrew. "It can either go through the cuticle and hit the melanin where certain colours will be re-emitted, or it can be reflected from the cuticle and go straight back out."

The amount of shine we see depends on the contrast between these two actions. And yet... why does dark hair appear so shiny if it absorbs so much light? "Imagine little pieces of silver lying on a white beach," says Andrew. "Because something that is white does not absorb any colour, so much light is being re-emitted from the cortex that you won't notice that there is a difference between the reflected light and the re-emitted light.

"But if you have black hair, the dark melanin absorbs all wavelengths of light. Now you've got a big difference because you have reflected light coming back from something that appears black. So if you put those little pieces of silver on a black beach you're more likely to see them because the only light coming from the beach is the light that's reflected."

Andrew is clearly desperate for a beach holiday. But he also explains that it's not just hair colour that has an impact on shine. "The cuticle behaves as a mirror and if it's thicker, more light will be reflected back. Similarly, if the light hits straight hair, it will bounce straight back, whereas if it hits curly hair, it will go in different directions."

I learn that the condition of the hair cuticle is also key. Thankfully I already know a bit about this outer layer, which is made of further tiny layers of protein, fats and amino acids (the building blocks of protein) and lined by chemical-resistant keratinocytes. Rather than fitting like a jigsaw, keratinocytes slightly overlap each other and slope downwards like tiles on a roof. These are then attached to a protective layer of fats which repels water.[46] If the cuticle is raised, uneven or damaged, the light hitting it bounces off in different directions like it would from a broken mirror, explains Andrew. "Sleek, straight, clean, black hair with a thicker, undamaged cuticle and coated with a reflective product is always going to be the shiniest," he concludes. You heard it here first.

Personal growth: the incredible lengths your hair will go to

Unlike the skin melanocytes, which have pigment on a non-stop production line,[47] melanin is only injected into the hair follicle when it is actively growing.[48] But hair growth is also routinely paused with fibres shed and melanin production is parked at this point. When the growth cycle rolls round again, the stem cells in the hair follicle turn the engine back on and start producing pigment-producing melanocytes again.[49]

When it comes to growth, not all your hair is in the same phase at the same time, otherwise it would all fall out en masse - not a great evolutionary feature. Instead, the follicles work collaboratively, meaning as one hair dies, another grows. Once, this would have ensured adequate body cover, but now it is just about keeping your scalp protected. While your body hair cycles through short stages of growth which take place over weeks and days, your scalp can maintain the growth phase for between two to eight years.[50] Ninety percent of your scalp hair is estimated to be in the anagen phase at any given time, though this decreases with age.[51]

Human head hair is capable of reaching amazing lengths. When I worked on the shopfloor in Lush Cardiff, my colleague and dear friend Diana was a veritable Rapunzel, with thick blonde hair down to her hips. If I encountered a blonde in search of hair care, I would wheel out this Welsh goddess wherein she would unfurl her locks commercial-style, and introduce her hero products (Daddy-O shampoo, naturally, a tonne of Marilyn hair treatment and so on). The effect was dazzling.

According to *The Guinness World Records*, the record holder for the world's longest ever documented hair belongs to Xie Qiuping, whose hair reached an incredible 5.6 metres when it was measured in 2004. Teenager Nilanshi Patel, whose locks measured 1.7 metres in 2018, held the record for longest ever hair on a teenager before she had a chop and donated her locks in 2021.[52]

Is there anything you can do to improve your hair growth? Not really, according to Dr Westgate: "Diet and lifestyle can affect the duration of anagen stage, but generally speaking only at the extremes. We know that extreme dieting will cause the cycle to be shorter, but hair

A fairytale-like depiction of Xie Qiuping who began growing her hair in 1973 at the age of 13. In 2004, it was over 5.6 metres long.

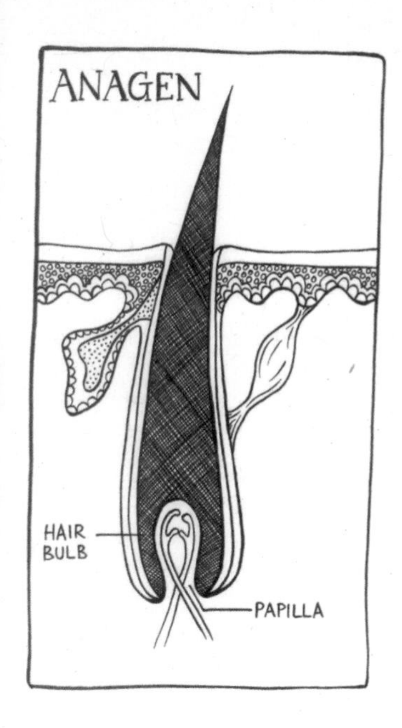

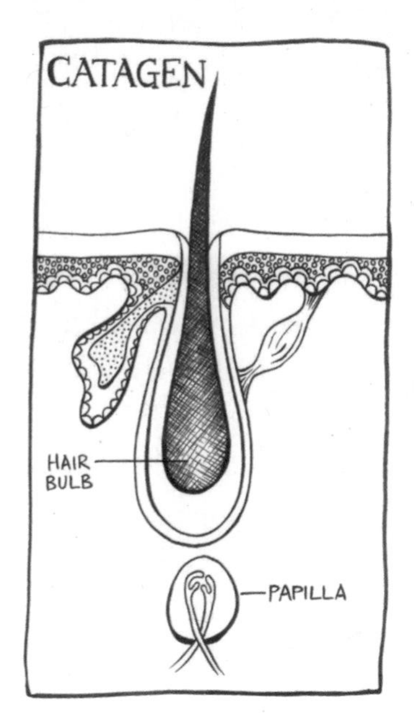

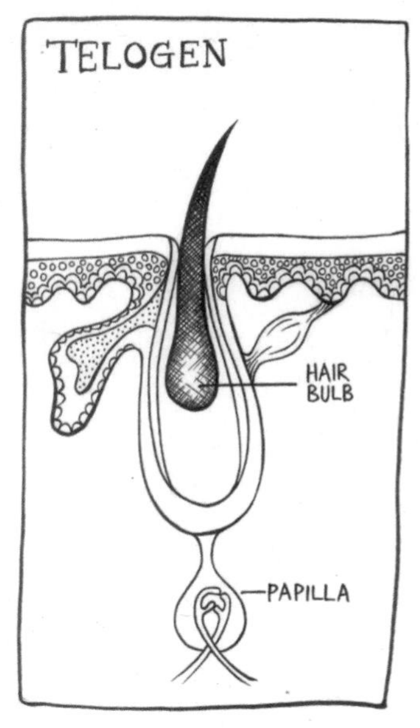

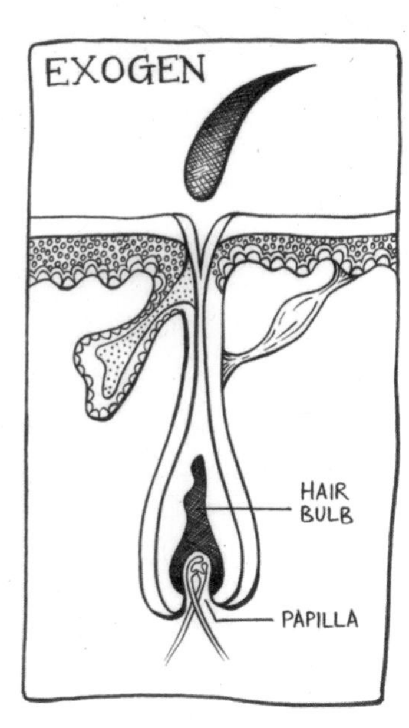

Scalp hair follicles cycle through repeat stages of growth, rest and shedding at different times.

is quite resilient. If someone's short of nutrients, the hair cycle stops, and the hair is shed, so someone might experience more shedding. But when the cycle starts up again that follicle still has the ability to produce the hair that it could have produced if it hadn't been subjected to the stress of the diet."

Before the growth stage is over, melanocytes in the hair bulb stop producing pigment and your follicle enters a much shorter stage called the catagen phase. Over four to six weeks, the follicle head stops feeding the hair fibre and the hair root degenerates. The fibre enters a period of rest known as the telogen stage, which lasts around two to three months, then a final exogen stage when the dead hair fibre is shed.[53]

Most of us lose between 100 and 150 hairs a day,[54] and this can also increase on wash days. While we may not notice it, human hair loss could still be linked to the seasons, with Google searches for hair loss increasing during summer and autumn months.[55] One small study of 14 men in Sheffield, UK, also found increased hair loss during the late summer months, peaking during August and September,[56] while another saw maximum hair loss at the end of the summer.[57] A much larger study - of 823 women this time - over six years in Zurich, Switzerland, found that the highest percentage of hairs entered the telogen stage during July, which would also correlate to shedding in the autumn.[58]

If these results check out, low levels of shedding in the European winter may just insulate our head during colder months, while peak hair fall after the summer solstice (June 21st) could provide protection from the sun during longer daylight hours.[59] Given that these statistics come from people who live in cooler regions where heat dumping isn't a massive concern and likely had long, straight hair textures, they may well differ in hotter places.

But shedding of hair in springtime also fits into common behavioural patterns in the animal kingdom, as Dr Westgate explains. "Seasonal hair loss probably harks back to pre-human ancestors when hair was a very important nest material. Lots of mammals and birds shed in the spring to 'feather' their nests, so to speak - that's literally what happens! So hair being shed in early spring is a part of mammalian evolution."

Growing pains

Aside from seasonal shedding, hair growth and loss can be disrupted during times of hormonal change or stress. If melanocytes are diverted from the hair follicle when the skin is harmed, the entire hair fibre can be deserted during major physical stresses.

Most new mums also notice hair loss a few months post-childbirth, after enjoying a longer anagen growth phase during the second and third trimesters of their pregnancy thanks to increased oestrogen levels.[60] Despite expecting it, I remember being horrified as handfuls of my hair came out in the bath for weeks on end a few months after I had my daughter.

The reason for postnatal hair loss is obscure but trichologist Iain Sallis attributes it to 'acute telogen effluvium': an umbrella term for shock hair loss, in this case triggered by birth.

"There are certain enzymes and hormones that are released when your body tends to come under stress," he explains. "Your body biologically stops the production of about 30% of your scalp hairs, and switches them into a dying phase because it needs the energy, proteins, and nutrition that it would usually spend on growing those hairs. The follicle doesn't die; it just stops producing the hair that it is producing at the time. Then you've got this three month process for the hair to actually be ejected. So, this is why all of a sudden, your hair falls out several months later. And then the hair mostly just grows back."

The (let's be honest) somewhat traumatic physical experience of childbirth has other effects. "Usually you've got this fall in iron due to blood loss," explains Iain, "a massive hormone dip and then you've got an excessive amount of shedding due to this shock process, which happened several months early. All these stresses definitely have an impact on the hair."

Blood loss aside, Dr Westgate cautiously suggests it could even be weakly reminiscent of mammalian nesting behaviour, giving our much hairier ancestral mothers the materials to improve their treetop beds known as nests. "You could imagine hair loss has a similar purpose as springtime shedding in pregnancy, when you need to have natural materials to help with nests and burrows and whatever else," she suggests. "The reason we have a cycle is partly due to the fact that you can't keep the same fibre forever, but it must also be because we need the hair for other reasons than to have it on our bodies."

Emotional, physical, or psychological shocks or stresses can also divert energy from the hair fibres causing later hair loss, such as chemotherapy. Yet a majority of people will notice increased natural hair loss as they age due to hormonal changes that affect the hair follicles. Your genes also determine your susceptibility to balding (which you can thank either parent for). The affected follicles become smaller in diameter, and produce very fine, short and non-pigmented hair fibres.[61] Typically, this is more common in men, affecting around 50% by the age of 50,[62] while most women will not notice pronounced hair loss until their 60s or 70s.[63] Female hair loss is usually also more widely spread across the crown of the head, while men tend to see a receding hairline.

Broadly speaking, White Europeans are likely to experience hair loss at an earlier age than African-Carribean and Asian populations. "This may be because Caucasian men complain about it more," remarks Iain, drily. "But also, they usually wear their hair a little bit longer, whereas many men of African-Caribbean descent, for example, shave their heads. And then if you look at the way that African-Caribbean women use their hair, with cornrows, twists, locs and wigs, you see that we all view hair differently and, therefore, you're not measuring the same variables."

Losing pigment: it's a grey area

I'm consistently referred to Professor of Dermatological Science Desmond Tobin when it comes to questions about hair colour. He has a stellar reputation in the hair colour world and he's written a lot of papers. He's also a super busy man, but his personal assistant kindly gives me 30 minutes to reel off my questions (I'm actually only allotted 20 - but Professor Tobin is generous enough to concede the ten). With time for niceties, I launch right in. Firstly, why can hair colour change dramatically throughout childhood? A lot of my friends who now lighten their hair, for example, say they were blonde as children.

Professor Tobin explains that hormones have a lot to answer for. "A healthy and normal pigmentation system of the human hair follicle changes a lot from birth to even the age of 20, and it's likely to be at least partly hormonal in most cases. Sex steroid hormones are very dominant in driving pigmentation, so a boy's beard area would go from consisting of colourless, fine hairs to dark-pigmented, strong hairs under the influence of sex steroids, particularly testosterone.

"Children with blonde hair will have already turned brown or darker by about five or six years of age," he continues. "The remaining ones will usually turn brown by puberty. It's only a very, very small number of typical Brits of Anglo-Saxon geographic ancestry (less than 5%) that will remain noticeably blonde after puberty, despite the fact that you see 30% to 40% of people walking down the streets apparently with blonde hair. You see the same sometimes in children who have vivid red hair that becomes quite auburn by the time they go through puberty."

Skip forward a few decades and finding that first grey hair can cause significant emotional distress. I turned 30 recently and for the first time my hairdresser gently asked if I had noticed any 'twinkly' hairs yet (I haven't). As a White woman, this is likely to happen sooner rather than later: Europeans typically begin to grey in their mid-30s, Asians in their late 30s, and Africans in their mid-40s.[64] But, of course, this is an average not a rule. When my daughter's lovely childminder (whose exact age remains private knowledge but let's say she's over 50) casually mentions that her brown hair is all natural, I'm both gobsmacked and filled with optimism.

The mid-thirties thing surprised me actually. That's because I actually don't know any mid to late-thirties women who go about their day to day life with noticeable grey hairs. Presumably a fair number are using hair dye, like I know many of my friends do for this purpose. I can't help but feel it perpetuates the idea that grey hairs at this age are unnatural.

When we talk about 'grey' hair we are essentially referring to unpigmented hairs that have stopped producing melanin. Against pigmented hairs - especially darker fibres, the impression we get is of grey. Professor Tobin tells me that, in some cases, you can see the transition from dark to light in single hair fibres in the lab. The contrast between light and dark is why unpigmented hairs are much more noticeable in brunettes while the hair of blondes and redheads instead appears to lighten with age. I only noticed the other day that my mum has somehow transitioned from warm blonde to icy silver under my very nose.

Professor Tobin explains that hair greying is modulated by an extensive range of genetic, psycho-emotional, age, metabolic and nutritional-related factors. These are big words. He helpfully summarises: "There is still no universally accepted model for why human scalp hair loses pigment. It starts in the anagen hair bulb, however, eventually the stem cell pool becomes depleted, at which stage hair greying is largely irreversible." Recent research is also showing that periods of stress can trigger loss of pigment in hair that is 'on the threshold' of greying. In some cases, this is reversible when the stressor ends. Stress, for example, will not induce hair greying in a young child but might in a 30-year-old, suggest the study authors.[65]

Hair typically does not just lose colour when it greys. The loss of pigment also seems to correlate with a change in the texture of the fibre, making it a little wirier and less manageable - you may notice that grey hair stands on end and is trickier to style. This may be to provide additional protection to the scalp after the loss of protective pigment, but it also makes the fibre harder to colour.

Rogue greys aside, our hair generally decolours as we age. Perhaps more surprisingly, our skin does too. This is big news to me, though it makes sense when I think about it: both are controlled by melanocytes and the number of these in your skin decreases by about 10% per decade after the age of 30.[66]

While you probably won't notice an obvious change in your skin tone, you may notice the loss of pigment in other ways. Professor Tobin explains, "Take a woman who has dyed her hair black since she was in her 20s. She may continue into her 30s and it still looks fine, but when she gets into her 50s and 60s it may start to look very harsh against her skin tone. That's largely because the skin tone of the woman has also blanched a bit with time, as well as the healthy glow of youthful skin – not just the colour of the melanin pigment, but also the pinkness of the skin."

"When it comes to the ageing effect of the hair follicle, it appears that the ageing of the skin and hair follicle appears earlier in White Europeans than in people of Asian or African origin. That's largely because genetic differences will play out in thousands of different aspects of their physiology, including their aging. But diet is also often very different between geographic ancestry populations as well, and sometimes diet can offset some of the impacts of physical/chemical forces like sunlight."

While a vitamin B12 deficiency can lead to premature hair greying, there's not a huge amount you can do to stop the inevitable, according to Iain Sallis. "By and large, your hair will de-colour according to your DNA," he says. "These cells that you are made of have a biological timer. The people you might look at and say 'Bloody hell, you look good for your age' have a slightly better genetic process than someone who looks 50 when they're 20. And that is just, unfortunately, genetic pot luck. Things can influence it like smoking and bad diets, but not a massive amount. You can't outrun your genetics."

You can conceal them though, as so many women choose to. I always assumed I would when I started to grey. But why is that? Why do we stress about grey hair so much? I can only speculate it's due to a very primal and ancient desire to appear young, particularly for women. It's a bitter pill to swallow when we wish to move away from being judged or defined by our looks, but perhaps it comes down to that old chestnut - mating preferences again.

Research suggests our traditional parenting roles still affect what we look for in a partner. While male fertility appears to begin declining after 40,[67] a woman is maximally fertile in her twenties and this begins to decrease from as early as 32.[68] Studies have shown that women tend to look for high-status men who are able and willing to divert resources to them and their offspring, while men have been shown to prefer younger partners who are able to have more children. This harks back to that subliminal primal desire to have lots of females raising their offspring.[69]

Interestingly enough, as men age and their fertility does decline, they have still been shown to prefer increasingly younger partners, apparently because of the subliminal knowledge that it increases reproductive success whether children are planned or not.[70] Although female choice probably decides the bulk of modern mating choices, retaining that mate - and this is painful to write - may still feel dependent on looking young and fertile. With hair condition a visual marker of age - and thus fertility and perceived attractiveness - the trap is sprung. Sigh.

And, of course, female insecurity is the beauty industry's bread and butter. Yet hair dye has a fascinating and very complex history and men too have fallen under its sway. Think that colouring your hair is a modern concept? Think again. We've been putting all kinds of stuff on our heads for thousands of years, some respectable like henna and indigo, others less so: putrefied slugs, metal pigments and cat blood. We've invented new technology to address an age-old desire - one that feels very uncomfortable but necessary to probe. Desperate though I am to agree with Mark's overwhelming confidence in female choice, I don't know that I'm going to like what I find.

The good, the bad and the social climbers: the intriguing roots of hair colouring

3

Head hair has been a source of gender, class and racial anxieties for thousands of years. It's a reminder of our primal past - a visible link to our closest primate cousins that needs to be tamed and cultivated as 'proof' of our civility. It's a malleable tool we can shape into fashions: a source of magic in fairy tales and subversive power in folklore.

Hair is also sexy. It's one of the only sites of noticeable human body hair that is not concealed by clothing. Clean, healthy and pigmented hair advertises our youth, fertility and 'good genes' to potential partners. All over the world, men and women also typically wear their hair differently to advertise their gender.

This does not always mean short hair for men and long hair for women, although this is the western norm. Male Tikopia islanders in Melanesia, Oceania, traditionally wore their hair long and bleached it with lime, while most women wore theirs cropped. Tasmanian men would similarly stain their long hair red with ochre obtained from roasted iron ores, and fought fiercely against British attempts to cull the practice during the brutal colonisation of Australia in the early 19th century.[1]

As the works of historians like Emma Dabiri are revealing, hair-styling is also inherently political. 'Flapper' girls of the 1920s rejected strict conservative female dress and cut off their long hair,[2] while advocates of the US Black Pride movement of the 1960s wore their hair in statement-making Afro styles.[3] Changing your hair so that it conforms to the status quo - or not - sends a powerful message.

Changing your hair colour carries a similar meaning. It can give individual agency or enhance a communal identity. It can conceal the signs of age and the inevitable social marginalisation that comes with it. An Iron Age Celtic warrior would bleach his hair into white spikes with limewater, then streak it blue with woad to spook his enemies in battle.[4] A wealthy Venetian woman in Renaissance Italy would lighten her hair to indicate her desirable high status on the competitive marriage market. A man in ageist, industrialised America would dye his grey hairs to hold onto his job for as long as possible.

Many of our early hair dye techniques were derived from the methods we used to dye fabric. For thousands of years, we experimented with pigments extracted from flowers, plants and bark - even insects and shellfish - to colour our clothes and materials. When temporary rinses and dyes were not satisfying enough, we got inventive, creating lasting effects with the use of mordants: substances that use a chemical reaction to make the dye bind to the fibre.[5] Different mordants suited different materials, and could be applied before, during, or after the dye process. Some dyes, such as alum (also known as potash - literally 'pot ash'), chrome, and tin, would brighten material, while others like copper (also known as blue vitriol) and iron would darken it.[6]

Cosmetic consultant and former industry chemist Dr Robert Hefford explains that many early recipes relied heavily on the metallic mordants to actually give them any staying power at all. "Metals have been used for a very long time in trying to colour hair," he says, "and were often obtained by using an iron or copper container and an acidic solution like vinegar or 'old wine' that dissolved some of the metal from the container and into whatever horrible mixture they had. This might act on its own, but more often the metal will interact in some way with a material derived from the plant or organic source, either as a mordant or a catalyst for oxidising things. These metals will chelate [bind] with anything organic and give you colours."

These primitive hair colouring methods would be honed over the years (modern gradual colourants are, indeed, still metallic) until the birth of the modern hair dye industry in the 19th and 20th centuries when a new class of dye was utilised: aromatic amines. These shiny new materials revolutionised the ease with which a person could colour their hair and gave uniform results. In the 1970s, however, they were under scrutiny for their potentially carcinogenic effects. While much of the beauty industry was anxiously looking to the future, Mark Constantine was looking back in time.

"I was having a good rummage through the drawers of history trying to find something we forgot, something I could nick," he remarks with a smile. "I would talk to painters and look at the pigments they used. I spent a lot of time talking to weavers at craft fairs and reading books on dyeing wool and then trying those same experiments - but they used to boil the wool in a mordant and, well, of course, you couldn't boil heads!"

Brandishing an eye-catching knitted vest with a diamond pattern, Mark draws my attention to the different colours in each segment. "Well it doesn't take long to have a conversation with a weaver before you find out that her mother knows all about mordants and dying with herbs," he says, as if that were obvious. "I got in touch with this lady, she spun some sheep wool into this tank top and dyed it with all the different herbs that I'd written about in the *Herbal Hair Colouring* book.

"Then she gave me a colour wheel telling me what she had dyed each section with, which I have since lost. But there were all kinds: alkanet, onion skins, henna, logwood... all of the herbs and plants that were in my little book. And I would wear that knitted vest when I had my henna parties. It's a little snug over the tummy now - I look like a football with bloody arms and legs - but it's still very lovely and very dear to me."

Not only a massive henna enthusiast but a pro at rifling through the bathrooms of antiquity (and his staff), Mark also advises me on where to begin my journey into the origins of hair colouring. I'm heading east to scrutinise the cosmetic cabinets of the Ancient Egyptians.

Looking good for the Afterlife: beauty secrets of Ancient Egypt

The Ancient Egyptians took looking good seriously, and by looking good I mean looking young. An iconic - if not entirely accurate - modern image of this superpower has been cultivated of razor-sharp black wigs, winged eyeliner and penchant for sending the dead off in spectacular style, and so it's fitting that they are responsible for some of our earliest evidence of cosmetics, including hair dye.

Egyptologist Professor Joann Fletcher explains, "The Egyptians always tended to portray themselves as eternally youthful, vigorous and full of life. This is all rooted in their firm belief in the Afterlife, where they would live forever in idealised form, doing all the things they had loved to do when alive, and of course, looking their best, quite literally."

New dynasties over the epic 5,000 year-long period may have heralded new fashions but a person's hair remained a key indicator of their social standing. Many Ancient Egyptian men would wear their hair cropped or shaven to cope with heat and lice, with wealthy men adopting a stylish shoulder-length wig. Elite women would often wear their hair long, supplemented with extensions - human hair was a valued commodity to be traded and turned into hair pieces or wigs. Strutting round town with an impressive toupée sent a clear message: you had the money to look good and to appropriate the hair of others.[7]
"The Egyptians were among the first ancient cultures to create wigs and hair extensions," elaborates Professor Fletcher. "These could be worn along with the natural hair, or sometimes in place of the natural hair. But when it comes to status, given the amount of hair required to make a complete wig - and the time and expertise taken - these were costly items and only really available to the wealthy. By contrast, hair extensions were far more cost-effective and therefore available to most people in society." (Professor Fletcher has previously taken to task those who assume hair extensions were only used by Egyptian women).[8]

Hair dyes were also a popular weapon in the beauty armory of any self-respecting Ancient Egyptian with a little spare income, and recipes from the period include the blood of a black calf or fat of a black snake boiled in oil.[9] Wealthy, high-status individuals took care to conceal greying hair and receding hairlines, which were symbolic of disempowerment. In art too, it is the lower status subjects who are usually shown with a receding hairline, greying or unkempt hair. White hair does not appear to have carried the same stigma at the height of the New Kingdom (c.1400-1200 BC), and was occasionally depicted on some higher-status people.[10]

Professor Fletcher was also part of the team to identify the oldest example of hair dye use in Egypt when she studied the remains of a woman from a cemetery at Hierakonpolis that dated back to an incredible c.3,400 BC. "Although tomb robbers had ransacked her burial in ancient times so we were dealing with fragments only," she explains, "enough remained to show that her hair had been elaborately styled with a central section of what could be described as almost loc-like hair extensions. And these - and her natural hair to which they had been attached - had all been coloured with henna."[11]

The Ancient Egyptians are among the first to be identified as using henna (*Lawsonia inermis*) as a hair dye and a nail stain[12] although this claim is not without controversy.[13] Henna has also always been Mark's very favourite herbal colourant. "Henna was always the best of all the herbs," he enthuses. "It gave really superb results and had such a long history of use. When I went to the British Museum and saw the beards that the female pharaohs wore to give them authority, I saw that lots of the mummies had hennaed hair."

It's true. Although historians differ in their belief of how popular henna was as a hair dye (some arguing that it was not in use at all, as discussed in Chapter 10),[14] the auburn-red tint derived from henna on dark hair was seemingly fashionable amongst the upper class[15] (or at least vastly preferable to greying hair, such was the Egyptians' preoccupation with appearing young). Henna may have also been used on greying hair as part of the famed embalming process, with dyed red hair found on a number of mummies including Pharaoh Ramses II (c. 1303–1213 BC).[16]
Professor Fletcher believes Ramses' potential use of henna was probably to replicate his original hair colour, which Egyptologists know was a rich auburn like that of his father Seti I. "This is particularly interesting," she explains, "since Seti himself was named after the ancient god

Seth, a deity associated with turbulence, storms and the colour red, and whose followers were known as 'red-headed forms' with a reputation as unruly misfits. Given their own hair colour, it is therefore quite likely that both Seti and his son Ramses turned any ambivalence toward their hair colour and their associations with Seth into a positive, stressing the god's great strength and rehabilitating him into Egypt's divine pantheon."

Was the iconic Cleopatra VII (69 BC – 30 BC) a henna fan too? Professor Fletcher believes so, based on an auburn-haired posthumous portrait that has been identified as the famous female pharaoh. Cleopatra's affiliations with Rome - she married Julius Caesar (100 BC – 15 44 BC) and Mark Antony (83 BC – 30 BC) [17] - where fairer hair was fashionable, may have encouraged her to tint her auburn hair a richer colour. She may have even been a fully-fledged redhead.

"It is entirely possible that Cleopatra's hair colour was at least enhanced with henna," argues Professor Fletcher, "since by the 1st century BC, red hair was hugely fashionable within Cleopatra's court in Alexandria and around the Greek and Roman worlds of which Egypt was by then a central part. Also the henna shrub was common around Canopus in Egypt's Delta region, a place where Cleopatra had a palace, while the best quality henna came from Askalon (Ashkelon) in Judaea, again, a region Cleopatra stayed on several occasions and from where she even issued some of her coins."[18]

Although hair dye was probably used predominantly by Egyptian women as men were more likely to shave their heads, its use is clearly linked to a desire to appear young on the part of both sexes. Part of this was about social power: being able to afford the means to maintain your appearance was an indication of status. Cosmetics in general were not highly gendered. While beauty was a prized trait in an Egyptian woman and her main responsibility was still judged to be domestic, she also enjoyed what I'm discovering was an unusual number of legal rights such as land ownership compared to her ancient peers.[19] A small number of women like Cleopatra even ruled as Pharaoh in their own right - not as a consort.[20]

Significantly, the Egyptians also believed that (amongst other trials) the physical body had to be preserved and recognisable to enable it to reunite with the soul in the Afterlife, so those who could afford to were invested in caring for their appearance.[21] Some of the spells in the *Book Of The Dead* (a collection of texts written to guide a person's soul through the underworld) even exact specifications about a person being clean, well-dressed and made up before they could invoke them.[22]

A youthful example was also expected to be upheld by the Pharaoh. Rulers celebrating thirty years on the throne today might expect a jubilee and a street party, but an Egyptian Pharaoh reaching this milestone had to prove they had the physical prowess to continue to rule. The festival known as the *Heb Sed* required an ageing ruler to take part in physical tests such as running around his palace to illustrate his divine youthfulness - the Pharaoh's living spirit being considered vital to the health of Egypt.[23] It's even been suggested that, in earlier times, the Pharaoh may have been murdered if he failed to complete the tests. Harsh crowd.[24]

Pretty hurts: going for gold in Ancient Greece and Rome

A wealthy woman is preparing for a hot date, Ancient Rome-style. An *alipilus* (arm-pit plucker) removes hair from her underarms using pumice or Venetian clay, while an enslaved attendant applies a salve of bear fat to her eyebrows and

An interpretation of a wall scene from Herculaneum, Italy, is believed to be a posthumous portrait of Cleopatra who stayed with Julius Caesar in Rome 46-44 BC. Notably, the figure has red hair.

manicures her nails. A cream containing white lead is used to whiten her complexion whilst another attendant paints delicate blue veins on her temples.[25] Her hair, naturally dark, has been treated with a bleaching soap made of goat's fat and beechwood ash to lighten it to a fairer, auburn shade. More daring ladies will insist on a higher proportion of ash in their bleach to lighten the hair further, bleaching the fibres literally to breaking point.[26] Still, as the writer of one contemporary letter consoles his thus afflicted sweetheart, "Do not worry, dear; now Germany will send you tresses from captive women."[27]

How romantic.

Growing up, like the Romans, I always knew blonde hair was special. Barbie reigned supreme, fairy tales were filled with Rapunzels, and Disney's most eligible princesses were always golden-haired. Blonde hair meant beauty, star quality and charisma. As a brunette child with a blonde best friend, I was, sadly, always going to be the Posh to her Baby Spice.

To be a natural blonde is to be special - it's a belief that's been ingrained in western society for thousands of years. It's rare, but without the negative stigma that has dogged red hair, and it's gold, giving it monetary appeal. The hair of most naturally blonde children darkens during puberty giving it associations with youth and purity. The (usually) corresponding light skin also adds a racial undertone to the reverence of light hair.

We can trace the reverence of blonde hair back to the Ancient Greeks. Amongst this predominantly dark-haired civilisation, fair hair was associated with health, wealth, youthfulness, and any number of Greek heroes. Indeed the finest specimens of Greek manliness such as Achilles and Ulysses were commonly depicted as auburn-haired by contemporaries such as Homer.[28] Lighter hair may have been considered to signify nobility and indicate the purest Hellenic bloodline. But while it was admired in all, blondeness became irrevocably entwined with female sensuality and beauty - the cult of goddess of love and fertility Aphrodite.

Prostitutes borrowed the famous deity's crowning glory, rubbing saffron (Crocus sativus) tints, yellow muds and coloured powders into their naturally dark locks. Wealthier prostitutes would even purchase blonde wigs at great cost from abroad. Golden hair afforded these sex workers visibility and status, drawing on the rarity of fair hair and the mythological allure of Aphrodite and other classical blondes.[29] Not only was golden hair now desirable for its classical illusions about Greek excellence, but it was also incredibly sexy.

And that was dangerous. In a society in which women were passed between male guardians and married as young as 15 to ensure their virginity,[30] female sexual power threatened the established status quo that reinforced male power, and the birth of undisputed sons. A typical Greek woman was not able to enter into financial contracts above the price of a "medimnos" of barley - enough for petty bargains at market but no major business transactions[31] - and the only significant public role she could play was in sacred ceremonies and rituals.[32] So, no matter what the reality of her situation was, a courtesan at least symbolised the kind of freedom no Athenian woman could hope to enjoy, and her blondeness added to her glamour.[33] It was to begin the long-standing contradictory appeal of female blondeness: both virginal, youthful beauty and dangerous sensuality.

Despite its associations with sexual lasciviousness and foreignness, blonde hair is also reputed to have become popular amongst Roman women when legionnaires began bringing back fairer-haired enslaved people from Western Europe. As domestic slaves were commonly coerced into sex with their masters, some historians have assumed this evoked the jealousy of Roman wives - although in my mind this is a classically reductive view of women. Perhaps rare genuine affection between an enslaved blonde and her master - and his favouring of her - might have triggered a wife's enmity, but sexual abuse probably didn't. The rise in numbers - and social status of - fairer-haired Germans in the Roman Empire over several centuries may have also contributed to the popularity of fairer hair.[34]

Red hair, mostly encountered in the 'uncivilised' Celts who fiercely rebelled against subjugation, did not appear to overcome its associations with barbarism in the same way.[35] It may have been that vividly red hair was associated with a certain tempestuousness that was not considered an attractive female quality. A famous supposed redhead of the period was Boudicca of the Iceni - a woman who exacted terrible revenge against the Romans when her land was taken and her daughters raped. We don't have much reliable information about Boudicca but Roman historians fixate on her savageness and flaming red hair - probably because it fits a stereotype about redheads cultivated since ancient times.[36]

An ancient brunette inspired to give nature a helping hand would bleach her hair with sapo: a soapy alkaline substance made of beechwood ash and animal tallow. This would have given dark hair a lighter, auburn tone. Walnuts and saffron could also be used to add red-gold hues.[37] Some women even ran the risk of destroying their hair completely as Roman poet Ovid (43BC-17AD) noted in Elegy XIV of his Amores: "I always used to say; 'Do leave off doctoring your hair,'" remarks Ovid's narrator curtly. "And now you have no hair left that you can be dyeing."[38]

Several high-profile Roman blondes mark the pages of history, such as Roman Emperors Caligula (12-41 AD) and Commodus (161-192 AD), who have both been noted as either bleaching their hair yellow or wearing a blonde wig.[39] However, female bleaching practices are typically condemned as an indication of lust - both for sex and power - by contemporaries. The famous beauty Poppaea (30 – 65 AD), second wife of Emperor Nero (37 – 9 June 68 AD) was famous for her 'amber' hair and the money she spent lavishly on saffron tints.[40] In his Satire VI, the Roman poet Juvenal also wrote explicitly about the apparently insatiable Empress Messalina (AD c.20-48) who reportedly "dared, at night, to wear the hood of a whore [...] with a blonde wig hiding her natural hair"[41] and sneak out of the palace to act as a prostitute in brothels. There, it is said, she frequently dislodged her headpiece, rendering her disguise useless.[42] Historians have since argued that Roman prostitutes were legally required to wear a blonde wig or bleach their hair as a symbol of their status.

But classicist Professor Kelly Olson says this was tripe. "The idea that Roman prostitutes had to wear blonde wigs is ridiculous. It's a modern misreading of a source that tells us about Empress Messalina's exploits that has been misinterpreted by modern historians. For one thing, wigs were expensive and most prostitutes would not have been able to afford them, and, in addition, the Romans had no way of enforcing that law."

As we speak virtually, Professor Olson confirms that, despite the backlash against bleaching, blonde was indeed the prized colour amongst the female masses, although it may have been a different shade to what we imagine blonde to be today. "The problem was they didn't have bleaches or peroxides," she explains. "There were a few substances that were reputed to lighten hair but nothing that was going to lighten their dark Mediterranean hair that much. The ancients also didn't have very precise colour terminology for a number of reasons and so it might be that

For those who could afford it, saffron has long been popular for adding golden tints to fair hair, especially amongst the women of Ancient Rome and Renaissance Venice.

everything on the red-gold-yellow colour band was termed blonde."

Criticisms of hair colouring were rooted in fears that women enhancing their desirability were undermining male control. Like Greece, Rome was a fiercely patriarchal society, meaning social and legal power was wielded by and transferred to men. Sexually liberated women who might have illegitimate children threatened the stable transfer of power, titles and privilege.

Greek poet Menander (c.342—292 BC) suggested that synthetic blondes were "outraging the character of gentlewomen, causing the overthrow of houses, the ruin of nuptials and accusations on the part of children."[43] Christian author Quintus Septimus Florens Tertullianus (c.155 - c.220 AD) went further, accusing bleached blondes of not only being anti-Christian but anti-empire. "I see some women dye their hair blonde by using saffron. They are even ashamed of their country, sorry that they were not born in Germany, Gaul!"[44] We might suggest that he was possibly more upset than the good Lord may have been - and yet his apocalyptic anger shows how deeply entrenched male ownership over female bodies was.

Professor Olson also tells me the Romans and the Greeks had a strong anti-cosmetics tradition. "Male writers are very prescriptive in Ancient Rome," she says, "they talk about what women should be doing rather than what they are doing (aside from the mentions of women who are using hair dye and are being ridiculed for it, either because it's not effective or because it's made their hair fall out). Yet, we have tonnes and tonnes of evidence that Roman women are using hair dye and cosmetics," she laughs, "so clearly they don't give a fig for the male anti-cosmetics tradition."

I'm intrigued that despite its associations with prostitution and captive foreigners, blonde hair captured the female imagination quite like it did. Was it a small but collective means of rebellion against the control held over their lives? A means of empowerment? Or did blonde hair symbolise a form of power or glamour missing from their lives?

"The age-old story is that women want to make themselves attractive to men and that's certainly what Roman men think they are doing," muses Professor Olson. "Of course there's never any mention of attracting other women - the Romans are a very phallocentric society and they operate according to very heteroerotic norms. But I wonder if women were using cosmetics because it made them feel good. It gave them a noticeable presence in a world where they really didn't have the same powers that men do. They couldn't vote, get into politics or have high-powered careers; the majority of them were really forced to be wives and mothers. They didn't have a creative outlet, so I wonder if cosmetics allowed women to be noticed for their appearance if they couldn't be noticed for their social activities."

She explains that evidence of men using hair dye is notably scarce, although this doesn't mean they didn't use it. "We assume men are embarrassed by going bald because we do have scientific treaties with lots of cures for baldness. So Julius Caesar was balding and always wore a laurel crown to try and disguise this. But grey hair, I think, would have been desired for men. It's kind of depressingly similar to today where grey-haired men are distinguished-looking and grey-haired women are just old. It really doesn't change - it's very depressing."

A number of recipes did exist to dye the hair black, including this treat from Roman author Pliny the Elder (AD 23-79): "one sextarius of leeches to be left to putrefy the same number of days in a leaden vessel with two sexterri of vinegar, the hair to be well-rubbed with the mixture in

The use of henna to colour the hair predates Islam in the Middle East, but a red beard became a popular indicator of religious piety amongst Muslim men.

the sun". He further advised taking the helpful precaution of holding oil in the mouth during application to prevent the teeth turning black.[45]

Yet, dyeing the hair dark didn't attract the same attention that bleaching did. Perhaps its effects were less obvious on the dark Mediterranean heads of the Romans or, if we consider the perils of repetitive pregnancies and childbirths, it may be that the women who survived to gain and conceal their first grey hairs were just not numerous enough to warrant attention.[46] I'm beginning to suspect though that the very brazenness of obviously bleached hair bothered certain Romans. To them, it represented uncontrolled female sexuality, foreignness, and had anti-empire connotations that hair darkening did not.

Deep dark secrets: hair dye in early Islam

In the ancient Middle East, long, luxuriant and finely oiled hair was the crowning glory of any man or woman but particularly royalty. Hair and beards were loaded with symbolism during the Persian[47] Achaemenid Empire period (553–330 BC) when the status of kings was reflected in the fantastic length of their beards.

Kings like Darius I (550-486 BC) also liked what they saw during the Achaemenid conquest of Egypt in the 6th century BC, and drew on the depictions of elaborately-styled Pharaohs to present themselves as powerful, youthful and divine. False hair would be woven into the beards and natural hair of the elite to display virility and rank, while prisoners of war could have their beards shaved in an act of humiliation. In doing so, ruling Persian classes modelled themselves in the image of the long-haired biblical heroes of Eastern antiquity like Samson, who lost his supernatural strength when his lover Delilah treacherously cut his hair. While long hair was prized, however, an important stipulation was that it needed to be well-dressed and cared for - unkemptness was associated with barbarism. Hair that was thin or of poor length or quality was also considered to symbolise ill health or uncleanliness.[48]

The beauty habits of Persian women are less documented, although a woman's most beautiful feature was commonly considered to be her hair and much attention was paid to its length and quality as an indication of fertility.[49] The veiling and seclusion of women, which predates the 7th century AD Islamic conquest, however, would have removed many women - particularly wealthy ones - from the public glaze. Covering the hair was intrinsically linked to female virtue and the concept of women being impure, particularly during menstruation and childbirth.[50] The importance of bathing rituals for women in particular to compensate for this impurity was probably reflected in the emphasis on the health and condition of their hair through which she showcased both her fertility and chastity.

The use of indigo (*Indigofera tinctoria*) and henna to colour and treat the hair also pre-date Islam in the Middle East (see Chapter 10 for the origins of henna use) and are referenced in pre-Islamic Arabic verses (one example reads, "The blood of many leaders of herds is in him, thick as the juice of henna in combed white hair).[51] The grandfather of the Prophet Mohammed himself, Abd al-Muttalib Shaybah ibn Hashim (480- 578 AD), is famously said to have been introduced to the custom of using a mixture of henna and a dark plant-based dye (possibly indigo) on his beard by a king of Yemen.[52] Yet, despite its ancient origins, male use of henna to dye beards was actively encouraged as a sign of devotion to the Prophet Mohammed, and when it came to colour the brighter the better. Professor of Islamic Thought

Ahmed El Shamsy believes there was an ulterior motive for this eye-catching look.

"My hypothesis is that Islam emerged as a reform movement of Abrahamic religions," he explains "and so wanted to keep within the biblical world of law. There is a section in the Bible that says that men should not imitate women. And so, while women may dye their hair to cover grey hairs, men should not imitate them and dye their hair in the same way. In Jewish law, as a man, you are not allowed to dye your hair or beard when it goes grey and you are not allowed to pluck the grey hairs either."

He continues, "Muslim leaders did not want Muslim men to hide the fact that their hair was greying, but to distinguish themselves in a communal way from the Jews. If you dye your hair an unnatural colour, you are indicating that your hair has greyed but you still look different. They went for a very specific colour and when they didn't have henna, they'd use materials like turmeric and saffron."[53]

Was women's hair dyeing of the same interest in Islam, I ask? "In these legal discussions, I don't see any mention, discussion or preoccupation with women using it at all," he replied. "It is solely about men; there appears to be no concern with women dyeing their hair. The original impetus seems to be that women do it and it is acceptable, but that men should not do it too."

Professor El Shamsy goes on to suggest that as Islam grew in numbers during the 7th century AD conquests, the pressure of appearing distinct fell on the new minority religions, not the Muslim community. With the spread of the religion into India and Northern Africa, the practice of dyeing the beard red only survived in some regions such as Yemen, Bangladesh and the Indian subcontinent, or amongst those particularly adherent to the example that Mohammed set. Beard dyeing, then, had truly become about identifying yourself as a fervent follower of Islam and the Prophet's example.

He also likens it to the type of culture war we are experiencing today with Covid-19. "Take the US; if you are a Conservative these days, you don't wear a mask. Donald Trump doesn't wear a mask. And if you are a man you don't wear a mask. But if you are a liberal, you wear a colourful mask. It just becomes a matter of people's identities and I think hair colouring stays like this."

Although beard dyeing using dark colours did occur, and became more acceptable towards the end of the 7th century, men caught using hair dye to deceive could face severe consequences. In one notable example, the second *Caliph* to the Prophet Muhammed, Umar ibn al-Khaṭṭāb (584-644 AD) dissolved a marriage (and had the husband beaten) after his new wife's very indignant parents complained that he had concealed his age by dyeing his hair black.[54]

Religious piety aside, being attractive for women was also considered important by some male hair dyers. "Don't you know that she [your wife] would like to see in you what you would like to see in her?" berates poet Al-Sharīf al-Raḍi (970-1016 AD). "If there are women who have become unchaste, it's because their husbands have taken little care of their appearance for their sake."[55] It's a staggeringly different attitude to western writers. Far be it for me to tell my partner to break out the Grecian 2000, but I have to admit it's a little nice to see men being held to unrealistic beauty standards.

Over 800 years later, British Officer Frederick Burnaby writes that dyed red beards were still a familiar sight in West Azerbaijan Province, Iran. Imagining this must be solely for attracting women (and showing the lack of cultural understanding for which we Brits were renowned), he writes, "Unless a man has his beard dyed a bright colour, he has very little chance of meeting with the approval of the fairer sex. A stout red-haired Welshman would have what is termed 'un grand succès' amidst the ladies in these regions."[56]

Pretty hurts: lightening up during The Dark Age

Medieval Europe took a clear stance on women's hair: loose hair, loose morals. During the 5th to 15th centuries, hair style, length, and colour were key signifiers of what role a person played in medieval society, their beliefs and even their sexual status. Good Catholic people were expected to follow strict rules about how to dress and present themselves, and women in western and central Europe were under pressure to wear their hair modestly in line with Christian principles. Covered and restrained hair signified those prized female traits: chastity, modesty and subservience.[57]

All scions of society displayed their status by their dress and hair style. The English who settled in Ireland in the 12th and 13th centuries were penalised for adopting long 'wild' hairstyles of the Irish, while Muslims in the Christian-ruled Iberian Peninsula (the bulk of modern Spain and Portugal), were subject to strict rules regarding how they wore their hair to identify them as 'other'. Scouts for Ango-Saxon King Harold II (c. 1022 –1066) famously assumed that the army of invading Normans was composed of priests due to their short hair and shaved faces in contrast to the hairy Saxons.[58]

Western reverence of blonde hair also showed no sign of abating and was firmly re-established to be the domain of virgins, chaste courtly ladies, and pious martyrs. Considered to be a sign of aristocratic roots and the epitome of chivalric female beauty, the virtues of blonde hair on both men and women was extolled but more so on women. In fact, golden hair was practically canonical in Medieval literary portrayals of feminine beauty in Europe,[59] with only Andalusian and Arabic texts[60] showing a preference for dark hair.[61] Given the rarity of natural blonde hair in adulthood, this posed a dilemma for many a maiden.

While very little written cosmetic information survives from the 6th to 11th century in Europe,[62] we do know some of the ways that a discontented brunette would lighten her hair - probably to the same honey-gold shade achieved by the Romans and Greeks beforehand. *The Trotula*, a 12th century Italian compendium of women's medicine, advised would-be blondes to apply a blend of celandine (*Ficaria verna*), root of agrimony (possibly *Agrimonia eupatoria*) and boxwood shavings then wash away with oat ash. Crocuses, white wines, and henna were also recommended.[63]

The Hebrew text *Sefer Ahavat Nashim* (Book of Women's Love) contains five recipes for blonde hair, including ginger oil, nettles in red vinegar, fresh pumpkin and iron shavings.[64] Recipes suitable for women of different incomes were published, citing ingredients from the common nettle to expensive saffron, indicating the desirability of blondeness across the social spectrum..[65]

The dedication applied by a would-be blonde to her hair may have even influenced fashion. By the end of the 12th century, female headdresses were becoming smaller and veils were becoming lighter, giving women's hair new visibility. Scholar Roberta Milliken makes the point, "Why spend three days dying your hair golden [...], not to mention buying expensive ingredients, only to cover it up entirely under a veil?"[66]

Obvious hair transformations, however, were treated with scorn or suspicion. Women faced a Catch 22 for aspiring to the beauty standards set by male writers: to be considered beautiful, one should be blonde, but to be falsely so, well, that was just the worst kind of vanity. Lightening your hair was a way to gain a rung on the social ladder, but a society intent on maintaining the divisions between nobility and peasantry also hated upstarts.

Professor of Medieval History Maria Montserrat Cabré explains the fear of deception had its roots in misogyny. "The artful pursuit of human beauty – through the use of cosmetics - was thought of both as legitimate and unlawful, depending on how, why and by whom it was sought. Supplementing beauty to the extent of surpassing one's place in the natural order was considered illicit in the medical and theological traditions. Nonetheless, for married women, the alliance between nature and art could be desirable, if with beautifying practices they prevented their husbands from falling into the sin of adultery, as Thomas Aquinas argued.

"If beautifying artifices were considered to be used to contravene or cheat the natural order - God's creation - they were thought to be illegitimate. This tendency to threaten nature was regularly ascribed to women, particularly in the misogynistic traditions that re-emerged in thirteenth-century Europe. The tension between the natural and the artificial expressed patriarchal anxieties over the maintenance of a natural order defined in male terms, since diatribes against the improper use of adornment and cosmetics with the aim to embellish their bodies were thoroughly directed toward women."[67]

If blonde hair was a way to get noticed in Medieval Europe and perhaps even enhance your status, greying or white hair signalled the end of any such ambitions. Medieval French allegory Le Roman de Rose describes Beauty as "Not dark or brunette" but with "long blonde hair falling to her heels", while Old Age is derided for her ugly white hair."[68] While humans were modelled in the shape of God, old age and death was believed by many to be an ugly consequence of Original Sin (another chance for Eve-bashing then). Much of western society was unashamedly ageist, and older individuals who did not live with family survived on the margins of society.[69]

To turn back the clock on age was impossible, but to care for the aging body was permissible. Medieval physicians believed that old age decreased the natural moisture and warmth from the body, and recommended a diet composed of warming, digestible foods, resting in a sunny room, bathing, light exercise and less sex.[70]

While depictions of young men in art and literature were typically biased by class, age was generally a great leveller for men in Medieval literature. Old men were mostly depicted as slightly comic, tragic, or a bit grotesque, no matter what their station. Old women, however, were a different matter - probably dangerous and allegedly prone to making poison once they entered the menopause. (Let's be honest, they weren't keen on menstruating women anyway.) The aged female body was said to be dominated by degenerate sexual desire, and was used to portray various sins such as 'lust' in Medieval art. So growing old was not a happy prospect for many men, let alone women,[71] which may explain why we also find dyes to darken the hair in publications like the Trotula, despite the popularity of blondeness.[72]

Good as gold: Renaissance blondes

Those with highlights continued to enjoy the high life well into the 16th century Renaissance period. During this time, the perceived values of blondeness were also enhanced by humourism: the prevailing European belief of the time that men and women consisted of four humours. These were blood, hot, wet and sanguine; yellow bile, hot, dry and choleric; black bile, cold, dry and melancholic; and phlegm, cold, wet and phlegmatic. Each individual was believed to have their own ideal equilibrium of the four temperaments, which were also associated with seasons, ages, essential oils and more. Imbalances to a person's particular brand of blood, yellow bile, black bile and phlegm caused illness and should be treated medicinally - either with a dose of the opposing humour or complementary health regimes.[73] This fascinating ideology inspired Lush's Renaissance Spa treatment, launched in 2020.

Professor of Renaissance History Michelle Laughran explains, "Hair colouring in Renaissance Italy was so common that 'washing one's hair' was used to refer to the process of dyeing, not cleaning. Most of what we know about hair-dyeing practices in the Renaissance comes from what were called the 'books of secrets'. These inexpensive and pocket-sized compendia of recipes were so successful in the early-modern period that it has been estimated that more than 350 different titles were printed in several editions just in Venice, which inspired translations and similar publications around Europe."

Female beauty standards were also tweaked in line with humourism. According to Italian scholar Giambattista della Porta (c. 1535 AD—1615 AD), the ideal, and let's face it, fairly unrealistic, Renaissance beauty represented an almost perfect balance between the three humours considered appropriate to women: fair skin and hair (phlegmatic), rosy cheeks (sanguine) and black eyes and eyebrows (melancholic). Choler (supposed to encourage quick temper and ambition) was not considered an appropriate feminine quality.[74] "Men, on the other hand," says Professor Laughran, "were much more likely to be allowed to express their passions; as a result, black recipes for male hair (that is, beards) suggesting gravitas, seem to be more common." In the period 1450 to 1540, Italian dye recipes for black hair are frequently noted as being suitable for the beard, unlike bleaching recipes.[75]

Strawberry blonde hair for women was especially popular in Renaissance Venice, akin to the majestic shades of the various Venuses painted by the great Venetian master Titian (c.1488/90-1576). Thankfully, this reddish-gold tone was achievable. "Veneziane were renowned for their 'arte biondeggiante'," says Professor Laughran, "that is, their practice of coating their hair with 'acque' (often composed of saltpeter, saffron, madder, wine, spermaceti, lime and silver salts) and then sitting on their rooftop terraces to allow the sun to lighten their tresses, all while wearing a crownless, wide-brimmed hat to protect their faces from tanning." Despite the widespread use and publication of hair colouring recipes, Professor Laughran says that obvious users of cosmetics, bleaches and hair dyes still faced backlash. "Clergymen did publish anti-cosmetic diatribes, most of which focused on the sins of lust in women and vanity in both sexes. However, even though Saint Jerome had originally railed against those who used cosmetics including dyeing their hair 'with that red that foreshadows the flames of Hell', hair colouring is not mentioned nearly as much in these treatises as face make-up. However, anyone – man or woman – who exaggerated their use of otherwise accepted cosmetic practices might be lampooned in published gossip or invectives, including people too old who were trying to appear too young or those whose application of colors was deemed too unnatural."

The dye recipes that say they are suitable for beards tells us that men were dyeing their hair during this period, but it's the female practices that have been scorned and written about in great detail. While beauty was an admired female attribute, male authorities were deeply suspicious of women who openly beautified. So why did they do it?

Professor Laughran explains that the line between cosmetics and medicines was blurred in Renaissance Italy, "Hair dyes were often literally considered 'remedies'. The processes of dyeing one's gray hair, for example, meant that any such procedures to seem young were considered tantamount to medicinal applications. If gray hair suggested a lack of youthful vigor, then coloring it would imply its presence."

"I also have wondered if people at the time might have utilized hair coloring "remedies" if they were looking to reinvent their personalities, as, for example, in a case of a dark-haired woman who might have tried to alleviate her abundance of melancholy by literally 'lightening up', she adds. "A cosmetic goal may well have even been to give the appearance that one's complexion was perfectly balanced, even though it might have been perceived as an unhealthy state for any individual who wasn't naturally born with it. This could have been another reason why cosmetics were often perceived by physicians as unhealthy."

I want to know more about the lives of the women who dedicated so much time and effort to bleaching their hair, so I'm reading up. While working class women may have tried bleaching their hair using more affordable recipes, one of the first things that becomes apparent is that many of the women bleaching their hair in this lengthy manner must have been reasonably wealthy with time to spare. Wealthy women would have been more restricted in terms of their freedoms, shielded from private male company so as not to harm their reputations and under intense pressure to marry well and form a powerful alliance for their family.[76]

So what was getting hitched like in Renaissance Italy? Well, for the working classes, reasonably casual. In fact, while they may have been subject to all sorts of social dangers from preying men to poverty, working class women could probably marry a chosen partner with reasonable ease - intent to marry on both sides was normally considered paramount to formally sealing the deal. But marriage became infinitely more high-pressure, competitive and expensive further up the social ladder.[77]

All marriages in Renaissance Italy required payment in the form of money, land or goods by the bride's family to the groom, however small. This was effectively life insurance for the bride, and she was supposed to receive the same amount back should her husband predecease her.[78] The law on women's dowries varied between city states in Italy - in Venetian law, for example, a woman's dowry was her personal property, while in others she might not be so lucky.[79]

Nevertheless, a competitive rise in dowry prices in the fifteenth and sixteenth centuries meant that families prioritised one or perhaps two daughters' marriages for consideration. This had a big social impact. Sources suggest that male heirs were furious about the size of the dowries being carved out of their inheritance, while snubbed daughters who didn't make a match would be sent to a convent.[80] Staggeringly, it's been suggested that 54% of Venetian noblewomen were in convents by 1581 and this continued to rise over the next century.[81]

Governments were not only concerned with the abundance of sexually active women deposited into a less-than-willing life of chastity, but also that so much private wealth was in the hands of women.[82] Dowries did not always offer women the financial security they suggested, however, and lawsuits from the time show a widow might have found her settlement drained or withheld when she needed to claim it. "Dowries could be a great source of investment capital for ambitious

Renaissance men," says Professor Laughran. "It was not uncommon for widowed women to have difficulty getting the dowry back from their late husbands' heirs though, either because it had been frittered away or else the heirs wanted to keep it."

Despite the inherent insecurity of a dowry, was marriage still a way noblewomen might gain some agency as a wife in the domestic sphere? Presenting oneself as the pinnacle of female beauty from a high-status family was surely - unfortunately - one way in which women could outshine rivals that included their own sisters. We could speculate that the women bleaching their hair were also making it abundantly clear they were not suitable for life at a convent too, given the criticism of the practice from church authorities. Professor Laughran agrees it's a reasonable theory, but cautions, "I do think cosmetics were used as strategies but whose exactly is a bit less clear. It might have been an expression of independence for some women, an area over which they had some control. Or the men in their lives might have even dictated cosmetics use since, for example, an attractive woman might not have needed as large a dowry."

The reality of women's lives within power-hungry Italian city state society proves complex to unravel. Yet, it seems likely that the romanticisation of blonde women combined with extreme marital competition to create this hair-bleaching culture. Blonde hair embodied several ideals that were considered desirable female qualities - youthfulness, virginity and virtue - while humourism ideals suggested that a blonde woman was well-balanced in terms of temperament. The depiction of golden-haired women by famous painters like Botticelli (1445 – May 17, 1510) and Titian built on the established Medieval trope of blonde beauty and grace.[83] Fair hair and its association with fair skin also implied the high rank that comes with a leisurely indoors life and nothing was more important to the ruling classes of the Italian city states than status.

With blonde hair set up as this intensely desirable female quality, perhaps hair bleaching was a means of gaining visibility for women within a repressive patriarchal society. If so, it was ultimately one that still pandered to the importance of female appearance.

Red hot royalty: Elizabethan England

Red hair was red hot in the English Elizabethan era - an astonishing turnaround after centuries of stigmatising in western civilisation. The rarest hair colour in the world had long been associated with dangerous 'others': 'barbarian' tribes that troubled Ancient Greece and Rome, transgressive women like Mary Magdalene, and Judas Iscariot, betrayer of Christ. A child with red hair was once charmingly said to have been conceived during menstruation [84] - and sex during menstruation was a big no-no according to the Old Testament.[85] All in all, it was a pretty rubbish time to be a bona fide redhead, unless you had fashionable auburn hair with hints of red and gold.

Enter Elizabeth I. Mistress of her own image, the English queen (1533 –1603) worked the 'otherness' of her natural red hair - supplemented by an abundance of wigs - to her advantage. Firstly, red hair symbolised her legitimacy as her red-headed father's heir (Elizabeth's mother Anne Boleyn (c.1501–1536), Henry VIII's second wife, was beheaded in 1536 on charges of treason and adultery). Secondly, as a lonely female Protestant ruler amidst a sea of dark-haired Catholic kings, looking different also suited Elizabeth's Virgin Queen brand.[86] (before he fell out of love, the queen's father had made himself head of the church, and been excommunicated, in order to marry Anne Boleyn.) Like the flame-haired Boudicca before her, Elizabeth would defend her kingdom against invading forces intent on restoring England to Catholicism and papal authority.

Nevertheless, it had to be portrayed in the right way. Under Elizabeth's careful patronage, her red hair becomes "lockes like wiers of beaten gold"[87] in sycophantic poetry of the time, and forms a magnificent yellow-tinged halo in approved portraits. The Queen was famous for cultivating a careful iconography with her portrait-painters and even ordering offensive portraits to be destroyed.[88] She was fiercely jealous of her younger cousin and Catholic rival, Mary Queen Of Scots (1542 –1587), interrogating the Scottish ambassador as to "whether my queen's hair or hers was best, and which of them two was fairest."[89] This rivalry was resolved when she had Mary executed for treason in 1587.

Upper class women who wanted to emulate this queenly figure of virginity rushed to tint their hair, using materials like rhubarb juice and sulphuric acid. With hair loss a common consequence of these caustic hair dyes (not to mention the use of lead to whiten the complexion), a high forehead and severely plucked eyebrows were in fashion for Elizabethan women.[90]

Male courtiers like Elizabeth's favourite, the Earl of Essex (1565 - 1601), would use materials like lead and quicklime to stain their beards red in homage to the queen.[91] In doing so, they were also declaring loyalty to Protestantism. The fashion even infiltrated the much-loved Elizabethan theatre and all but four of William Shakespeare's (1564 –1616) 37 attributed plays alone mention beards. Some surviving plays from the period even specify the beard colour of characters, meaning a suitable prosthetic needed to be procured by hook or by crook.[92]

Turns out today's beardy hipster subculture owes a lot to the Elizabethans. I mean, you can just imagine these bright young things swigging back their cold-brew coffee and planning a yoga retreat once their peace treaty with Spain is all tied up. As the queen grew older, her wigs grew blonder and her outfits more elaborate, her face decadently powdered in a sheen of youth. She ordered elaborate paintings to immortalise her image, and would not appear in court until she had been carefully dressed, powdered and squeezed into her elaborate disguise.[93] The royal wardrobe contained numerous wigs to pad out her thinning hair - one warrant alone signed by the Queen in 1602 ordered payment to be made for "six heads of heare, twelve yards of heare curl and one hundred devises made of heare curl."[94]

Professor Laughran says, "When Elizabeth was young, she played 'hard to get' as an ingenious strategy to encourage ambitious men at home and abroad to behave (and, say, not plot against her) in the hopes of being able to marry her and have the lucky one's progeny become English royalty. However, all of her makeup couldn't disguise the fact that she was aging, so when marrying her in order to have an heir by her was no longer a possibility, Elizabeth transitioned her image into a quasi-sacred one, not unlike the Virgin Mary. As a result, her image (including her makeup and hair colour) thus became more like a religious icon or statue — ironically, a living version of the Catholic ones that had been destroyed during her father's reign — to which a kind of chivalric devotion was encouraged among retainers."

Elizabeth knew that so much of her virginal power depended on being unattainable but desirable or revered; appearing old, and, by association, weak would be dangerous to her brand and even her life. Grey hair would be unthinkable - a dagger in the heart to the image she carefully portrayed to the world. It's a stark reminder that even a queen who refused to do what was expected of her (both as a woman and a monarch) by producing a heir, recognised that her appearance was essential to her appeal. She may have been the most powerful woman in the kingdom, but it was still known as a kingdom for a reason.

The good dye young: status, spectacle and spinsterhood in early modern society

4

Elizabeth's dedication to spectacle and illusion may just have started something. When her Scottish nephew, James Stuart (1566-1625) succeeded her on the English throne, the theatrical extravagance of his predecessor's court showed little signs of abating. In fact, after reigning in poorer Scotland, James revelled in his new-found wealth, dressed to impress and spent extravagantly.[1] While he was a shrewd statesman and seemingly happily married with legitimate children, he was also openly attracted to his male favourites at court who vied for his favour. His Jacobean court became renowned for scandalous gossip and splendorous styles,[2] leading to accusations of effeminacy.

"It was the court that led the fashion," argues historian Lawrence Stone, "and a philandering Queen followed by a homosexual king no doubt gave an added incentive to the movement [of conspicuous consumption]: both Elizabeth and James had an eye for the well-dressed young man."[3] While previously attractive women had been placed at the heart of court by their ambitious families to curry royal favour, it was now the turn of dapper young men.

Along with sumptuous male fashions, makeup was also becoming increasingly popular in aristocratic circles - used by noblewomen to create a pale complexion, red lips and cheeks. In a change of heart, black eyebrows and dark hair were firmly in vogue - probably to emphasise a gentile lady's fair skin[4] - and later dye recipes from the 17th century included oak roots, walnuts, old red wine and oil myrtle.[5]

King Louis XIV of France (1638 – 1715) is often said to have been the first to introduce wig wearing to the French court after he lost his hair prematurely due to illness,[6] and his English cousin Charles II (1630 –1685) is commonly believed to have brought the custom to England after the Restoration of the Monarchy in 1660. Englishmen of all classes, however, wore wigs in the late 17th century, from the aristocrats featured in elegant portraits to the enslaved men described in advertisements for escapees.[7]

A man's style of wig originally stood for a particular profession, rank, or character, taking the place of natural hair as an aesthetic to be 'read' in the Medieval period. Very few men - only the extremely poor - would have gone bareheaded, with servants and enslaved Africans[8] serving as domestic servants commonly gifted wigs by their superiors.[9]

The fashion for big wigs and big hair, dusted with colour, however, has become synonymous with aristocratic debauchery as the fashion grew for towering hairpieces at the end of the 17th century - wigs that only the truly wealthy could afford. The popular so-called 'full bottom' wig required around ten heads of hair and cost upwards of £50 - a relative fortune. So great was their value that economic writers in 18th century Britain stressed that British hair should be raised and harvested and duty slapped on foreign imports.[10]

To their joy, the upper classes found that a wig could hide a multitude of evils: greying or thinning hair and baldness (a side effect of the syphilis that was rife during the period).[11] They could also be boiled to remove lice and perfumed to cover less-than-pleasant smells by one's wigmaker.[12] Women, expected to keep their 'natural' hair (however supplemented it was with false hair, powders, pomades and padding), did not enjoy the benefits of having a removable headpiece.[13] Once a lady's crowning glory had been carefully sculpted, she would wear a huge nightcap made of iron mesh to keep out mice at night, and carry a thin hooked scratcher to discreetly remove parasites from her headgear.[14]

Like monstrous wedding cakes, these immense wigs and padded creations would be dusted with powder, initially to de-grease them but later for fashion. White-haired wigs were considered particularly prestigious, and court-goers wanting to imitate this style on the cheap would use white powder to colour their hairpieces. Hair style quickly became a status symbol and size mattered - the larger a lady's barnet, the larger her family's wallet. "The women were of such enormous stature that we appeared as grasshoppers beside them," recalled one contemporary.[15]

The messy process of wig-styling and powdering meant that specially designed 'powder rooms' were built into the gentry's houses for the procedure. Without access to corn-starch or Cyprus powder, the working classes used household flour to deodorise and colour their wigs instead. It caught on further afield too; Polish and Russian nobles were known to flaunt their wealth by giving their servants powdered wigs to wear as part of a uniform and one Russian family was reported to have eighty footmen who each wore a powdered wig.[16]

Wigs, however, caused a lot of social anxiety. They were worn by men but made of women's hair, and not aristocratic women either, blurring the lines between gender and class that the Church was so keen to keep distinct. Publications in France debated the value of sourced hair - not only its geographic origin but the type of woman it came from. Author of 'Illicit Wigmaking in eighteenth century Paris',[17] Professor Mary K. Gayne explains, "Published texts and legal memoirs point us towards hair from Normandy, and, in these, they refer to the strength of the hair. The famous 18th century French *L'Encyclopédie*, on the other hand, highlights the desirability of hair from women who have not yielded to debauchery or prostitution."

Nowhere was the fashion more flamboyant than France. Male and female courtiers alike paired their ostentatious wigs and hair pieces with thick layers of rouge and face paint in the reign of King Louis XIV and his son Louis XV (1710 – 1774). Facial hair was plucked or removed, and some courtiers wore eyebrows made of mouse fur. Outside court, female citizens would rub their eyebrows with ripe elderberries or burnt cork to blacken them, and use nuts, roots, white lead, litharge, quicklime, and salt to dye their natural hair dark. Red hair was, unsurprisingly, not in fashion, but neither was blonde hair until the second half of the century.[18]

Now red hair not being in fashion I'm used to, but blonde? I seek out historian Professor Morag Martin, author of *Selling Beauty: Cosmetics, Commerce, and French Society, 1750–1830*,[19] to find out more.

"Well, darker hair was definitely the most fashionable shade until the time of Marie Antoinette from the mid to late 18th century," she confirms. "That's partly based on the theory of the humours, which suggests dark hair is stronger, more stable and less temperamental. But I also think it's because, when blonde hair did come into fashion, they were really into 'cendre' or ashy blonde shades that mimicked the effects of hair

Marie Antoinette's elaborate wigs (pictured with her boat-shaped 'coiffure 'à l'Indépendance ou Le Triomphe de la Liberté')

gained notoriety during her husband's reign.

powder. They had this fear of anything red, and a lot of blonde bleaching does start veering towards strawberry blonde. Even Marie Antoinette wore powder; she rarely went without it. They wanted a very cool, greyish colour which was difficult to achieve. So I think the initial popularity of dark hair was down to a combination of fashion and convenience. It's always easier to make your hair darker than lighter."

Professor Martin continues, "If anyone was dying their hair up until the 1780s, it was women and probably women with red hair, because male hair was hidden beneath wigs. They would want to dye their natural hair to match the horse and human hair they were adding in. The most desired hair type or 'look' would curl well, hold its shape, and have a nice uniform colour. I have an interesting advert from 1764 which says you can have your hair turned dark brown if your hair is red or too blonde. So, there is a certain blonde that is not popular."

The fair-haired, ill-fated Marie Antoinette (1755 – 1793) certainly popularised ashy blonde hair. She established a fashion for wearing the hair high off the head in towering coiffures sustained with false hair, wool cushions and steel pins, and dusted elaborately with hair powder.[20] Her hairdresser would create elaborate scenes to reflect current affairs, and once famously, created a naval-inspired 'do' to celebrate a French victory against the British during the American Revolution.[21] In 1775, underground weekly publication *Correspondance littéraire secrète* reported that she sent for silks in the same shade as her hair, sparking a new fashion for 'blonde dresses".[22] A wig made from natural blonde hair could also be charged at a high price and the Parisian Wigmaker Guild busted numerous unlicensed manufacturers that were undercutting the value of genuine blonde wigs by selling poor-quality bleached hair.[23]

Professor Mary K. Gayne explains that genuine blonde hair charged a premium for several reasons. "Blonde hair was difficult to attain and not without risks to work with, so, from the wigmakers' perspective, it had the highest value. Its expensive price is at least partly linked to its volatility. Blonde hair doesn't hold its colour over time, therefore, working with blonde hair added an extra step to the process of making a wig. Once a wigmaker started preparing hair for the wig, they put the hair through a series of cleaning steps. The worker clamped locks of hair to the table and used cards to comb out whatever dirt or other undesirable materials might be in it. And, some texts say, for hair that is blonde, particularly light grey or almost white, that before curling it, they took the locks of wrapped hair and dipped them into indigo.This tinting with indigo prevented blonde wigs from reddening."

Wigmakers had to be wary they were not being sold field hair: bleached hair sold as genuine blonde. "Before the discovery of chlorine bleach in the 1780s," says Professor Mary K. Gayne, "they would soak hair in an acidic liquid, oftentimes urine, and then lay it out in the sunlight to create a bleached effect. Afterwards, it was particularly important for the liquid to be washed fully from the hair. If it wasn't, later processing activities would reveal the blonde hair to be adulterated hair. Legally, field hair was forbidden by the Wigmaker Guild and the failure to dilute the liquid fully from the adulterated hair often caused hair purchasers to report the use of field hair to guild officers.

"Hair that was lightened in this way was used to give greater mass to the wig or to bulk it up, but field hair was not suitable for the curled parts of blonde wigs. For that, truly blonde hair, typically being human hair or horse manes, was required."

Ageism was also rife in the period, particularly towards women who could be considered 'past it' at as little as 25. Marie Antoinette herself was said to only invite young women to her parties as she could not imagine that "past 30, a woman would dare appear in court". Old women were pitied and meant to respectfully shun the limelight, while old women attempting to hide their age were despised.[24] But although ageing women who used excessive make up, false hair and dye were ridiculed, the extravagant fashions offered a tempting means to extend their inclusion at a court that glittered with opportunity and privilege. I think old age, and the marginalisation and invisibility that came with it, would have been a frightening prospect for many women.

Yet such excessive displays of wealth and artifice drew building scorn. In 1716, English aristocrat Lady Mary Wortley Montagu (1689 – 1762) wrote of the "monstrous" female fashions she saw at court in Vienna: "They build certain fabrics of gauze on their heads, about a yard high, consisting of three or four stories, fortified with numberless yards of heavy ribbon. [...] Their hair is prodigiously powdered to conceal the mixture, and set with three or four rows of bodkins (wonderfully large, that stick out two or three inches from their hair) made of diamonds, pearls, red, green, and yellow stones." Snippily, she concludes, "You may easily suppose how this extraordinary dress sets off and improves the natural ugliness with which God Almighty has been pleased to endow them, generally speaking."[25]

Lady Mary's attitude was not uncommon by the second half of the century. With the decadence of the elite incensing the working classes, the writing was on the wall for big wigs (and indeed bigwigs). English women found themselves penalised by the law for adopting the fashion for excessive hair do's and cosmetics and concealing their natural looks from suitors. A 1770 Act Of Parliament was proposed declaring that "all women of whatever rank, profession or degree, whether virgins, maids or widows, that shall from and after such an Act, impose upon, seduce and betray into matrimony any of His Majesty's subjects by the scents, paints, cosmetic washes, artificial teeth, false hair, Spanish wool, iron stays, hoops, high-heeled shoes and bolstered hips, shall incur the penalty of the law now in force against witchcraft and like misdemeanours, and that the marriage upon conviction shall be null and void."[26] Although not passed, it had a sobering effect. The fear of witches, of deceitful women, of loose women whose children might not be yours, had reared its ugly head once more. It was time to re-establish the gender status quo.

A follow-up 'wig powder tax' established by English Prime Minister William Pitt (1759 – 1806) in 1795 sounded the death knell for the fashion, while international working class discontent left sensible citizens ditching their wigs for less inflammatory attire.[27] Rather than functioning as a status symbol, hair powder signified indifference to the nation's poor.[28]

Across the channel, The French Revolution (1789-1799) dealt a death blow to the declining extravagant fashion and heralded the emergence of a new 'natural look' for hair and makeup that heavily criticised the artifice and trickery of cosmetics.[29]

Professor Mary K. Gayne explains that the symbolic power of the wig sealed its fate. "The wig represented privilege in the Old Regime. When a man in the late 17th century walked into a specific location donning a full-bottomed wig, he marked his association with the State. By the last third of the 18th century, privilege began to crumble, but people still desperately wanted, or at least, needed, access to it. They found that they had difficulty navigating society without privilege, yet they recognised that privilege itself was part of the problem.

"In reading many of these critiques and looking at the caricatures which appeared later, you perceive that wigs are crossing boundaries. They've drifted beyond the realm of the nobility, into a space where, perhaps, privilege shouldn't be defining relationships. And, with that, a critique that men are becoming feminine surfaces. Workers who are making a display of privilege on people's heads are drawn with exaggerated feminine qualities, in terms of their stance and gait. And so, we can read attitudes from these texts about the tensions that men faced regarding the pressure to craft meaningful lives within the context of privilege. We see similar, related changes in women's appearances that are being scripted on to the bodies of women, as well."

Yet, Professor Martin explains that the end of wig-wearing heralded a new opportunity for hair dye in France. "Interestingly, advertisements for hair dye increased during the French Revolution because wig-wearing stopped," she explains. "The manufacturers of hair accessories before the Revolution shifted their business towards new hair products like dyes and there was also an increase in men dyeing their own suddenly visible hair."

The attacks on hair dye, when they came, were also less critical than they were of face makeup. "I see people attacking hair dye outwardly for the first time in the 1820s," continues Professor Martin, "and these criticisms were very much focused on safety and condemning the chemicals being used. They warned against burns and allergic reactions. There were fewer attacks based on falsity since most people were not trying to dye their hair artificial colours. The moral argument is focused more on saying that you should be happy with what you have, rather than suggesting that hair dye will somehow corrupt young women. Importantly, the spread of natural fashion doesn't mean that men and women give up cosmetics, it just means that they reconfigure how they wear them. Hair dye becomes a way to continue to beautify without people knowing."

Not so beautiful: hair dye's slavery links

During this period, hair dye also had a far uglier purpose. Human traffickers engaged in the Trans-Atlantic Slave Trade would either dye or shave the greying hair of enslaved African people being sold to work on Caribbean plantations to make them appear younger. Wise to these tricks, buyers would check the teeth of victims to gauge their true age and rub rags through their hair to look for dye residue.[30]

For enslaved African people, hair arrangements had complex social and cultural meanings, with the highest ranking men and women adopting the most ornate styles. The hairdresser held a special, trusted role in community life, thanks to their intimate job of washing, arranging, and dressing people's hair using specialist combs designed to minimise breakage.

Elaborate patterns, styles and colours were rooted in meaning. Tribes like the Qua Qua wore their hair plaited and twisted, adorned with palm oil and red earth,[31] while messengers of the Oyo Kingdom had their heads shaved every fifth day, leaving a circular patch on the crown that was worn long, braided and dyed with indigo.[32] Dasenech, Pokot and Turkana men would cover their hair with mud and sometimes add blue pigment or feathers to create a headdress known as a 'chignot',[33] while Masai women shaved their heads and anointed them with red ochre.[34] Grey hair was a symbol of pride for tribes like the Yoruba, the men of which typically shaved their head and beard until old age when grey hair (ewu) and a beard (irugbon) were celebrated signs of wisdom.[35] Untreated, unkempt hair was a sign of bereavement, ill health and depravity to many communities.[36] Deprived of the tools and time to tend to their hair, enslaved Africans were forced to become inventive with household products like bacon grease to condition their hair, and cornmeal as a scalp cleanser. Coffee would be used as a tint, while axle grease would be used to both dye and straighten the hair. While rich westerners took immense pride in their hair, similar sentiments towards Black hair were unceremoniously squashed, leading to centuries of pressure to assimilate to White standards of beauty.[37]

Long, dark and handsome: Eastern hair ideals

In East Asia, the finest hair has long been considered to be the lengthiest, shiniest and blackest - and not just for women. In traditional China, both men and women wore their hair long unless they were monks or nuns (criminals also had shaved heads),[38] and shiny black hair was considered an important sign of vitality. Hair loss was considered to show ill health, old age or infirmary,[39] while one alarming medieval source even claimed that white hair was a sign of a shrinking brain.[40]

Yet the pressure on women to appear youthful was extensive. Indeed, the ripe old age of "twice eight" (16 years old) was considered to be a women's prime in various famous writings from Japan and China during the 18th and 19th centuries. Long, raven-black hair and dark eyebrows signified vitality and youthfulness although the hair would be worn in different styles according to fashion and region.[41]

Conformity to the norm was also highly valued. "The Chinese understood beauty (mei) as the pleasurable sensation that people feel when viewing something orderly and harmonious," writes historian Professor Bret Hinsch.[42] As late as 1905, Japanese historian Yoshisaburo Okakura (1868-1936) stated that an ideal female beauty would have "long, straight, jet-black hair." Explaining further to his audience in a lecture in London, he added, "Blue eyes and blonde hair, the charms of which we first learn to feel after a protracted stay among you, are regarded [by the] Japanese as something extraordinary in no favourable sense of the term. A girl with even a slight tendency to grey eyes or frizzly hair is looked upon as an unwelcome deviation from the national type."[43]

Fifteenth century Chinese women would use pepper imported from Southeast Asia to maintain glossy black hair,[44] while medical compendium *Pên T'sao Kan Mu*, published by physician and herbalist Li Shih-chên (1518-1593) in 1578, also details hundreds of different herbal prescriptions. These included the use of walnuts (*Juglans cathayensis*) to blacken the hair and whiskers, and galla fruits (*Galla chinensis*), pierced and dried in a sand bath, to be used as hair dye.[45] Until the 19th century, the Japanese practised 'shiragazome': hiding grey hair with tannic acid and iron salts.[46]

But when it came to maintaining that much revered dark hair, the Iranians were the pros. "Black hair", wrote French merchant Sir Jean-Baptiste Chardin (1643 – 1713) in 1711, "is most in esteem with the Persians, as well the Hair of the Head, as the Eye-brows and the Beard[.] Those of the Persian Women, who have not Hair of that Colour, dye and rub it over with Black to improve it."[47] The Persians had a secret weapon in their hands: the henna plant. The much-honed and effective method of combining indigo and henna into a blend known as 'henna reng' gave them superior hair-darkening powers and plenty of other benefits to boot. It combined beautification with medicinal purpose: indigo was used to promote hair growth, treat itching, fevers and head lice,[48] while henna was believed to improve the complexion and treat serious ills like leprosy and cholera.[49]

The use of henna reng to dye the hair was a widely accepted and encouraged practice. Compare this to attitudes towards hair colouring in the west and it's a bit of a turnaround. But then, whereas western hair dye methods, as with other cosmetics, would mostly be performed privately, I'm learning that long, social bathing and cosmetic rituals were a key aspect of life for Iranian society. Men and women of all means would visit public baths regularly at different times,[50] though the wealthiest would dedicate a generous proportion of each day to tending to one's appearance and local gossip. "They have their reward," reports one source in 1884, "for the henna dyes the hair a beautiful warm, chestnut brown; hence gray hair is unknown amongst Persian ladies."[51] Like the Ancient Egyptians before them, using henna was an act of hygiene and self-care. The ritual was also established in Middle Eastern culture, endorsed by the Prophet Mohammed, and the act of application felt comforting and healthy. Just compare that to the burns suffered by bleaching women in the west, where the process definitely felt medically unsound.

I also think henna reng benefited from not being in the sole domain of women. In fact, the use of many cosmetics and hygiene regimes were not specific to women, with medieval Islamic men also using basics like kohl.[52] Portrayals of beauty were largely ungendered in literature and art in early Qajar Iran (1785–1925), and both youthful men and women were described in ways we would deem 'feminine' by today's standards. This would change when Iranian society absorbed European anxieties about young men being portrayed as beautiful.[53]

Hair was also hugely symbolic for a ruler's image in terms of indicating power and youth. Very long, dark beards were considered the height of manliness amongst the Iranian aristocracy during the 18th and 19th centuries, and this trend trickled down. "Nothing can exceed the attention paid by a Persian to his beard," wrote English writer Frederic Shoberl (1775–1853) on a trip to Iran, where he reported that the average man dyed his beard with henna reng fortnightly and carried a comb and mirror on his person at all times.[54] Earl of Albemarle George Thomas (1799 – 1891) recounted an amusing anecdote from his travels in Iran, in which, "In addition to the usual process of an eastern bath, the barber had dyed my moustaches before I was aware of his intention."[55]

The second king of the Qajar dynasty of Iran, Fath-Ali Shah Qajar (1772 –1834) was considered to cut a particularly dashing figure with his sweeping, jet-black beard, much embellished in oil paintings and embroidered Kashan carpets. Memoirs of a servant of the later Naser al-Din Shah Qajar (1831-1896) also reveal that the henna used by members of his harem would be closely guarded and hidden from others, especially jealous wives, sisters or mothers-in-law in case it was adulterated.[56]

When Naser al-Din Shah Qajar attended the 'world's fair' or *Exposition Universelle* held in Paris in 1878, he brought with him a number of dye materials including madder, nutgalls, henna and indigo. Luckily, he also brought his physician, who then demonstrated to attendees how henna and indigo could be combined in a two-step process to dye the hair.[57] The Shah's "shining blue black" moustache is also referenced by Intrepid Victorian naturalist Isabella Bird (1831 –1904), who visited the Middle East before his assassination in 1896.[58] Mrs Bird recalls that her own undyed greying hair was a course of constant interest to the Iranian women she spoke to during her travels, and while in Iran, she also recorded a typical hair dye process performed by the bath attendants of wealthy Bakhtiari women.

These attendants would apply pastes of henna to their mistresses' long hair to give it an auburn tint, followed by a paste of indigo, left on for two hours. She watched fascinated as, over the next 24 hours, the resulting khaki green shade darkened to a rich blue black.[59]

Henna reng continues to be popular in the Middle East today. Yet, while henna is mentioned in 14th century Castilian poetry, and included in a hair colouring recipe in 16th century Italy by our Italian friend Giambattista della Porta (the guy with the very specific idea of Renaissance beauty in Chapter 3), its western commercialisation came predominantly in the 19th century.

Hair colouring on the quiet: pride and prejudice in the 19th Century

A common image of the Victorians is one of hysterical women covering up table legs for decency's sake. Though fun, that urban myth probably isn't true. But what's certainly true is that after the extravagant fashions of the 1700s, the 19th century saw more modest hairstyles return to fashion in the west. In France and the US, obvious cosmetics were associated with the aristocratic rule both nations had overthrown in the preceding century, which led to the reprisal of homespun remedies and natural complexions.[60] With wigs out of favour, men and women had to seek out subtle cosmetic treatments for greying and balding hair.[61]

Black hair was popular in the early to mid-19th century Britain[62] as embodied in the sleek, demurely-styled dark hair of the young Queen Victoria (1819-1901). The youthful queen, who ascended to the throne at the age of 18, was a welcome breath of fresh air after a line of elderly and unpopular kings of the Hanoverian dynasty, and depictions of her virginal youth were used to revive support for the monarchy.[63] Victoria's branding was focused on family values and female modesty and the queen was openly disapproving of cosmetics.[64] Like any respectable married woman of the time, she wore her hair tied back and displayed a fresh complexion. Despite the modest image she portrayed, however, Victoria was also steely, hot-headed and passionate. She famously gifted her beloved husband Prince Albert (1819-1861) a risqué portrait of herself with her neck bare and long hair unravelling that he displayed in his private quarters.[65]

Dark hair had another benefit - it emphasised the whiteness of a lady's skin when a fashionably consumptive pallor was all the rage.[66] A common disease of the period, tuberculosis, was actually considered highly desirable for society ladies as it was not physically disfiguring like syphilis but instead thought to induce a state of melancholic loveliness in women.[67] Invalids were frail, pale, pure and confined to the home - clearly the ideal Victorian women. I've read enough Victorian era children's literature (*What Katy Did, Little Women, Heidi, The Secret Garden*) to recognise that the saintly invalid trope penetrated this genre too. Hair was also massively sentimentalised in death, with locks being used in jewellery and given as keepsakes.[68] Attractive hair was important even for the deceased.

Obvious cosmetic use was frowned upon, but a thriving market of subtle 'hair restorers' emerged: products marketed to appeal to a respectable Victorian lady's desire for discretion.[69] Some were also falsely sold as vegetable colourants with exotic names such as 'water of Persia', while lead-based 'restorers' were sold in blends of sulphur, glycerol and perfumed water.[70] A respectable lady had to be careful where she spent her money however. Popular American magazine *Ladies' Magazine and Literary Gazette* recounts the folly of a young woman who coloured her greying hair using Imperial Hair Restorer. The moral of

Indigo could be combined with henna to create lustrous dark browns on the hair - a technique for which the Persians became famous.

the tale? Her hair turned peacock green.[71]

Readers of *Anne of the Green Gables,* published in 1908 by Canadian author Lucy Maud Montgomery (1874 – 1942) and set a few decades earlier, will recall an incident in which flame-haired Anne buys dubious dye from a peddler and turns her locks khaki-green. Earlier in the novel she reflects sorrowfully on her natural, highly undesirable hair colour: "Yes, it's red," she said resignedly. "Now you see why I can't be perfectly happy. Nobody could who has red hair. [...] I think to myself, 'Now my hair is a glorious black, black as a raven's wing.' But all the time I know it's just plain red, and it breaks my heart. It will be my lifelong sorrow."[72]

Red-tinted hair did enjoy something of a reprisal in the west, however, and socialites such as russet-haired Italian opera singer Adelina Patti (1843 – 1919) are often credited with popularising henna.[73] The subject of John Singer Sargent's racy *Portrait of Madame X*, young Parisian socialite Virginie Amélie Avegno Gautreau (1859–1915) was also said to tint her hair with the plant..[74] But I think true credit should go to the Pre-Raphaelite movement of the mid to late century which revived the fashion for auburn shades of hair with hints of gold on women. This group of painters and writers were fascinated with female hair - particularly the golden-red shade - and it was explicitly romanticised and sexualised in their work.[75] It continued to be popular in Asia and the Middle East also, and by the late 1930s, henna and indigo were being cultivated in some regions of India solely for local use as a hair dye.[76] The romanticism of auburn hair also coincided with the increasing popularity of 'physiognomy': the dangerous pseudoscience that proposed a person's character was displayed in their features. Dark hair was considered to indicate strength and power[77] - not ideal qualities for a society that still operated on patriarchal values and feared the rising call of women's rights.[78] In contrast, women with fair hair were increasingly seen as fragile and in need of protection.[79]

It's a surprising return to the ideas tossed around by followers of humourism during the Renaissance that venerated blonde hair in women but felt black was really more suitable for men. Texture was key too - revealing the racist attitudes underlying these medieval ideas. Theories like these were exacerbated by pseudoscientists like American Orson Squire Fowler (1809 –1887) who was part of the movement that tried to categorise the global population into inferior and superior 'races'. In one of his many openly racist works, he wrote that fine, light, or auburn hair signified "quick susceptibilities, together with refinement or good taste" while those with red or coarse hair were best suited to physical work outdoors.[80]

By the latter half of the 19th century, blondes were replacing the dark-haired heroines of earlier Victorian literature. In May 1866, Punch magazine noted this new social phenomenon with a telling caricature that showed a dark-haired lady saying to her hairdresser, "and so, Mr. Frizzelind, you think I ought to have my hair washed yellow! And pray, why?" "Well, Ma'am," replies the hairdresser, "black hair is never admitted into really good society now, you know!"[81]

Hairpieces also saw a reprisal in popularity as styles became a little more daring. Selling hair became a way of making money for the destitute - or unscrupulous undertakers wanting to earn a bit on the side. India was also a popular source of human hair that could be bleached and styled into hairpieces for the society lady.[82]

Victorian women were clearly receiving a lot of contradictory messages about their looks.
Beauty was becoming very feminised after the gender-bending aristocratic extravagance of the 18th century and they were presented with images of beautiful, desirable women with long flowing

hair. Yet, at the same time, most Victorian women lacked any agency and were fiercely repressed, told their place was in the home and that their reputation must be purer than snow. They had the virtues of marriage and motherhood drilled into them from a young age. Morality tales and melancholy artwork bewailed the reputation of a woman who had a child out of wedlock (oops - too late for me), and harped on about the dangers awaiting to corrupt innocent females.

Marriage was the ultimate goal. A woman might even achieve a reasonable degree of autonomy in the domestic sphere - provided she made a good one, of course. Given that the ideal marital age for women was suggested to be half that of her beau's plus seven years,[83] she faced great competition and a ticking clock.

Presenting one's self as a paragon of beauty and morality was key to attracting the right man which may be why Victorians were dying their hair and using subtle cosmetics. Spinsterhood was akin to social exile,[84] and to be over 30 and unmarried was to be considered an old maid. In contrast, a majority of middle-class men married in the early 30s. Divorce might not have been the done thing but widowhood was also a troubling reality for many women. 19% of marriages would end in death within a decade in the 1850s, and the number of widowed women over 35 was double that of widowed men.[85] Only the youngest and prettiest women had a chance of remarrying and gaining some social status again as a wife[86]

So, like the Venetian blondes before them, I think that cosmetics like hair dye were a means of agency for Victorian women under intense pressure to find a good husband. Subtlety was key though. Too much and you were clearly a woman looking for casual sex. (That may also have been why bleaching recipes were initially out of favour.) By the end of the century, visible makeup was - worse! - taking on the rebellious mark of the career woman set on female emancipation.[87] Yet men were also common users of hair dye during this period, as we can see from the burgeoning advertising industry in America. An 1851 advert for a barbershop in Boston, Massacheuts advertised two hair dyes,[88] while 'Scalpine', created by medicine entrepreneur H. H. Warner (1842–1923) in the 1880s, promised to cure premature hair greying.[89] Archaeological excavations at Camp Nelson in central Kentucky have also uncovered broken bottles that once contained hair dye, possibly used by soldiers when posing for early photographic portraits.[90]

Pierre Gustave Toutant-Beauregard (1818–1893), the Confederate officer who instigated the American civil war by an attack on Fort Sumter in 1861, is said to have startled his company when his brown hair turned snow white over the course of a few weeks. He had been unable to get his French-made hair dye through the United States' naval blockade of the Confederate states.[91]

There were several reasons for the growth of a male hair dye market. The death of wig-wearing after a century of comfortably concealing one's head had given western men a new anxiety about their hair. They were also under pressure to look younger though for different reasons than women.

The young working class man's muscular body 'hardened' by tough labour was increasingly admired as the epitome of manliness in art and literature in the late 19th and 20th centuries when thinness was associated with poverty. Upper class men would wear 'brown paint' to emulate a tan and follow dietary plans to build body strength.[92] Strength and youth were highly desirable masculine qualities, but, by the turn of the 20th century, age discrimination was forcing working class American men out of employment.

The emerging auto industry, remarked American political activist Robert W. Dunn (1895–1977) was "a young man's industry".[93]

The rise of mass production corresponded with increased life expectancy but the hirers of fast-paced assembly line work were unrepentantly hiring younger men. With older, higher-paid men turned away from work and often first in line for redundancy, the pressure to look young in the workplace sent more men to drug stores. They purchased dyes to colour their hair and shaved greying moustaches. Ageing workers in a range of occupations including steelworkers, auto-workers and machinists were reported to colour their hair, some using shoe polish. Reports followed that older men in the steel industry were even darkening their hair with soot from the furnace.[94]

This was clearly desperation, not fashion. Working class male identity had been built on the notion of 'honest toil' and providing for a family, but the over 40s found themselves increasingly considered past their prime. Wives and mothers supplemented income with factory work and the grown children also took over as key earners for their fathers.[95] Those first grey hairs signified social marginalisation for a whole generation of men and the more practical problem of providing for a family. Hair dye was the solution they reached for.

Does she or doesn't she? The industry that advertising built

5

The 19th century was a massive turning point for the hair dye industry. Until that point, most commercial dyes had consisted of messy metallic and natural components mixed together with somewhat unpredictable results. The entire operation still had that under-the-counter feel. But the seeds of a professional hair dye industry, based on more predictable, quick results, were sown in this century.

It began with pyrogallol: an organic compound first obtained in 1786 from nutgalls: the outgrowths produced by insects that puncture tree bark to insert their larvae.[1] Pyrogallol was the very first synthetic organic dye developed for use on human hair, although the use of nutgalls and tree bark in historic dyes was not new. Fabric dyes had long been derived from wood,[2] while nutgalls would be stewed in water to create a deep brown dye, or mixed with iron to create a dark blue or black.[3]

Yet, extracting pyrogallol from nutgalls for use on the hair was a new concept, first suggested in 1845. Alone, pyrogallol acted as a progressive dye, gradually tinting the hair as it darkened in response to oxygen, but adding ammonia gave a more potent colour. Henna could also be added to create a rich, more lasting brown shade. By the 1880s, however, reports of skin irritation led to pyrogallol's ban in several European countries.[4]

A more lasting breakthrough occurred with hair bleaching. While hydrogen peroxide was discovered in 1818, it wasn't until 1867 that London-based 'chemist-perfumer' E. H. Thiellay, and Leon Hugo, a French hairdresser, demonstrated its effects at the Paris *Exposition Universelle* in 1867, where it far outperformed previous bleaching methods.[5]
Famous courtesan of the period Cora Pearl (1836 –1886) was said to use hydrogen peroxide to bleach her dark hair yellow.[6]

By the turn of the century, hydrogen peroxide had practically replaced all previous bleaching materials in Europe and the United States.[7]

Yet one discovery would supersede all of these.

In 1856, an 18-year-old student at London's Royal College of Chemistry, William Henry Perkin (1838–1907), made a discovery that would dramatically change the way we dye hair and launch the petrochemical industry. Hoping to create the anti-malarial drug quinine, Perkin experimented with a simple aromatic amine called aniline and coal tar - waste sludge from Victorian gas lighting - that he believed had a similar chemical structure to quinine. But instead, he was left with a thick, black substance that left behind a bright purple colour which transferred to cloth.[8]

He later reported: "On experimenting with the colouring matter thus obtained, I found it to be a very stable compound dyeing silk a beautiful purple that resisted the light for a long time, being very different in this aspect to the Archil colour [derived from lichen] which was sometimes used in silk in that period."[9] Perkin had done the

Nutgalls would be stewed in water or combined with metal mordants to create varying shades of brown, black or navy.

impossible: he had found a way to extract colour from coal, rather than plants or sea urchins. Now he just had to find a way to extract money from the same discovery.

To the disgruntlement of his chemistry teacher Professor August Wilhelm von Hofmann, Perkin dropped out of college to patent and manufacture the colour he named “Mauveine”. His father pooled the family’s capital on establishing a dye works, his brother ditched an archaeology course to help, and Perkin moved his Mauveine operation out of the garden shed.[10]

Despite the seeming brilliance of his invention, Perkin spent the next two years unsuccessfully touting Mauveine to printers and industrialists. Downhearted and probably regretting his decision to ditch a promising scientific career, he was having little fortune. In 1856 however, he was in for an extraordinary stroke of luck when purple became the most desirable colour in the western hemisphere.

First, the incredibly influential Empress Eugénie of France (1826-1920) declared that mauve was the colour that suited her eyes. To what must have been his abject despair, Perkin had been unable to patent Mauveine in France. Fortunately, British Queen Victoria then wore mauve to the Princess Royal’s wedding. Amidst the ‘mauve madness’ that followed, Perkin spent time pitching Mauveine and offering technical support to dyers across the country, and his purse-friendly, fade-resistant colour exploded onto the scene. As one chemist later noted at a gathering of the Society of Chemical Industry, “If a fairy godmother had given Perkin the chance of choosing the precise moment for his discovery, he could not have selected a more appropriate or more auspicious time.”[11]

Long after mauve had enjoyed its moment, discovering the world’s first synthetic aniline dye gave Perkin a Midas-like legacy. Fifty years after his discovery, coal-tar derivatives had spawned 2,000 artificial colours (as well as artificial perfumery components and sweeteners), and were preserving canned foods for soldiers, and had enabled German bacteriologist Paul Ehrlich (1854 –1915) to develop pioneering immunology and chemotherapy programmes.[12]

While his star student went on to make a fortune, Perkin’s former professor August Wilhelm von Hofmann (1818 –1892) had not been idle with his time. He had been the one to initially discover the aniline that was so fundamental in Perkin’s discovery, and, with perhaps an unsurprising change of heart, Hofmann began to stake out his own piece of the coal-tar pie. In 1863, he identified a coal-tar-derived aromatic amine that darkened on exposure to oxygen. This was para-phenylenediamine (commonly known as PPD): a highly allergy-inducing but very useful colour-changing compound.[13]

What Mauveine had done for coal-tar, para-phenylenediamine was to do for hair dye.

Chemists discovered that by adding a secondary molecule to para-phenylenediamine called a coupler, they could develop a wide range of colour options, making the new dye infinitely more exciting.[14] When combined with hydrogen peroxide, and ammonia these so-called aromatic amine dyes offered rich dark coverage in contrast to the duller, greenish hues derived from metallic bases.[15]

It was an exciting commercial breakthrough, quickly seized upon by a mysterious entrepreneur known as Monnet et Cie of Paris who obtained a patent in 1883 to use para-phenylenediamine or its derivative para-toluenediamine (first synthesized in 1877)[16] with an oxidising agent as a dye for fur, hair and feathers. This was followed by several further German patents awarded to chemists Hugo and Ernst Erdmann that increased the range of materials like para-

William Henry Perkin had the golden touch, finding a way to extract a lasting purple dye from coal tar.

phenylenediamine and introduced their use with hydrogen peroxide.[17]

The material flooded the fur and textile industry thanks to its durable colour and sharp results.[18] By the mid 1980s, new para-phenylenediamine-based hair dyes also trickled through to other European countries and North and South America via manufacturing lines for hairdressers to prepare individually in their salons.[19] It was an immensely exciting commercial breakthrough for dye technology but it came at a terrible cost.

Dying to be beautiful: allergy

The newly synthesised para-phenylenediamine was a potent skin sensitiser, capable of eliciting severe allergies in manufacturers and customers alike.

I speak to toxicologist Dr David Basketter, a leading specialist in hair dye allergy, to find out exactly what this means."Well, a skin sensitiser is a chemical substance that by virtue of being able to react and covalently bind to skin proteins makes them appear foreign to the body," he explains. "Your body then mounts an immune reaction to them, which is seen as the induction of contact allergy in an individual. If this happens, in the normal course of events, the person will get a skin rash in response to further exposure to the same chemical to which they have become allergic. That same rash is called allergic contact dermatitis or sometimes allergic contact eczema."

As Dr Basketter will explain in Chapter 9, para-phenylenediamine requires oxidation to become reactive, though we still don't know exactly what it is about the substance that makes it such a potent allergen. What is clear, however, is that continued exposure can lead to increasingly severe reactions and even fatalities. It was reports like these that dogged the wonder dye's progress into manufacturing lines across Europe and the United States at the end of the 19th century and start of the 20th. Workers in the dye, textiles and rubber industries suffered from ulcers, eczema, skin infections and asthma due to the restrictive nature of the dye on the airway. Wearers of furs reported similar reactions.[20] Hair dye customers were also exposed to allergy through the distribution of unregulated, unstandardised colourants containing para-phenylenediamine.

Erdmann himself retracted on his earlier enthusiasm for para-phenylenediamine as a hair dye, warning in 1895 that the material and its derivatives "are not in any way altogether suitable for all the requirements that hair dyes must meet [...] because of the strongly poisonous action of this base, and its property of producing swellings and eczemas on sensitive skins." He devoted his time to developing a code of safety for workers using para-phenylenediamine in the fur industry, but supported a ban on the substance in hair dyes.[21]

Erdmann's warning was ineffective. Despite its side effects, hairdressers and customers alike loved the rich colours delivered by para-phenylenediamine-based dyes and were loath to give it up. They were already used to using dyes that fell into two categories: the less effective, less harmful type and caustic, painful sorts with unpredictable results. Bad reactions had always been a risk, without the pay-off of good results.

The appeal of an effective hair dye was evidently strong. The public prosecutor of the Seine Department of Paris, France, recorded 142 related burns and allergy complaints in 1902 alone, and, in 1909, famous actress and courtesan Caroline Otéro (1868 –1965) reportedly suffered serious burns from a 'para' lotion she was using.[22] In 1906, para-phenylenediamine was reclassified as a poison in Germany with retailers told to include the warning on products marketed to customers.[23] Austria swiftly followed suit.[24] This did little to stop hairdressers and customers from importing unregulated products from abroad.[25]

Doctors recorded with alarm some of the fatalities that followed. In 1933, a 21-year-old hairdresser's apprentice was admitted to Manchester Royal Infirmary with abdominal pain, jaundiced skin and swollen feet. Her periods had stopped six months ago and her urine had been darkly coloured. She died six weeks later of liver atrophy attributed to her contact with para-phenylenediamine dyes at work.[26]

Six years later, doctors recorded the case of a 51-year old woman who was admitted to hospital in New York with palpitations, weight loss, shortness of breath and discolouration of the skin. The cause was her para-phenylenediamine-based hair colourant and she died on the ward two months later. A post-mortem revealed pigment granules had infiltrated and damaged areas of her brain.[27]

When pre-prepared hair dye with standardised shades became available to salons in the early 20th century, the stage was set for a showdown between two technologies: historic, metallic-based dyes and the new highly effective, highly sensitising para-phenylenediamine formulas. But it was to be something else entirely that shaped the future of the hair dye industry: fashion.

Battle paint: Para-phenylenediamine versus pyrogallol

The founder of L'Oréal, Eugène Schueller (1881–1957), is often falsely credited with making the first truly commercial para-phenylenediamine hair dye: an invention that kickstarted L'Oréal on its journey to dominating the beauty industry. While today the company has massively diversified its offerings, their founder's rags to riches hair dye invention story remains close to their heart. I grew up watching spokespeople like Cheryl Cole and Eva Longoria swish their glossy locks around on the small screen, whispering those magic words, "You're worth it".

Today permanent hair dyes containing para-phenylenediamine from brands like L'Oréal make up around 70% of the world hair dye market.[28] Yet, Schueller's pioneering colourant did not contain para-phenylenediamine for one key reason: he did not trust it.[29]

Instead Schueller's famous dye, created in 1907, was based on pyrogallol and metallic salts (copper and iron). A budding French chemist, he applied the opposite procedure to oxidation, by using a reducing agent to delay the reaction between the pyrogallol and metallic salts until the mixture was exposed to oxygen when applied to the hair.[30]

Much like Perkin before him, Schueller quickly realised the potential of his product, which could be marketed as an alternative to the allergy-inducing para-phenylenediamine dyes. His patent application in 1907 declared that "aside from their toxicity, which has led to them being banned in several countries," existing para-phenylenediamine-based dyes did not produce an effective and predictable colour and claimed that his product was harmless and far more effective. In 1909, he began selling his dye under the name of L'Auréale – meaning 'halo' - operating under the company name of Société Française des Teintures Inoffensives pour Cheveux (The French Harmless Hair Dye Company). He would quickly rebrand as L'Oréal.[31]

In 1914, he introduced L'Oréal Compound Henna: a mix of henna to bind the colour to the hair but with tannin, pyrogallol, nutgalls and other colouring agents to create brown shades.[32] These hair dyes, he argued in his publication *De l'innocuité des teintures pour cheveux* (The Safety of Hair Dyes), were infinitely safer than dangerous para-phenylenediamine-based dyes.[33]

Para-phenylenediamine, however, was not going anywhere. In 1910, the first range of mass-market standardised commercial hair dyes containing para-phenylenediamine was released by French hairdresser Gaston Boudou (1870-unknown).[34] Known as 'Inecto', the 11 shades delivered predictable (and reproducible!) results and delighted hairdressers were willing to defend them fiercely, arguing that allergic reactions were the consequence of inexperienced customers using them incorrectly at home. Their wheedling was to no avail and para-phenylenediamine was classified as a poison in France in 1911.[35]

It did not dent the popularity of Inecto abroad. The manufacturers expanded the range to 18 shades in 1917 under the name 'Inecto Rapid'[36] and in 1919, Inecto reached the United States where it was received warmly by hairdressers, but also triggered large-scale reports of allergy and dermatitis.[37] These spurred on Inecto chemist Ralph L. Evans to introduce a new line, 'Inecto Rapid Notox', based on related aromatic amine para-toluenediamine in 1924. He also standardised aromatic amine colouring procedures and made it simpler for customers to switch from metallic compound hennas to oxidative amino dyes.[38] It was a move determined to steal Schueller's customer base.

But, although a fierce marketing campaign assured customers that Notox was so safe it did not require a patch test in promotional literature, customers continued to react severely to the now para-toluenediamine-based products.[39] As para-toluenediamine is the main alternative still found in 'PPD-free' permanent hair dyes today, I ask Dr Basketter whether it's truly less problematic.

"Well, the whole point of para-toluenediamine was that it was not as allergenic as para-phenylenediamine," he muses, "but manufacturers have to use a higher level of para-toluenediamine to get the same kind of performance. So, with higher exposure, you then tend to reduce the benefit of the lower allergy risk because it's not just the potency of the allergen but also the dose that people are exposed to. Many would say that actually in practice para-toluenediamine probably sensitises almost as many people as para-phenylenediamine."

Previous action against Inecto had been unsuccessful due to various dodgy changes of ownership and name, but it was in the US that lawsuits finally caught up with the manufacturers.[40] In addition to its 'safe' branding, the manufacturers also came under fire for advertising their product as "penetrating in its action [able to deposit] the colour inside the hair shaft, where the natural pigment originally grew." It's how modern permanent hair dyes work, but this claim was fiercely discredited by chemists called upon as witnesses, according to whom, "there is no dye known to the medical or chemical profession that can penetrate to the inside of the hair".[41]

However former industry chemist Dr Robert Hefford thinks this particular claim could just have been true. "Remember they didn't have electron microscopes in those days," he advises. "Para-phenylenediamine dyes can penetrate to the centre of the hair, but if you don't have a pH high enough, it's not going to penetrate the hair very far. So, one would imagine that the early para-phenylenediamine products did penetrate the hair shaft. How far would depend on what extreme of pH they were at. It's a mystery wrapped up in all the marketing and positioning that was going on to get people to buy their products."

New technology or not, The Federal Trade Commission ruled that Inecto Notox was a "dangerously toxic, deleterious and harmful product, containing a toxic dye-base, and toxic, poisonous and injurious ingredients or properties" and the company was ordered to cease and desist.[42]

But it was too late. Despite their effects on many unlucky customers, the convenience and colour range that these unregulated aromatic amine dyes provided meant a large number of customers were already addicted, while safety-conscious clients instead opted for Schueller's 'safe' metallic and compound henna blends.

But the latter's claims of safety were equally problematic, says Dr Hefford. He explains, "Schueller presented these products as the safe alternative to the use of 'coal-tar dyes', and the battle between the two technologies went on through the 1920s and 1930s, but today very few metal-based hair colouring products exist due to toxicity concerns. Up until quite recently you could find warnings given in oxidation hair colouring product instructions telling you not to use them if the hair had been coloured with a metallic dye or a 'compound henna'.

"Using hydrogen peroxide on hair that contains metal ions can lead to heat, excessive hair and scalp damage and strange colour effects. If the use of metals was suspected, hairdressers used to take a small cutting of the hair and treat it with some hydrogen peroxide. If metals were present, the peroxide would start to decompose and produce oxygen bubbles."

While compound hennas were initially popular because they offered coverage without the threat of serious allergy, it was actually a change in fashion that put the nail in the coffin for these products as women adopted another new technology: permanent waving AKA the perm. The hydrogen peroxide used in the perm procedure made compound henna incompatible with the new style, and it fell out of favour as the perming process became simpler and more popular in the 1930s.[43]

Schueller had already seen the writing on the wall, and had an abrupt change of heart regarding aromatic amines. In 1931, he launched 'Imédia': a perm-friendly oxidative dye containing para-phenylenediamine.[44] As much of his marketing touted the 'harmless' nature of L'Oréal's hair dyes in contrast to his rival's aromatic amine dyes, this was a risky move, and he took the liberty of advising customers of an antidote to allergic reactions as well as asking them to perform an initial patch test. To his relief, the colourant was a runaway success.[45] Yet, rather than rely on hair dye alone, Schueller was also a canny businessman who set about massively expanding and diversifying L'Oréal's beauty offerings to customers in the decades to come.[46]

His competitors-to-be had also been busy. In 1934, American chemist Lawrence Gelb and his wife Joan bought the rights to a new range of hair dye formulae for $25,000[47] from a German chemist while on a trip to Paris, and used them to found the Clairol Company in the United States.[48] Joan, the glamorous face of the brand, soon adopted the alias Joan Clair for her sales pitches to salons, and 'Clairol Oil Shampoo Tint' was a success.[49] This product was also advertised as the very first commercial hair dye to penetrate the hair shaft and give more natural colours.[50] Whether Inecto beforehand had achieved this or not, remains unclear. Clairol has certainly been credited with this development since, so we can say that the marketing campaign was a success.

Miss Clairol was considered a breakthrough product for many in the industry, but it had its inherent weaknesses: mostly that dark-haired customers still had to pre-lighten their hair before its use. The peroxide tablets that needed to be combined with the dye were also prone to deterioration - a problem amplified by the material shortages and delays triggered by the Second World War in 1939. When competitors Roux introduced a formula based on liquid peroxide, Clairol embarked on seven years of research to provide an even better product than their rivals.[51]

Does she or doesn't she? Commercialising hair colour

The chemistry may have advanced since the nineteenth century, but attitudes towards dyed hair were still frightfully Victorian. More women were dabbling in the illicit glamour of widely sold cosmetics but bleached hair was still widely deemed the domain of chorus girls and prostitutes by middle class housewives who companies like Clairol recognised had to be their core demographic. They had to somehow make hair colour classy.

However, Clairol had two key advantages in its quest for commercialising blondeness: cinema and White racial anxieties. Despite Nazi propaganda using blonde hair to weave a myth of White German supremacy, White segregated America too was emotionally invested in the clean-cut, all-American blonde. This fair-skinned, fair-haired emblem of Americanness was a response to fears about inter-racial society and relationships.

The brassy bad girls of early '20s silver screen were being rewritten as wholesome heroines, and a series of 'racial adventure' films in the '30s pitted the beautiful blonde against bestial others with depraved motives - most notably King Kong.[52] White anxieties towards racial integration were high, and much racism was directed at the visible, segregated African American population. Japanese Americans also received racial abuse after the bombing of Pearl Harbour in 1941. The image of Rita Hayworth, a dramatically reinvented and bleached-blonde Spanish actress turned Hollywood star, was even painted on a test Atomic bomb.[53] Conversely, on the other side of the war, Nazi leaders had also adopted fair hair as an icon of 'Whiteness', perpetuating the myth of a pure Aryan race under siege from racial mixing (This was despite many key Nazis looking notably 'un-Aryan' themselves). Blonde hair, with those well-trodden connotations of innocence, vitality, health and youthfulness, was the poster child for perfect German genes.[54]

Some Jewish people in Nazi-occupied territories bleached their hair or their children's hair in an attempt to assimilate. Jewish actor Leo Reuss undertook an incredible subterfuge by bleaching his hair and skin and taking on a new acting persona in Austria.[55] Austrian-Jewish Olympic swimmer Ruth Langer lightened her hair and escaped to England in 1938 with a fake baptismal certificate.[56] Interviews with Jewish Holocaust survivors have even found that those with lighter hair and eyes had a better chance of survival than those with dark features. Were they less likely to be subject to documentation checks? Did guards at concentration camps have a vague positive bias that saved their lives?[57]

But the true horrors of the Second World War did not dent the popularity of blonde hair in Hollywood - it was instead used to sell passive female ideals to a generation of war veterans and newly independent women. After capably filling their husbands' work shoes during the war, post-war polls suggested that between 60 and 85% of women in non-traditional roles did not want to leave them. Male film-makers responded with the 'dumb blonde' stereotype that still plagues blondes today, first propelling Marilyn Monroe (1926–1962) to fame and equally stifling her. Blonde hair symbolised incredible sensuality but was also non-threatening to veterans who were pitched a return to home comforts: adoring wives, angelic children and picket fences. Women were being told that the most desirable, adored icon of womanhood sought the approval of men around her. They were being told to go back to being mothers and homemakers.[58]

It was in this era of conservatism that Clairol introduced Miss Clairol Hair Color Bath: the first home hair dye that could lighten, tint, condition, and shampoo hair in one step in 1950.[59] They had a difficult job ahead of them. While blondeness was embraced as part of the American dream, obviously bleaching one's hair still carried a heavy stigma, and the task of making Clairol's hair dye commercially profitable fell to junior copywriter Shirley Polykoff. Polykoff (who had been a bleach blonde since the tender age of 13) perceptively realised that discretion would be the key to success and launched a hugely successful advertising campaign to reassure customers their natural colour would not be rumbled. "Does she or doesn't she? Only her hairdresser knows for sure" is still regarded as one of the most successful marketing lines of all time.[60]

In contrast to high glamour hair dye ads of the time, Polykoff also insisted that Clairol's models were mainstream and respectable. Her brief stated: "Shirtwaist types instead of glamour gowns. Cashmere-sweater-over-the-shoulder types. Like larger-than-life portraits of the proverbial girl on the block who's a little prettier than your wife and lives in a house slightly nicer than yours."[61] Ads also showed golden-haired mothers pictured with golden-haired children to show just how closely Clairol could colour match. In a stroke of marketing genius, Clairol reinforced their homely image with softer terminology, advertising 'colourants' rather than 'dyes' that 'lighten', 'tint, and 'colour' rather than 'bleach' the hair.[62] "If I've only one life... let me live it as a blonde!" proclaimed follow-up ads.[63]

Names like 'Lady Clairol Whipped Creme hair lightener' (launched in 1951) were also carefully chosen to indicate class. Clairol teaching technician Vern Radusky recalled, "People identified lightening and bleaching the hair with a certain kind of individual. She was a bit fast, or more aggressive, or she was a showgirl. We wanted to give the product an aura of elegance and dignity to counteract that image."[64]

A small company without money to throw around, these clever adverts were combined with strong salon relationships, and Gelb and his small sales team toured the country pitching Miss Clairol's benefits to salons and cosmetic exhibitions.[65] Bruce Gelb, who ran Clairol alongside his father and his brother, Richard, remembered demonstrating their new product at the International Beauty Show near Madison Square Garden. "They were astonished," he recalled. "This was to the world of hair color what computers were to the world of adding machines. The sales guys had to bring buckets of water and do the rinsing off in front of everyone, because the hairdressers in the crowd were convinced we were doing something to the models behind the scenes."[66]

Clairol hair colour had an unprecedented impact. "Thank you for changing my life," gushed one satisfied customer. Another wrote, "My boyfriend, Harold, and I were keeping company for five years but he never wanted to set a date. This made me very nervous. I am 28 and my mother kept saying soon it would be too late for me." After dying her hair blonde with Clairol, the ecstatic writer (later revealed to be Polykoff herself) reported "that is how I am in Bermuda now on my honeymoon."[67]

Other competitors also entered fray during this period, notably perm pioneers Wella with 'Koleston' hair conditioning cream tint in 1950[68] and Alberto-Culver with shampoo-in permanent hair colouring in 1955. A low-key L'Oréal also began selling hair dyes in New York under the name of Cosmair, Inc in 1954.[69]

In addition, the first hair dye in the

brand established by the late great American entrepreneur Madam C. J. Walker (1867–1919), who manufactured and sold beauty products to Black women was advertised in 1958.[70] This would be followed by other brands like Tintz, who created hair dyes that catered specifically to men and women of colour ("Natural or straight? Color it black, baby, but by all means colour it!").[71]

Yet, just as quickly as American women were embracing hair dye, their lifestyles were changing. Convenience was taking on new importance and the development of shampoo-in hair colouring was the future. Helena Rubinstein's Tintillate was first off the mark in 1962, but it was Alberto-Culver's New Dawn in 1963 ("So easy, so beautiful, you'll think your hair colored itself!) that the concept really took off.[72] Clairol retaliated with 'Nice 'n Easy' in 1965. A dreamy ad showing a beautifully bouffant woman running through the fields into the arms of her partner teamed with Polykoff's accompanying slogan, "The closer he gets the better you look", struck gold.[73]

Clairol represented 60% of American sales in the 1970s,[74] but the challenge from the company new on the American scene, L'Oréal, came in the form of 'Preference' in the 1970s. It was a more expensive product than Clairol that promised better results and delivered one of the most famous slogans of all time: 'Because I'm worth it'. This slice of marketing genius was delivered by another young female copywriter, Ilon Specht, who persuaded the male creative team to use her feisty soliloquy and ditch their planned use of a wafting, mute model. Their bet paid off; a new wave of feminism was in the air and 'Preference' went on to surpass Clairol's 'Nice 'n Easy' as the leading hair colour brand in the US.[75] The company also adopted the supremely catchy and empowering slogan for their entire business.

Advertising made a wealth of difference to hair care sales. New formats also rained down on consumers: shampoo tints, gels and cream for at-home use. In the 1950s, only 4% to 7% of American women were estimated to dye their hair, but, in 20 years, that number had risen to over 40%.[76] Between 1995 and 1998, retail sales of home hair dye for Black American women rose by 8.3% with 42% of those choosing to dye their hair opting for blonde or red shades.[77] By 2004, a staggering 75% of American women were said to colour their hair.[78] Clairol's picture-perfect housewifey ads had persuaded a generation of women that looking good (which meant looking blonde) for their husband was commendable, but L'Oréal brought hair dye into the modern era by associating it with self-empowerment and a touch of rebelliousness.

By the 1970s, men were also being targeted. Companies promised dye-shy men discretion with slickly-packaged progressive dyes that gradually darkened the hair by leaving metallic salts on the shaft without penetrating the cuticle. This was not new technology and had been adopted by plenty of working men during the industrial revolution, but it was given a fresh lease of life through marketing campaigns, playing on old anxieties about ageing.[79]

Then came temporary colours. While introduced in rinse form as early as 1922 in the US,[80] temporary colours really took off at the end of the 20th century when obvious hair dye use took on new political meaning, typically anti-establishment. Adopters of the 1970s Punk movement in the UK and US became famed for their use of bright hair colours over bleached spikes of hair,[81] while adopters of the western 'Goth' subculture teamed dramatic makeup with hair dyed midnight black.[82] '90s teens in Japan experimented with reddish brown hair to rebel against strict conformity standards in Japanese schools,[83] and some schools responded by forcing even naturally fairer-haired students to dye their hair dark.[84] For decades, politicians in the ruling Chinese Communist Party have dyed their greying hair a uniform jet black in a demonstration of youth and uniformity.[85]

Legally blonde: legislating for hair dyes

Critics of hair dye were still prevalent during the early 21st century, but they were no longer primarily interested in women's morality but their health. As a burgeoning European market developed for commercial hair dyes, some governments, concerned by serious contact allergy reports, labelled para-phenylenediamine as a poison, effectively banning it, for a time - Germany and France in the early 20th century as discussed[86] and Sweden in 1943 (the latter also prohibited the use of para-toluenediamine between 1943 and 1964).[87] These bans were overturned in the late 20th century in line with EU legislation[88]

In Great Britain, the 1933 Pharmacy And Poisons Act required all hair dyes containing phenylenediamines or toluenediamines or their salts to be labelled "Caution: This preparation may cause serious inflammation of the skin in certain persons and should be used only in accordance with expert advice."[89] Over in the USA, the 1906 Pure Food And Drugs Act controlled the use of colourants added to food and drink, but did not extend this coverage to aromatic amine hair dyes. This lack of regulation had tragic consequences, such as this case reported in 1920. George Hoffman, a lawyer practising in New York, appealed to the United States Bureau of Chemistry for help on behalf of his sister, who had purchased a dye called The Empress.

"Within 36 hours", he wrote, "her eyes were affected seriously; it required about two months' time and the assistance of the most skilful physicians obtainable in the city of Hartford to save her eyesight [...]. It is useless to attempt to describe the physical and mental agony suffered by the young woman who is about 47 years of age."[90] Despite pressing the case that the dye claimed to contain "no substances injurious to the hair", the Bureau of Chemistry was powerless to act because hair dye was not a food or drink.[91]

When Franklin Roosevelt became President in 1933, a reform of the act was part of his administration's agenda. This became particularly important with the increase of American customers swapping the salon for cheaper dyes to use at home during the period of economic depression.[92] The FDA produced public exhibits to support their need for more regulatory control over food, drink, medicines and cosmetics such as one memorable display at the Chicago World's Fair. This was to become anecdotally known as 'The Chamber Of Horrors'. First Lady Eleanor Roosevelt was horrified to see 'before' and 'after' photographs of a woman blinded by Lash Lure: an eyelash and eyebrow dye containing para-phenylenediamine.[93] Widespread coverage of the story led to a decline in eye cosmetic sales and an angry response from mascara manufacturers.[94]

I tried several times to read another article that showed graphic post-mortem images of a 52-year old woman who died after using Lash Lure only a year later. My stomach wasn't strong enough - I had to get my partner to extract the tragic facts for me instead. The victim, who had her right eyebrow plucked and Lash Lure applied to her brow and eyelashes, quickly experienced excruciating pain and swelling to the extent that she could not complete the treatment. Admitted to hospital with bleeding and ulceration of the eyes, she succumbed to sepsis eight days later. Doctors examining her said the plucked eyebrow had increased the capacity of the para-phenylendiamine-based mascara to enter her

Images seen by First Lady Eleanor Roosevelt at the Chicago World's Fair of women blinded by Lash Lure saw a steep decline in eye cosmetic sales. This design is an interpretation of a Lash Lure advertisement from the time.

system, resulting in a 'violent local and systemic allergic response".[95]

Five more years of campaigning in the US followed,[96] but it was another tragedy that finally triggered action by Congress. In the autumn of 1937, more than 100 people died from an untested drug designed to treat sore throats: Elixir Sulfanilamide.[97] The deaths led to the swift passage of the 1938 Food, Drug, and Cosmetic Act through Congress, which increased the Food and Drug Administration's authority to regulate drugs and cosmetics. The legislation stated that colours used in cosmetics had to be certified by the FDA, but such was the power of the lobby that coal-tar dyes were exempt from this regulation as long as they had a caution on the label warning about skin irritation and eye injury. Mandatory patch-testing instructions were deemed to be enough protection for customers against the danger of severe allergic reactions.[98]

Further attempts to ensure hair dye manufacturers' tested their ingredients for safety before they were sold were thwarted by a fierce industry response in 1962, with businessmen (and women) threatening devastation of the industry and the swift growth of a black market. "Mr Secretary," asked the Chairman of the hearing, quickly grasping the importance of the issue, "[...] you do not want unnecessarily to interfere with our ladies' opportunity to become the most beautiful women in the world; do you?"[99]

As customers grew more dependent on hair dye, and manufacturers remained dependent on oxidative coal-tar formulas, a stalemate was in place. Concern over hair colourant use, however, was soon to switch from allergy alone to cancer.

The hair dye industry - like the cosmetics one - has worked hard to turn colouring your hair into a form of female self-empowerment and self-expression. Gone are the ads showing adoring husbands and pinny-perfect housewives with their blonde curls. Now we are shown glamorous career women who somehow manage to juggle the school run with morning television slots and have the time to dye their hair over the sink before pick-up at 3pm. Where are the twinkly-haired 30-something women on primetime TV, presenting the news, taking the lead in a sitcom? At the salon, having their hair coloured, that's where.

We are also being targeted early. In recent years, hair dye brands have turned the weaknesses of temporary and semi-permanent hair colours into a marketing triumph, selling increasingly younger customers formulas promising commitment-free fun. Hair colourants have become a new form of fast fashion, available cheaply in DIY formats for those unable to afford a salon visit. Market research in 2019 suggested that 72% of Italian 16-24 year old users and 69% of Spanish hair dye users of the same age were interested in trying vibrant new colours, while 40% of 18-24 year old customers in the US also regularly experiment.[100] More customers are now encouraged to colour their hair themselves at home from a younger age. Once hair dyes thrived on promising subtlety, but now they are also proudly bright and beautiful.

Temporary hair dyes have successfully recognised the zeitgeist for the younger generation's desires for fun, self-expression and creativity. But there's no denying that, whatever they peddle to younger users, this entire industry depends on exploiting female fears about growing old.

Significantly, permanent hair dyes - the most reliable and long-lasting form of grey coverage - account for around 80% of the hair dye market worldwide.[101] Market research in 2011 confirmed that a majority of European women decide to colour their hair to conceal greys.[102] Even women in cultures like China, India and Japan with a tradition of respecting older generations have heaped pressure on women to conceal this normal sign of aging[103] (one 1990s Indian advert memorably showed a young woman with greying hair being addressed as 'Aunty' until she dyed it.)[104] In 2013, L'Oréal spokesperson Jane Fonda (then aged 75) urged women to "Keep your colour, never give up. We are totally worth it."[105] The message is clear: the patriarchy isn't dead, ladies, your value still depends on looking young.

In 2015, when the Duchess of Cambridge stepped out with a few grey hairs at her roots, it made headlines, with celebrity hairdresser Nicky Clarke calling the look a "disaster". "Unfortunately it's the case for women - all women - that until you're really old, you can't be seen to have any grey hairs," he bluntly told the Daily Mail. That the Duchess was pregnant with her second child - and a number of expecting women choose to avoid hair dye for health concerns (see Chapter 4) - was apparently beside the point.[106]

Academic Professor Mary Beard regularly receives abuse for her 'witchy' long, grey hair - hair that is apparently completely inappropriate and even repulsive for a female documentary presenter according to some.[107] Yet, you don't see David Attenborough being told to get down to the salon. Why? Because Mary Beard's lack of input into her appearance is also received as a lack of effort into her work. We're told it's female laziness. Greying hair is not only unattractive on women, reads the bottom line, but unprofessional.

There was a strong element of anger behind the barbed words too - especially in those delivered by female critics. Reading between the lines, Mary Beard is letting the side down by revealing the truth of female aging. Worse, she was liberated from what she dubbed 'the grey hair conspiracy', and her critics were not. The backlash was inevitable.

Like many women, when I make an effort with my appearance I can resolutely swear it's for myself alone. But, deep down, I know it's for society. I am arming myself with the confidence and tools to take on the multiple female roles waiting for me: mum, employee, partner, daughter, friend, woman. I suspect I'm not alone in this, though I would cheerfully have lacerated (verbally) anyone who suggested it only a year or two ago. No-one wants to feel manipulated still by the sexist legacy of our past. We want to swish out of the hairdressers with 'I'm worth it' hair and nail every hour of our complex lives. Who instead wants to probe that uncomfortable truth: why am I less 'worth it' with grey hair?

I'm somewhat relieved to write that I no longer think concealing grey hair is due to a subliminal, primal urge to look young for your partner. I'm frustrated to concede instead that it's down to thousands of years of social conditioning telling women their value is in their youth and fertility, not their intelligence, their careers, their other talents. Our painful patriarchal history has left us with open wounds.

Over the last century, cosmetics have gone from being frowned upon to being a female obligation. Men who dye their hair or try to hide a receding hairline are treated with a vague sense of pity and embarrassment. It's a shameful secret. But women are told it's expected of them. However much social progress we are making in the 21st century, women are still fed the line that physically aging makes them unattractive and less valuable, whether that's in the media, in the home, or the workplace. The pressure to conform, to remain young, is all around.

Frustratingly, I'm aware of my own desire to meet this unrealistic beauty standard. I don't have any grey hairs yet (despite my daughter's best efforts) but I know I will want to conceal them when I do. I want to feel confident in my appearance, I want to feel young. It's infuriating.

But until younger women with twinkly hairs are normalised in the images we are fed, a pregnant woman in the public eye can step out with grey hairs without backlash, and a prominent academic can wear her hair how she likes without getting a positively medieval reaction, I have to accept that my attitude is expected.

But, consider the concerns about the safety of hair dyes, and societal pressure on women to dye greying hair becomes ever more distasteful.

True colours: scandal in the 1970s

6

In the early 1970s, Mark was training as a hairdresser and trichologist in various positions between Dorset and London when worrying reports started appearing in the press concerning hair dyes.

First, a popular hair dye ingredient, 2,4-diaminotoluene, was found to be carcinogenic when it was fed to rats.[1] Then an explosive paper from American biochemist Professor Bruce Ames declared that nearly 90% of hair dyes on the American market contained DNA-altering ingredients.[2] His paper, published in 1975, was followed by others that found a number of the same ingredients caused tumours in animals.

The reports confirmed Mark's worst fears about the aromatic amines he had been handling in hairdressing salons. They also added fuel to his desire to create the most natural products possible. As a consequence, when he was working in a hairdressing salon in Poole as a trichologist many years later, he didn't like aromatic amine dyes although he learned all about them. Instead, he invested energy and time in creating products based on natural ingredients. "Such was my interest," Mark recalls, "that I became a member of The Herb Society: a British society founded in 1927 as a place for like-minded botany enthusiasts to practise herbal medicine. Then I was approached by Dr Malcolm Stuart from the Herb Society, who said, 'Look, people are really concerned about hair dyes and cancer, can you research it and write a booklet about it for us?' It was the first thing I ever wrote."

In 1978, Mark's *Herbal Hair Colouring* was published by the Herb Society; only a year after he had left his trichology job to establish natural cosmetics company Constantine & Weir with beautician and friend Elizabeth Weir.

Mark's dislike of synthetics may have set him apart within the beauty industry, but it did reflect a wider concern about chemical usage. Professor Ames' discovery came during an era that prioritised industry and economic recovery after two world wars but also ignited concern from environmentalists due to the heavy-handed use of the cheap new fertilisers, pesticides and herbicides developed during the war.[3] The hair dye health scandal was preceded by concern about the dead birds, foxes, and other wildlife piling up in verges, gardens and forests. Poisonous compounds were found in eggs and dead fish floating in the rivers.[4]

Public concern was first truly mobilised in 1962 by ecologist Rachel Carson (1907–1964) who published *Silent Spring*: a book that blew the lid off an increasingly carefree industry attitude towards pesticide usage. In this explosive title, she argued that the previous scourges of humankind, chickenpox and the plague, had been replaced by hazards of our own making: carcinogenic materials that were damaging human health and essential ecosystems.[5]

Industrialists were quick to react to *Silent Spring* with accusations of scaremongering, communism and female hysteria. In a letter to President Eisenhower, US Agriculture Secretary of the time, Ezra Taft Benson (1899-1994) wondered why "a spinster was so worried about genetics",[6] while *The New Yorker* magazine received the following letter: "Miss Rachel Carson's reference to the selfishness of insecticide manufacturers probably reflects her Communist sympathies like a lot of our writers these days. We can live without birds and animals, but, as the current market slump shows, we cannot live without business."[7]

But, despite industry attempts to represent Carson as anti-business, *Silent Spring* had a big impact on a society reeling from post-nuclear fallout. It has since been credited with instigating the environmentalism cause.[8]

It was in this era of industrialism versus environmentalism that the dangerous nature of contemporary hair dyes became public knowledge. But it wouldn't have without the pioneering work of Professor Ames who spent ten years developing a test that would revolutionise the way we test a material's carcinogenicity: the potential to cause cancer in living tissue.

Transforming the face of carcinogenicity testing: the Ames test

All cancer begins in cells. Your body is made up of 100,000,000,000, and each one has a specific role in keeping you healthy. At the centre of each cell is a control centre called a nucleus, which contains chromosomes made up of thousands of genes. These genes act like instruction manuals, telling your cell what to do, when to divide, and when to die. If damaged, either by chance during routine functions or by contact with a mutagenic or carcinogenic substance, they can give faulty instructions and alter your cells.[9]

When potentially carcinogenic substances enter your body, one of three things happen: they can change spontaneously into other substances, they are excreted unchanged, or they are metabolised by your enzymes. Most drugs take the final pathway. Your liver, kidneys and lungs play an essential role in breaking these drugs down into less potent substances that can be eliminated from the body. Many hazardous substances can be deactivated by your body, but, on occasion, they remain, or even become, more toxic during the process. If a substance has or gains carcinogenic potential, it can damage the DNA in your cells[10]

It takes several specific mutations working together in a cell to cause it to become cancerous through significant DNA damage. Abnormal cells can then divide uncontrollably and invade other tissues, forming tumours. As we grow older, our

Rachel Carson's *Silent Spring* lit a fire in the belly of environmentalists when it was published in 1962.

chances of accumulating these faulty mutations naturally increase because our cells have gone through many more division, replication and repair processes. This means the incidence of most cancers rises significantly with age. Somewhat depressingly, it has been suggested that currently one in three of us will die of cancer, and that, even if fantastic new cures for heart disease, strokes, and pneumonia are developed, these will only increase our lifespan by a few years.[11]

Despite this gloomy figure, there is also significant evidence that up to 80% of 'induced cancers' - that is, cancers we can attribute to an external cause such as smoking - are avoidable if we make lifestyle changes, such as altering our diets, protecting our skin from sunburn, and avoiding exposure to carcinogens (like tobacco).[12] Some cancers can also be kept at bay for long periods of time, if not cured.

During the 1970s, testing substances for their potential to cause cancer was dependent on long-term population studies and live animal experiments. The first option was expensive, slow, and had to consider a number of different lifestyle factors, the latter cruel and held under very different conditions to human exposure. Rather than trying to investigate a material's carcinogenicity, Professor Ames developed a revolutionary test that would instead assess a material's mutagenicity: its ability to cause changes to human DNA. P Mutagenicity and carcinogenicity are not interchangeable. But, as changes to DNA are one starting point of cancer, a high number of carcinogens are also mutagenic.[13] The extent to which the two correlate has been a subject of fierce debate for decades, (and, nowadays, we know that cancer is not only caused by gene mutations)[14] but it was this principle that formed the basis of what is known as the Ames Test.

Now in his nineties and working in nutrition from his home in California, Professor Ames is happy to recall the series of events over the phone. "I was trained as a biochemist," he reveals, "but I took a genetics course around when I was getting my PhD at Caltech [The California Institute of Technology] and that got me interested in mutagens and mutagenicity. People thought cancer was due to viruses, to genetic change; there were a lot of theories at the time, but, being half a geneticist, I knew that DNA damage had to be involved. And I saw that there was no easy test for mutagens, so I decided I would develop one."

Taking a chemical that he wanted to test for mutagenicity, first, Professor Ames mutated a

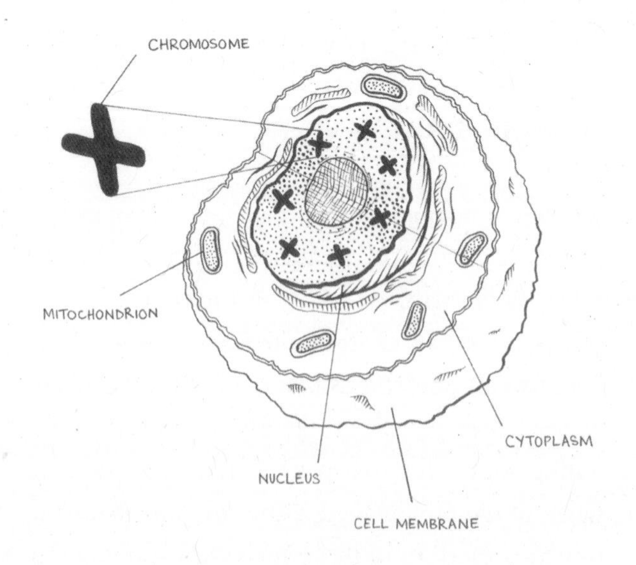

It's in your DNA. Human genetic material is stored within chromosomes housed within your cells.

strain of salmonella bacteria so that it was unable to produce histidine: one of the 20 essential amino acids needed by living organisms to survive.[15] In theory, the bacteria should have been unable to reproduce. Keeping one petri-dish as a control - a variable that is kept the same throughout the experiment - Professor Ames then introduced the potential mutagen he wanted to test to the other. He was looking to see if the bacteria in this second petri-dish reproduced, meaning the suspect chemical had reversed the salmonella mutation and enabled it to process the histidine after all.[16] If it did, it was proof that the chemical was mutagenic and probably carcinogenic too. To the science world, it was devastatingly simple - and economic.

In the following years, Professor Ames developed and improved his assay.[17] "A lot of aromatic amines need to be metabolised; they aren't directly mutagenic," he explains. "In humans, when a chemical enters the body, the liver converts it to an active form. So, I incorporated a little mouse liver so it acted as a kind of primitive human metabolism. Then I tested every known carcinogen to see if it showed up as a mutagen and a high percentage of them did, but when I used large molecules that were known to be carcinogenic, they couldn't get through the bacterial cell wall. And so, I made a mutation in the bacteria so the chemicals could get in more easily."

By the mid 1970s, Professor Ames' laboratory had demonstrated the mutagenicity of numerous common substances like cigarette smoke,[18] a flame retardant used in children's pyjamas[19] and - significantly for us - 89% of 169 tested commercial hair dyes on the market at the time.[20]

The hair dye public health crisis specifically came to light by chance after Professor Ames taught an undergraduate class at Berkeley. He recalls, "I told the students to bring in something from home to test in the assay, and one undergraduate brought in his girlfriend's permanent hair dye, which turned out to be really mutagenic. So, I gave my technician $100 and sent her out to the local drugstore to buy up all the permanent hair dyes. It turned out that most of them seemed to be mutagenic. That was interesting because people were putting them on their skin. So, I tested them all and I wrote a scientific paper, and I sent it to all the companies in the world, telling them 'You better do something about this.'"

Shockingly, however, the conclusions of Professor Ames' and his peers did not lead to a sudden tightening of regulations. Instead, they were widely dismissed by many national governments, including Britain's, which questioned the reliability of the Ames Test on the basis that mutagenic chemicals were not always carcinogenic in humans. UK Prices and Consumer Protection Minister John Fraser (1934-2017) even argued in the House of Commons, "there is no evidence these substances present a health hazard."[21]

Professor Ames remembers feeling frustrated by the slow actions of regulatory bodies. "I was somewhat naive," he recalls, "I thought all these regulatory bodies would adopt my bacterial assay and force industries to use it. And I was completely wrong because the bureaucracies that do the regulation are very conservative and they don't try anything new. Every industry in the world wrote to me for my bacterial strains and tests, but it took five or ten years before the regulators finally caught up and told the industries to use the tests when they already were."

With 40% of American women said to colour their hair by the 1970s,[22] Professor Ames' work triggered a flurry of frantic research. Follow-up studies found that women with dyed hair had significant chromosomal damage,[23] and a number of mice and rats treated with hair dye ingredients also developed tumours.[24] Further research confirmed that hair dye could penetrate the scalp and enter the bloodstream to be excreted in the urine[25] - something doctors studying the cases of para-phenylenediamine poisoning in the early 20th century had reported.[26]

The industry strikes back

The hair colourant industry was seriously rattled by the findings. Not only was their highly profitable industry under threat but they had few alternatives to the materials under scrutiny. Although some materials (such as the previously mentioned animal carcinogen 2,4-diaminotoluene)[27] had been removed from production as knowledge of their toxicity improved, there had been little innovation in colour development for the previous 50 years, and most hair dye manufacturers relied on the same small colour palette of about 10 to 15 ingredients. They were heavily reliant on a small number of primary intermediates like para-phenylenediamine: small compounds that penetrate deeply into the hair fibre, oxidise, and darken, and most of these had been patented by 1926. These were combined with a range of colourless couplers that would influence the final shade, add warm or ashy tones, and better colour stability.[28]

The mutagenicity crisis sparked a decade of fierce debate and frantic testing and formulation when the National Cancer Institute found that mice and rats fed 2,4-diaminoanisole, a popular coupler that created blue tones, and a number of direct red yellow dyes, developed tumours.[29] Para-phenylenediamine, the material that had caused so much allergy concern, was found to induce elevated incidences of liver tumours in female mice and kidney tumours in rats but these were not considered to be statistically significant and it slipped the net.[30]

In the US congress in 1978, the debate came to a head. Industry representatives contested the data from the animal studies conducted by the National Cancer Institute by arguing their own data, based on animal skin-painting tests, supported the ingredients' safety. They also fiercely opposed a notion that the FDA should be granted additional powers to regulate hair dyes, arguing that materials found to be carcinogenic in animal-feeding tests needed more research to prove they were a risk to humans. Fundamentally, they insisted that customer risk was a societal issue - not a scientific one, and the benefits of self-esteem outweighed cancer risks:

"If you are going to tell the public about risks from hair dyes, then you must also tell the public about the risk from caffeine that has been shown to be an animal carcinogen, egg yolks and egg whites that have been shown to be animal carcinogens, and tannin in tea that have been shown to be an animal carcinogen," stated representatives on behalf of the Cosmetics, Toiletries and Fragrances Association.[31]

The minutes from the hearing make fascinating reading. It's the full force of the lobby unleashed: the livelihoods of millions at stake, the importance of cosmetics to consumer self-esteem, the comparative risks of driving, flying - even peanuts. I tried in vain to track down one of the spokespeople - a former director to Clairol - but if he is still alive he wasn't biting.

I also read, with great interest, evidence given by Professor Ames to support the call for labels on hair dyes. He argued, "Even if they weren't carcinogens, mutagens are substances that damage the genes and if they get to the human germ cell line they would cause birth defects in our children and grandchildren." Critical of the sensitivity of all animal cancer tests in general, Professor Ames nonetheless described the industry's own animal skin-painting studies that concluded the materials were not carcinogenic to be "completely inadequate".[32]

"One problem is that you can set up a cancer test so the chances of it coming out positive are really pretty low. For example, tumours appear exponentially with time,[33] so if you do an eighteen-month experiment it's not nearly as good as a 24-month experiment. In addition, if you use a small number of animals, the chance of finding a carcinogen is much less because of statistical problems. So, if you picked an aromatic amine carcinogen that was similar in structure to those to be tested you could show that those tests would actually pick it up. Well, they didn't do that. They used a small dose and a relatively small number of animals and all kinds of conditions were set up so the chances of detecting a carcinogen were low."

He continues, "There are about 250 million women dyeing their hair and so you'd like to know about a hair dye material that would cause a one percent increase in cancer. That would be hundreds of thousands of women. Well, there's no way you can do a test in fifty animals to tell you that because of statistical problems."[34]

Despite the scolding industry representatives received from scientists during this explosive hearing, I'm shocked to find that FDA still gained no further regulatory authority over aromatic amine hair dyes. Although many manufacturers removed the most problematic materials voluntarily,[35] FDA attempts to force manufacturers and hair salons to provide warnings about products containing some animal carcinogens were obstructed in 1980, when a number of affected hair colouring companies obtained a staying order to delay legal proceedings.The FDA later consented to a court order to place warnings only on hair dye products considered to pose a cancer risk following a 'quantitative risk assessment'.[36]

Under pressure: the power of the lobby

Overseas in Poole, Mark was following the headlines with alarm. But when he got stuck into the scientific papers on hair dye and cancer, he also noticed a massive problem. "I could see that they didn't understand the difference between bleaching, metallic salts, highlights, and whether the dye was on the scalp or not. The amount of variation was huge because they didn't understand the basics," he explains.

In an attempt to offer help, he made contact with molecular carcinogenesis consultant Dr Stanley Venitt, who had demonstrated the mutagenicity of a number of hair dye materials

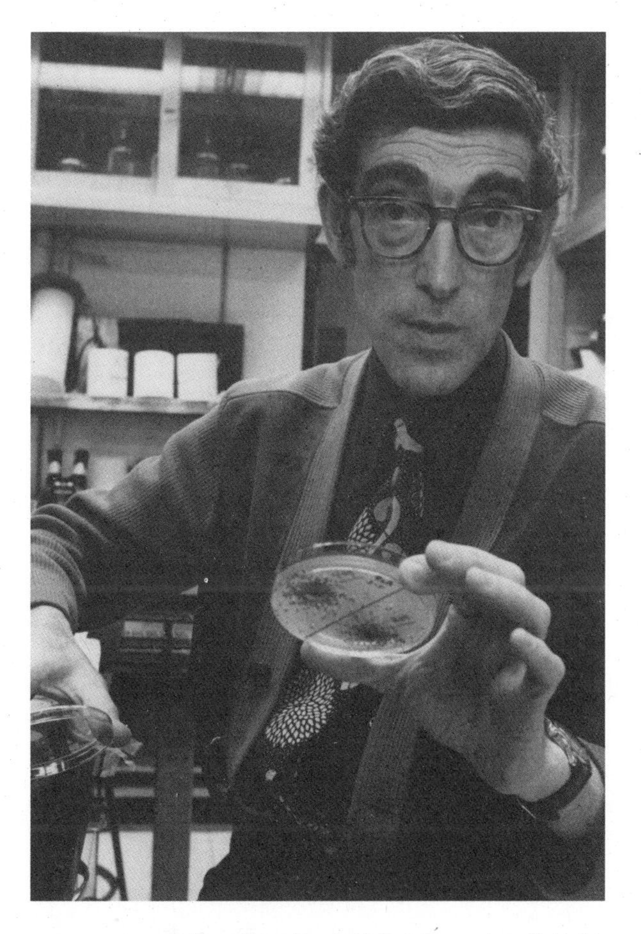

Professor Bruce Ames holds the infamous Ames Test in his hands, in this photograph taken in around 1976.

himself. [37] Dr Venitt introduced him to the big guns: the epidemiologists running the large, long-term studies. "Stanley was a very lovely man," Mark recalls. "We talked, and he got me down to Royal Marsden, introduced me to the right people, and I ended up writing all the questions for a large epidemiological study of mothers whose children had died under the age of five of rare cancers. It was here that I saw how much better epidemiological studies were compared with animal tests which were leaving people exposed."

"But I never got the results because, in-between this long study, they decided I was anti-science. And of course I was never anti-science, I was just anti that form of science. And I would still argue in any public space that the animal tests were not just unethical, they were invalid and they were part of the obfuscation. Everything that I've done since with our work fighting animal testing has been with the knowledge that for the improvement of public health and a real understanding of the dangers of hair dyes and cancer we needed better information."

Although Mark never received any results, thankfully, his friend and very diligent colleague, fellow Lush Co-Founder Helen Ambrosen, kept a wad of papers from the good old days that I am able to leaf through. I find a letter with Mark's suggested questions, referencing Dr Venitt and an epidemiologist he has also mentioned before: Professor Julian Peto. Armed with this knowledge, I track down the study Mark contributed to: The United Kingdom Childhood Cancer study - an investigation into the possible causes of childhood cancer throughout England, Scotland and Wales over the period 1991 to 1998.[38] It's still being used as a valuable piece of research now.

Then I find a follow-up study using the same data that looks at the relationship between maternal exposure to materials including hair dye and childhood leukaemia and lymphomas, published in 2008.[39] It looks like Mark's questions were indeed used, but I can only find one study that has used the data to look at hair dye in pregnancy specifically. In this case, hairdressers exposure to hair dye during pregnancy was not found to increase the risk of leukaemia or lymphomas.[40]

Having turned Sherlock, I decide to track down Dr Venitt and Professor Peto too. As Dr Venitt retired some time ago, he proves tricky to trace. He no longer has contacts at various associated universities, but I send a message to the chairperson of a club I believe his wife had a membership with, cross my fingers, and wait.

Professor Julian Peto is far easier to track down. A current fellow at the Academy of Medical Scientists, he has in fact been actively publishing on the Covid-19 pandemic in 2021, and an administrator passes on my message'. When we speak, he says he's never been personally involved in research regarding hair dye and cancer, and isn't ready to settle in for a long chat. Presumably he's pretty busy this year.

But I have a surprising breakthrough when Dr Venitt (who is as lovely as Mark says) contacts me by phone, and makes a very generous offer to speak to me in person. I hop on a train to his idyllic countryside house, hidden off the beaten track down a country lane. I even see a deer from his doorstep. Over tea and biscuits, we talk about Brexit, birding, and - of course - his work. It's a very humbling experience.

"Well, I did a degree in what was called botany, but they don't call it that any more," he says, "They call it plant sciences to make it slightly sexier. Then I did a PhD in biochemical genetics and applied for a job at what is now known as the Institute of Cancer Research.

The people I was working with then were interested in finding out what the target was for cancer. Everyone thought it was proteins, because they were the only things that are really complicated and the structure of DNA wasn't elucidated till the 1950s. It took a long time to convince people that DNA was the target. Over 30 or 40 years we've gone from knowing absolutely nothing about cancers to knowing an enormous amount. So, it's a huge journey that's happened, and I've been sort of incidental in that. But I was also a spectator of it as well, and that's quite exciting."

Like Professor Ames, Dr Venitt published a number of papers showing the mutagenicity of hair dyes in the 1970s and '80s.[41] He also became embroiled in industry attempts to find alternatives when L'Oréal patented a new primary intermediate known as 2-(2',4'-diaminophenoxy) ethanol. It was a very close relative of the carcinogenic 2,4-diaminoanisole that Professor Ames had first identified as problematic. Lab studies, they said, had proven it was devoid of any genotoxic activity. Venitt's curiosity was kindled.[42]

Dr Stanley Venitt (photographed at the Institute of Cancer Research in 1992) published a series of revealing papers about the mutagenicity of hair dye ingredients. Photo information: Institute of Cancer Research in 1992.

"The industry spent so long looking for a safe analogue of 2,4-diaminoanisole and L'Oréal, in particular, made lots of compounds," he recalls. "They dug this one out and said, 'This is it, this is the one; it's not mutagenic!' When those papers came out, I was absolutely staggered because they devoted a whole issue of *Mutation Research* to this single compound, saying that in every test they did, it was completely negative. But it was so closely related to 2,4-diaminoanisole that it sparked my interest."

Using both a purified commercial 2-(2',4'-diaminophenoxy)ethanol and a batch made by an organic chemist and authenticated by two labs, Dr Venitt says he and his colleagues went to enormous lengths to make sure the compound - which came out as a "screaming mutagen" - was identical to L'Oréal's.

"We were very confident that this was the same compound that they'd made and tested. We went into it very thoroughly because we knew that if we were trying to publish it, there'd be all sorts of opposition, they'd say, 'Well, it's not the right compound.' And I wrote it up, but then I thought, well, why are these people getting negative results? So, I went through all the papers, line by line."

I've read the paper, which goes into great detail about the shortcomings of all the other laboratory studies on 2-(2',4'-diaminophenoxy) ethanol, and, let's just say, I wouldn't fancy Dr Venitt writing my school report. He explains to me that some of the problems with the studies were pretty blatant. He also believes that data was withheld. "Once the data had been released to the people who commissioned the study, they can do what they like, and they can publish it or they can not publish it. I have a very strong suspicion as to what happened."

Industry pressure is nothing new to Dr Venitt, be it from the cigarette, agricultural or beauty quarters. "I was on these committees for many, many years and experienced the extent to which large bodies of interest groups like the tobacco industry and the food industry can apply pressure. It's very difficult for individual scientists to stand up against them, because they can amass enormous legal and financial power.

"I gave up meat for about ten years after I was on a committee that licensed veterinary products because of what I learned about the drugs used in intensive farming. Lots of the vets on the committee had research that was financed by the very large drug companies who had huge interests in factory farming. And the only thing that keeps factory farming alive are antibiotics and other things that stop animals dying. It's an awful business."

Dr Venitt's proudest achievement was his contribution to the decades-long battle to finally ban cigarette advertising in the UK. It wasn't until 1992 that tobacco advertising was banned in the UK - another example of the immense influence a fabulously wealthy industry can wield. I'm shocked when he reveals it took seven decades to persuade the government to ban advertising of cigarettes. *Cigarettes!*

Dr Venitt nods. "Their lobby was fantastic. They used to entertain those people who they knew would be opinion-formers. The advertising ban was inevitable in the end because even the thickest politician could see that smoking was terrible." He concludes, "so, over the years, I've been quite interested in the power of lobbyists, the most powerful being the tobacco lobby. But exactly the same tactics are being used by the food industry to support the continuing sales of sugars and palm oil, and if you try to cut their activities in any way there's a very powerful reaction against it."

Back on the subject of 2-(2',4'-diaminophenoxy)ethanol, he reveals that his paper got tremendous attention from particularly meticulous referees. "Normally you only get two anonymous referees who comment on the paper and say what they think about it, whether it should be published or whether it's got errors. In this case there was a great list of them. I wasn't very popular, but it didn't really worry me because I knew that it was a sound bit of work."

Mark also got a taste of the hair dye lobby when he attended a talk Dr Venitt was giving on his paper's findings. Some L'Oréal representatives were also in the audience. "They knew that they were a disgrace," he says, "because they stood up at the end and said, 'You paint us as unscrupulous.' Venitt's point to them was, 'You've changed 2,4-diaminoanisole by one hydoxymethyl group and reissued it. If that isn't unscrupulous, it certainly lacks scruples.'"

I'm curious to see whether 2-(2',4'-diaminophenoxy)ethanol is still used after all this debate in the 1980s. Forty years later and there it is under the EU's restricted substances list, available for use in hair dyes and eyelash colouring products today.[43] After my eye-opening talk with Dr Venitt, I don't know whether I'm surprised or not.

Modern hair dye regulation

While manufacturers and scientists locked horns over hair dye in the 1970s and 1980s, by the latter decade, American and European regulatory bodies were finally creaking into action. The long, slow arms of the law, however, took different approaches.

The newly established European Union

(EU) began to legislate hair dyes more strictly, banning 11 popular materials during the 1980s[44] and then putting forward plans to create a 'positive list' of safe hair dye ingredients.[45] This gave manufacturers the opportunity to provide safety dossiers for a list of hair dye ingredients they wanted to champion. Nearly five decades later, we still only have a list of prohibited and restricted ingredients and materials continue to be regularly banned and restricted - recently in 2006[46], 2015[47] and 2019.[48]

As of 2020, para-phenylenediamine is allowed in finished hair dye products at a maximum on-head concentration of 2% within the EU.[49] Permanent hair dyes within the EU also require a caution regarding allergy (a concern explored more fully in Chapter 9), but patch-testing instructions are not mandatory, although they are added by manufacturers.[50]

Many other nations around the world follow a similar regulatory approach to the EU when it comes to hair dye regulations, although with their own lists of approved and restricted materials and maximum concentrations. Japan once had a very restrictive approach to oxidative (aromatic amine) hair dyes, which are considered 'quasi drugs' and were subject to strict regulations, but this changed in 2001. Nowadays, as in the EU and USA, manufacturers or sellers are responsible for ensuring that any marketed or imported cosmetic is safe.[51] The People's Republic of China operates a similar system in practice to the EU with lists of banned and restricted ingredients, but has also published a positive list of dye ingredients that does not yet exist within the EU.[52] Member countries of the Association of Southeast Asian Nations[53] and Southern Common Markets in South America[54] also follow similar rules to those of the EU.[55]

In the United States, aromatic amine hair dyes (referred to as coal-tar hair dyes) continue to be subject to legislation rolled out in 1938 that leaves them largely self-regulated though legally required to carry a warning. In contrast, other colour additives have been subject to regulation by the FDA, and prior required approval since many children in the 1950s fell ill from eating a type of hazardous Halloween sweet.[56]

While the FDA has the power to take action against a cosmetic that contains "a poisonous or deleterious ingredient that may make the cosmetic harmful to consumers", it is unable to do so against an aromatic amine hair dye as long as the product contains adequate directions for a skin test. It must also contain the following statement: "Caution - This product contains ingredients which may cause skin irritation on certain individuals and a preliminary test according to accompanying directions should first be made. This product must not be used for dyeing the eyelashes or eyebrows; to do so may cause blindness."[57] Manufacturers, however, must follow the recommendation of the Cosmetics Ingredient Review Expert Panel, which recommends that on-head concentrations do not exceed 6% (significantly higher than the EU's 2% maximum).[58]

As recently as 2018, the FDA faced a legal challenge from Combe International, manufacturer of 'Just for Men' and 'Grecian Formula', when it began the process of banning lead acetate - a non coal-tar derived ingredient traditionally used in progressive dyes, despite Combe International claiming to have replaced it anyway.[59] Why? Presumably because they didn't want to be left open to legal action by previous customers.

The mutagenicity crisis was a storm that manufacturers managed to weather through delay tactics, debate and eventual reformulation, making them dependent on a much smaller number of ingredients in their patents. As I investigate the history of hair dye regulation, the tension over these materials is palpable - the industry desperately depends on their approval. As former Vice President for Technical Development at Clairol Robert Corbett himself noted in 1999, "It is evident that these patents will create major problems for the industry if it should lose the approval for the use of para-phenylenediamine, p-aminophenol, and 2,5-diaminotoluene [AKA para-toluenediamine]."[60] But as the net tightens on ingredients like para-phenylenediamine, can aromatic amine hair dyes weather the fresh wave of concerns surrounding allergy and cancer? Inevitably, I'm drawn to an unavoidable question: are modern hair dyes safe?

Should you or shouldn’t you? Hair dye and cancer

7

Animal testing: ethics and efficacy

During the national lockdown in the spring of 2020, I noticed a new trend on social media: rainbow hair. Parents desperate to cheer up their kids (and who can blame them) were dyeing their children's hair all the colours of the rainbow and sharing them online. "Before anyone tells me off," posted one mum alongside a picture of her handiwork, "the colours are all vegan - completely safe!" Her kids (whose hair admittedly looked great) looked to be about seven and ten years old.

A few years ago, this trend would have passed me by, but now I'm a spectator on numerous parenting groups on my limited social media platforms, usually joined between the sleep-deprived hours of 11pm and 5am during my maternity leave in 2017.

But, in the spring of 2020, my finger hovered anxiously over the 'comment' icon underneath that rainbow hair picture. Other mums excitedly tagged their friends and commented ("Love it, trying this weekend"). The thing is, I completely get it. What child wouldn't want their hair dyed a bright colour? My daughter (three-going-on-eighteen) would kill for pink hair, and parents are desperately trying to inject a little fun into their kids' lives during the Covid-19 pandemic.

But, oh no, "Stop!" I desperately wanted to type. "Hair dyes are not tested on children. Vegan doesn't mean safe." It concerned me how little understanding there is on hair dye, and not just because, come September 2020, there were still parents asking how to get the stuff out of their children's hair before school finally started again.

Since Professor Ames' work in the 1970s, hair dye has been consistently, but not conclusively, linked to an increased risk of some types of cancer. Shifting through the many studies and opinions has been eye-opening. "When it comes to hair dye, it's very difficult to extract the truth of the situation," agrees former molecular carcinogenesis consultant Dr Stanley Venitt. "On the one hand, you've got an industry pushing the stuff. On the other hand, you've got a huge proportion of the population socially addicted to it. And then you've got people saying 'Well, it might do you harm.' It's very difficult for the general public to disentangle what's true and what isn't."

Assuring the safety of cosmetic products and the ingredients they contain is a complex process which a 'responsible person; - usually the manufacturer or distributor - must take responsibility for within the EU. Unlike in the USA or Japan, a product can also be only either a cosmetic or another type of product; it cannot be both - say a pharmaceutical and a cosmetic - at the same time. [1] Currently, Britain follows this model also, with some minor changes, despite its exit from the European Union in 2020.

To sell a cosmetic product within the EU, a suitably qualified person on the company's behalf, like a toxicologist, must conduct a safety assessment. The company must electronically submit this, a description of the cosmetic, details of the manufacturing process, proof of effect, and data on any animal testing performed to meet safety assessments or to address legal selling requirements for markets outside of the EU to an online portal.[2]

In some cases, such as if they have been found or are believed to be potentially carcinogenic, mutagenic or toxic to reproduction, new ingredients require further independent assessment. Companies hoping to prove the safety of a new ingredient to sell their product within Europe will compile a dossier of studies on the material that their in-house toxicologist considers to be safe in its intended use. This can include existing lab data from in vitro studies (using bacteria or cultured cells), ex vivo studies (using tissues from animals), in vivo animal studies (conducted on live animals), epidemiological studies that look at human exposure in the real world and information about human exposure to similar ingredients. Companies are also encouraged to share information to avoid repeating tests.[3]

The dossier is submitted to the Scientific Committee on Consumer Safety (SCCS): an advisory board to the EU composed of independent experts who assess the evidence and either make a recommendation or say there isn't enough evidence to conclude the safety of the ingredient. The SCCS will also review the use of an ingredient in usage if new data becomes available. If the material in use cannot be determined to be either safe or unsafe, it typically remains in use until more information is presented or animal testing has been performed.

Lush toxicologist Chloé Raffalli explains, "In toxicology, the safety of a product is based on the safety of the ingredients. If you prove that one of your ingredients is safe then you do not have to do additional tests for every single product that contains this ingredient. For hair dyes, the industry has always managed to argue the safety of the ingredients like para-phenylenediamine, because those products are not applied daily and are rinsed off. This is why they do not have to test the finished products."

After years of extended deadlines, animal testing for cosmetic ingredients and finished products sold within the EU has been illegal since 2013.[4] - except for in certain circumstances outlined under the Registration, Evaluation, Authorisation and Restriction of Chemicals regulation, known as REACH. This allows the testing of cosmetics ingredients on animals if previous data falls short or proves inconclusive.[5] REACH's governing body has been criticised by The Animal-Free Safety Assessment (AFSA) Collaboration as recently as 2020 for "systematically requesting unnecessary animal data despite a legal obligation to promote non-animal methods."[6]

As well as being under strong criticism for their inherent cruelty, the validity of animal testing data has been under scrunity for decades. Dr Venitt believes that while animal studies are currently still necessary in the testing of anti-cancer drugs, they are inherently flawed. "Animal testing is still incredibly crude," he explains, "but to mimic the precise metabolism and circulation of a chemical in the system, it's going to take a hell of a lot of convincing that an alternative is as good as testing it in a mouse," he admits. "If you're inventing a drug that you're going to stick into a massive population of people, you have to test it in some system that gives you some evidence on whether it's going to kill everyone."

Yet, as he explains, in his quiet countryside home one frosty January morning, defining what high-dose, short-term animal tests can reliably tell us about low-dose, long-term human exposure is unrealistic. "I was on a government committee for years," he explains, "and various people tried to make us work out a sort of relationship between tumours you see in animals, bacterial mutagenicity, and the risk of cancer in humans. People produced models that varied by 10,000-fold. And it was all rubbish; we said over and over again, 'It's impossible to produce an algorithm that will say because it causes tumours in rats and mice or pigs, firstly, that it will cause those tumours in humans because it probably won't. And, secondly, humans are usually exposed to very low doses over time while you give these experimental animals large doses over short periods of time."

Professor Ames agrees. "Obviously, they can't do cancer tests on people, so they do them on rats and mice but, because that's expensive, they find the level of chemical that kills the animal and back down to the maximum tolerated dose. Well, it turns out that if you get a high enough dose of any chemical it is cell killing. Extra cell division, inflammation: all those things are known to cause cancer. If half of the chemicals in the world are carcinogens, that's because this high dose is killing cells and causing inflammation. There's something defective about the way you're testing it."

On the flip side, epidemiological cohort studies examine human exposure. These studies follow two groups over a long period of time. For example, one group composed of hair dye users and one not, to consider the cancer incidences of both to see if any relationships can be drawn. Despite being expensive and slow to conclude, this is the closest we can get to real-life human exposure. However, as Dr Venitt explains, it's virtually impossible to get a clean study. "The only thing you could do is to take a group of people and give them hair dyes for 20 years and tell them not to smoke, not to gain weight, and not to have babies and see what happens."

To gain the best understanding possible about the work done in this area, I too have had to read a great number of epidemiological and animal testing papers. As a Lush employee and an animal-lover, the latter has been difficult to reconcile myself to. Lush has been vehemently anti-animal testing in cosmetics since its beginning, and the company founders, including Mark, have held those values for much longer. The company is committed to not only campaigning against animal testing in cosmetics but also funding pioneering new methods of safety testing in the name of better science and animal rights.

Fighting animal testing: what the Ames Test did for Lush

A conversation with Lush co-founder and inventor Helen Ambrosen tells me that Professor Ames' work didn't just make big waves in the wider industry, it had a big impact closer to home. After working for UK governmental agency The Institute of Terrestrial Ecology, Helen joined Constantine & Weir as a formulator in 1982, bringing her expertise in botany and love of natural skincare to the table. Gaining patents in bubbles bars, toothy tabs and more, Helen created the henna brick in 2001 (a story we'll explore in Chapter 11) and this product also triggered her work in finding alternatives to animal tests.

Talking to me in the lab she shares with Mark, Helen recalls, "I knew that we'd had a safety analysis on our henna completed using a test created by Professor Bruce Ames that did not use live animals, and I was really proud of this. I didn't know, however, that the test still relied on the use of rat liver. When I became aware of this, I spoke to Mark about it and we argued (which we sometimes do!). He said, "Well, what are you going to do about it?" So, I thought, "Well, I had better get going!"

"Besides being cruel and unethical, I have

always believed that the use of animals in testing does not give the correct results. Alternative tests were beginning to become far more sophisticated and predictive in the 1980s and 1990s, so using them and championing their development became a passion. Bruce Ames' work was a hugely significant step forward in the development of alternatives to those tests. It also triggered a lifetime of work for me in helping to find alternative ways to test our products that did not involve animals at all."

When Helen and her colleagues founded mail order business Cosmetics To Go (the company that preceded Lush) in 1988, she threw herself into developing and researching replacement methods. As well as developing the Assisi test - a skin irritancy test that did not use animal serum[7] - Helen, Constantine & Weir co-founder Elizabeth Weir, and scientist Gill Langley also compiled a dossier of all the alternatives to animal tests that existed at the time. "It meant that for the first time there was a document where all the alternatives were listed, explaining the status of their development, and giving the contact details of the scientists who were doing the work," remembers Helen. "It went everywhere, including to the European Parliament. I received a letter back from an EU Commissioner that said, 'Thank you for doing that. If you hadn't done it, we would have.'"

FIGHTING
ANIMAL
TESTING

Lush's Fighting Animal Testing logo

It wasn't the end of Helen's work. "During his work with Anita Roddick and The Body Shop," she explains, "Mark had originally come up with the concept that ingredients used in the manufacture of products should not have been tested on animals for at least four years. This had become a cornerstone for the Cruelty Free movement. But, as Cosmetics To Go began to be successful, it became clear that this focus on the ingredient did not address the fact that the company that material was bought from could still be heavily involved in animal testing. The focus needed to be on the profile of the company itself, not just the ingredient.

"This experience led to the evolution of our policy, and today Lush only buys ingredients from companies that are not involved in animal tests. Adopting this policy enables us to support companies using the science we have trusted for decades, thanks to our own previous development and exploration in this area."

But, along with her colleagues, Helen still felt it wasn't enough. The founders and directors of Lush wanted to give scientists and companies much greater networking opportunities and so, in 2012, they launched the largest prize fund in the non-animal testing sector: The Lush Prize. This

Fighting Animal Testing, London, UK, 2015

biennial award offers funds of up to £250,000 to trailblazers in the anti-animal testing sphere, as well as publicity and the opportunity to meet like-minded people and companies.

"This global prize fund rewards the scientists who are making great breakthroughs, (including young scientists in these challenging areas) and recognises that communication and training on these subjects is also key to creating much wider international awareness," Helen says. "Financial support for particularly ground-breaking projects has helped the work continue and evolve, and Lush has donated large sums of money to labs and individuals researching and working in this area (Lush Prize has given £2.44 million to 120 winners in 28 countries so far)[8]. The prize ceremonies also provide ample opportunity for celebration!"

One of the biggest success stories of the Lush prize has been XCellR8: an animal-free testing lab that provides data for chemical industries and cosmetics businesses including Lush. XCellR8 Co-Founder and previous Lush Prize winner Dr Carol Treasure, who generously gives me some of her time to discuss animal testing, has dedicated her career to developing cruelty-free and more reliable alternatives.

She gives me her opinion on the current state of play when it comes to carcinogenicity testing. "Many aspects of human health now have internationally approved animal-free tests, but carcinogenicity has remained challenging to model. Regulators currently expect companies to perform animal studies that are widely regarded as flawed on both scientific and ethical grounds. They are poor predictors of carcinogenicity in humans due to a range of factors. These include the fact that rodents metabolise substances very differently from humans, which has a major impact on how those substances are handled by the body.

"Also, laboratory animals are kept in very controlled conditions – and human life just isn't like that. There are so many genetic, environmental and lifestyle factors that all add up to determine how healthy we are. Our cells have amazing natural defences against toxic substances, and cancer can develop when those defences are overloaded – this can be a cumulative effect over time, and caused by multiple factors. Real life is complex and that's why it's hard to make accurate predictions under laboratory conditions – this applies to the old animal models as well as new animal-free tests."

XCellR8 is one of the testing facilities pioneering new methods of assessing an aspect of carcinogenicity known as genotoxicity: damage to the genetic information within a human cell causing DNA mutations or changes in the structure or number of chromosomes. Any of these mechanisms may lead to cancer. We could call it a step up on Professor Ames' pioneering assay.

"An advantage of animal-free models, such as cell culture," says Dr Treasure, "is that we can study very specific events in human cells that are known to increase the likelihood of developing cancer later on. A number of approved animal-free tests are now available to study genotoxicity, which can tell us whether a substance is going to make cells more likely to become cancerous. Genotoxicity doesn't always lead to cancer, but these tests provide a much more scientifically advanced approach than the traditional animal studies, helping us to understand the mechanisms involved and to assess the overall risk. A lot of research continues in this area, and in the future there will be even more sophisticated approaches using both cells and computer modelling to predict carcinogenic potential."

So you can understand, given Lush's investment in alternatives, why reading animal testing papers in the course of researching this project has been a horrible, if necessary, experience.

For their faults, I find myself also trusting the epidemiological studies looking at hair dye exposure that I have read more closely than I do the existing animal-based trials because they show real-life exposures. From my conversation with Dr Venitt and Professor Ames' comments in the previous chapter about how easy it is to conduct low-sensitivity cancer animal studies, I am wary about what is not being published in animal testing data - and what is.

When I speak to leading breast cancer surgeon and researcher Professor Kefah Mokbel, he also makes the point that while hair dye manufacturers invest in research to prove that their ingredients are safe, they do not invest in research looking at the long-term health impacts of hair dyes. "None of the epidemiological research done on hair dyes is sponsored by manufacturers," he tells me over the phone. "They could actually improve their standing by sponsoring research into hair dyes and the public would probably respect them more if they did. But, I think, the lobby is powerful and focused on one thing: selling products."

Cancer and hair dyes: the official line

The current state of affairs is a bit messy.

Ingredients-wise, much attention is focused on para-phenylenediamine, its derivative para-toluenediamine and much more modern derivative 2-Methoxy-methyl-p-phenylenediamine. Both of the latter were designed to be less allergy-inducing alternatives to para-phenylenediamine (more on that in Chapter 9).

All three had mixed results in in vitro mutagenicity tests but none were considered to be mutagenic by the EU's Scientific Committee on Consumer Safety (SCCS) after the committee reviewed live animal studies in 2012.[9] Insufficient data (or in 2-methoxymethyl-p-phenylenediamine's case, no data at all)[10] was submitted by either manufacturers or scientists to make any conclusions about their carcinogenicity, although the panel suggested, "It is unlikely that para-phenylenediamine in oxidative hair dye formulations would pose a carcinogenic risk to the customer."[11]

Despite this, hair dyes have been linked to some types of cancer - specifically some types of non-Hodgkin's diseases and acute leukaemia - by the same authority since 2010. The risk of developing cancer in relation to personal use of permanent (meaning aromatic amine-based) hair dye, they said, was primarily related to users starting to dye their hair before 1980, but not exclusively. Next to the use of only permanent hair dyes, the risk increased with long-term and regular use. Frequent, long-term female users of hair dyes in the USA (where para-phenylenediamine is by far the most prominent primary intermediate in use) were also concluded to be at increased risk of bladder cancer.[12]

Although the SCCS raised "no major concern regarding genotoxicity and carcinogenicity of hair dyes", they warned that the evidence provided was small and did not show the effects of the combined ingredients of permanent hair dyes.[13]

In 2010, The International Agency for Research on Cancer (IARC) concluded that occupational exposures to hair dye are probably carcinogenic to humans, based on limited evidence, but personal use of hair dyes were not classifiable as to its carcinogenicity.[14]

It's no wonder the public isn't getting a clear message.

One of the first difficulties is that individual hair dye materials are being tested in one way and hair dye products in another. We are seeing two 'batches' of evidence: laboratory studies on the mutagenicity and carcinogenicity of specific hair dye materials mostly submitted by hair dye manufacturers, and human epidemiological studies submitted by scientists. The former are telling us that hair dye ingredients are pretty safe, the latter suggesting perhaps that hair dyes themselves are not as safe as we would like.

Concerningly, recent research from India appears to confirm that hair dyes are more toxic to human cells than their individual ingredients, causing chromosomal abnormalities and disrupting healthy cell division.[15] A separate study also found that aromatic amine dyes oxidised animal DNA, causing it to fragment.[16]

Of course, exposures to hair dyes also vary greatly from person to person. Because hairdressers mix and apply hair dyes regularly, they are normally considered more at risk than personal users of hair dye at home due to their increased opportunities for skin penetration and inhalation. Ventilation in the workplace, the number of colouring procedures they perform daily, the thickness of the gloves they use - if they wear gloves at all - all have an impact on how much hair dye material enters the body, not to mention the genetic differences that affect how we metabolise it.

Hairdressers have also been exposed to a number of hazardous materials over the years, other than hair dyes, including bread-and-butter hair styling product Brilliantine, which was found to contain carcinogenic colours in the middle of the 20th century,[17] and formaldehyde, used in some hair straightening procedures.[18] So assessing hair dye risk specifically can be difficult.

But it's customers using hair dye products at home that particularly concern me. They may well be doing so without gloves and the expertise that limits skin contact to the dye. Salons are legally not allowed to colour the hair of a customer under the age of 16, (although notable exceptions have made the news)[19] but with no age restrictions on hair dyes in shops, anyone can pick one up to use at home.

As Lush toxicologist Chloé explains, the safety of hair dyes is assessed according to adult body mass, not children or young teenagers. "When the experts of the SCCS calculate the margin of safety of an ingredient," she says, "they consider the typical body weight of a human to be 60 kgs. Usually, teenagers under 16 have a weight under 60 kgs, so they cannot guarantee the safety of the hair dye." When I see the rise in younger customers using hair dyes, I can't help but feel concerned.

Since these conclusions a decade ago, a number of recent studies have raised questions again over the potential carcinogenicity of hair dyes. With a strong cup of coffee, I tackle the most significant head on.

Bladder cancer

Cases of bladder cancer (the growth of abnormal tissue in the bladder lining)[20] might have dropped by 42% in the UK since the early 1990s, but it is still the eleventh most common cancer here[21] and tenth internationally.[22] Unfortunately, it has also gone hand in hand with hairdressing for centuries. That's because the bladder is a key pit stop for a number of hazardous chemicals en route to excretion, including aromatic amines.

Take para-phenylenediamine, for example. Less than 1% of applied para-phenylenediamine is estimated to penetrate the skin's very outer layer (known as the stratum corneum) during a single colouring procedure under lab conditions. More than 80% of the material that enters the outer layer of the skin will be detoxified by an enzyme known as NAT1.[23] The rest is then processed by the enzyme NAT2, which predominantly operates in the liver, small intestine, and colon tissues,[24] and is excreted in the urine (the majority of which within 24 hours).[25]

Aromatic amines are also found in products from the chemical and rubber industries, as well as paints, fungicides, cigarette smoke, plastics, metal and motor vehicle exhaust and pollutant emissions.[26] Because a majority of these industries were (and still are) male-dominated, men have had higher rates of bladder cancer for decades[27] Tobacco remains the single most significant cause[28] because the harmful chemicals in cigarettes are filtered by the kidneys into your urine, which is stored by the bladder.[29] So reliable studies looking into the relationship between bladder cancer and hairdressers need to consider the smoking habits of the participants.

But even if we exclude the studies that do not adjust for smoking,[30] three large international meta-analyses (meaning studies that gather together and analyse existing evidence) covering the period 1956 to 2009 all found a significant increased risk of bladder cancer to hairdressers[31] - one as high as 30%.[32] Symptoms of cancer can take decades to develop after a carcinogenic exposure, making it difficult to assess whether bladder cancer rates amongst hairdressers have declined or not. With that in mind, none of these analyses were able to conclude that there had been a conclusive reduction in risk since hair dye reformulation in the 1970s and 1980s, and all took smoking into consideration. So, it is certainly possible that, until further more recent studies are conducted, either hair dye exposure continues to increase hairdressers' risk of bladder cancer or that they continue to be exposed to other DNA-damaging agents.[33]

'Increased risk' is a vague term. "What exactly does it mean?" I ask internationally renowned professor of breast cancer surgery and researcher Kefah Mokbel, who explains that making a conclusion comes down to the resources and evidence available. "To prove causation requires a lot of animal and laboratory studies, randomised studies and dose-response relationships. So positive studies in general use the statistical approach of the null hypothesis: that is to say, 'we have observed an association between this and this and it is statistically significant so it's not caused by chance.'"

With that cleared up, what do we know about personal users of hair dye and their risk of bladder cancer? Four out of five large analyses have not found a significant risk increase for personal use of hair dye.[34] When I take a closer look at all the data included, I see that most of the studies that did find an increased risk for hair dye users were based in the US and Asia. This feels significant because, historically, para-phenylenediamine has been a popular hair dye ingredient in these regions,[35] with heavy use of dark coloured dyes that contain higher concentrations of the material natural amongst dark-haired populations. Given that para-phenylenediamine has also been found to induce cell death in human urothelial cells at low doses,[36] and higher levels of micronuclei (damaged bodies after cell division) have been found in cells on the urinary tract lining of female hair dye users,[37] it makes sense that these users would be exposed to increased risk.

Research has also unearthed a concerning find. Small but notable studies in Turkey, the US and Sweden have found traces of proven bladder carcinogens including 4-aminobiphenyl in hair dyes (and, in the latter case, hair-waving products). This suggests that banned chemicals may be formed as byproducts during the synthesis of chemicals like para-phenylenediamine, which then enter hair dyes.[38] If widespread, this would mean both hairdressers and hair dye users are coming into unwitting contact with bladder carcinogens in their products.

But there is another factor in play when it

comes to bladder cancer risk and that's genetics. Everyone eliminates drugs like hair dye from the body at different speeds, meaning the exposure time to harmful materials differs person to person. We can particularly see this in the case of bladder cancer, which is linked to the efficiency of NAT2: the enzyme responsible for the unenviable task of metabolising and excreting certain drugs and chemicals like aromatic amines from our small intestine and colon tissues.[39]

Evidence has shown that hair dyers who have genetic variants that enable them to metabolise and excrete drugs quickly (known as rapid NAT2 acetylators) are at less risk of bladder cancer,[40] presumably because the materials are being speedily removed from their body rather than held in the urinary tract. Unfortunately for hair dye users, the majority of rapid NAT2 acetylators belong to nomadic hunter-gatherer populations.[41] They are far more likely to use their speedy drug metabolism to detoxify wild plants and undercooked meat they've eaten, rather than hazardous home dyes they've picked up from the supermarket.[42]

Instead, fixed, farming-reliant populations are more likely to be composed of slow NAT2 acetylators who metabolise drugs more sluggishly. This includes a large slice of the hair dye market - white Europeans.[43] - who consequently may be more vulnerable to the aromatic amines in their hair dye.

Hair dye aside, finding a cheap, reliable and quick method of determining whether a person is a rapid, slow or medium NAT2 acetylator could revolutionise the drugs industry as a whole, enabling doctors to have a much better idea of how individual patients will react to different doses of medication. But as of yet there is no set way to test this, (although scientists have tried out different methods with caffeine and other drugs),[44] or plans to roll it out widely.

Lymphomas

Lymphomas (also known as hematopoietic cancers) are cancers that attack the white blood cells in your immune system. They are commonly categorised into two types: Hodgkin lymphoma (also known as Hodgkin disease, and the rarer of the two) and non-Hodgkin lymphoma.[45] Both types have increased significantly in the UK since the 1990s,[46] with non-Hodgkin lymphoma the sixth most common cancer in the UK in 2017[47] and the 11th internationally.[48] This has led to a flurry of research to pinpoint the dramatic rise in cases, and put hair dye usage under renewed scrutiny.

Although the level of risk increase is not clear, a number of meta-analyses and occupation-related studies conducted between 1925 and 2004 have all suggested that hairdressers have an increased chance of developing non-Hodgkin lymphoma specifically.[49] Interestingly, I don't see any particular patterns of increased risk according to region, unlike in other studies. Three studies found that this risk was specific to female hairdressers,[50] although two later analyses (covering the period 1950 to 2004) indicated that the risk had decreased for hairdressers recently.[51] This might suggest that the reformulation of hair dyes in the 1970s did reduce danger.

However, a large bank of recent evidence suggests personal users of hair dye are at increased risk of developing non-Hodgkin lymphoma,[52] particularly women,[53] frequent users of dark colours,[54] and those using hair dyes for over 20 years.[55] One meta-analysis made a bold claim based on 16 studies: the risk of non-Hodgkin lymphoma in a population with high hair dye usage was 14%, and recommended that people who have been using hair dyes for more than 20 years should minimise their exposure.[56] In addition, a study in 2016, using three types of popular permanent hair dye in India, found that all were toxic to white blood cells - a target of lymphoma cancers.[57]

The bank of existing evidence suggests that unprofessional use of home hair dye may be putting customers at risk, particularly long-term users of dark, permanent shades. Significantly, the home hair dye industry has boomed since its origins in the early 20th century. By 1992, North America, Europe and Japan had thriving retail trades and home hair dye sales that represented 50 percent to 75 percent of their total business,[58] and by the turn of the 21st century, an estimated 55 million Americans were using home hair colourants, including 30% of American teens.[59] Estimates have even suggested that at least half of the adult population in Europe and the United States use hair colourants with permanent hair dyes comprising approximately 80% of the market in the US and Europe - even higher in Asia.[60]And the use of home hair colour has only intensified since the Covid-19 lockdown.

Leukaemia

Leukaemia is a cancer of the blood that usually begins in the bone marrow: the spongy tissue at the centre of the bones that produces blood cells. Leukaemia patients may have too many blood cells or too few, or they may be faulty, making it hard for the body to transport oxygen, fight infections, and control bleeding.[61] Defined as acute or chronic, depending on how quickly it progresses,[62] leukaemia is currently the 12th most common cancer in the UK.[63]

For hairdressers, consistent associations have been found with some forms of leukaemia: lymphocytic leukaemia (cancer of the lymphocytes, which fight viral infections) and myeloid leukaemia (cancer of the myeloid cells, which fight bacterial infections, defend the body against parasites and prevent the spread of tissue damage).[64] A review of 16 studies between 1966 and 2009 suggested that leukaemia risk for hairdressers was elevated, but not statistically significantly.[65] This meta-analysis did not differentiate between the different types of leukaemia, which would have been helpful. However, the studies that found the highest risk increase for hairdressers were both Italian, and both mentioned chronic myeloid leukaemia specifically.[66]

This is interesting for several reasons. The Italian population is predominantly dark-haired and so hairdressers would probably be applying a high number of dark colourants to customers wanting to cover grey hairs. Interestingly, market research in 2018 and 2020 also found that Italians are one of the least accepting European countries of grey hair[67] and that 43% of Italian consumers used a hair colouring product at least once a month.[68] Lush product inventor Alessandro Commisso explains, "Italian women are very glamorous, and a glamour nonna with perfectly done hair is the standard really. It's very unusual to see anyone with grey hair. I don't know my mum's natural hair colour, and I'm ok with that." Italians also show a heavy preference for permanent hair shades,[69] and dark shades of these contain the highest concentration of primary intermediates like para-phenylenediamine and para-toluenediamine.

Another global meta-analysis found that female hairdressers specifically were at increased risk of chronic lymphocytic leukemia, based on the evidence of ten studies assessing patients diagnosed between 1988 and 2004. The authors attributed the risk increase to exposure to hair dyes or hair treatments more commonly used by women rather than men.[70] In 2014, this association was noted again in a review of 13 international studies.[71]

When it comes to personal hair dye use,

a strong relationship with leukaemia risk was reported for studies using data from the 1970s and 1980s.[72] Shockingly, one found a 70% increased risk of leukaemia for hair dye users who began colouring their hair with permanent dyes before 1970.[73] This risk decreased in the 1970s, which could relate to the wide removal of the carcinogenic 2,4-diaminotoluene from hair dyes in 1971.[74] This risk increase has decreased since the reformulation of hair dyes, though statistically significant links remain for lymphocytic leukaemia again, use of permanent or dark hair dye, hair dye use amongst men, and use beyond 15 years.[75]

Hair colouring products have also been linked to illnesses related to, and occasionally preceding, leukaemia. Some of the earliest cases of hair dye poisoning reported in the 1930s described patients with symptoms of aplastic anaemia: a serious condition in which the bone marrow and stem cells do not produce enough healthy blood cells.[76] In rare cases, this can develop into acute myeloid leukaemia. Cases of aplastic anaemia patients with liver damage and associated macrocytosis (larger than normal red blood cells), which doctors believed were caused by hair dye exposure, continued to be sporadically reported into the 1970s and 1980s.[77] Interestingly, para-toluenediamine was particularly implicated.

Why? I do some swotting up. Both para-toluenediamine and para-phenylenediamine are derivatives of benzene: a compound linked to an increased risk of developing aplastic anaemia and leukaemia.[78] Research on para-toluenediamine is lacking, but para-phenylenediamine has been found to damage the red blood cells, which can lead to anaemia.[79] DNA breakages have been found in white blood cells (which are the cells affected by leukemia) exposed to para-phenylenediamine,[80] while hair dye users have also been found to have slightly higher levels of white blood cell DNA damage after colouring their hair.[81]

Given that dye products used to contain higher doses of para-phenylenediamine - and para-toluenediamine is needed in even higher concentrations to have the same effect - these historic sufferers, some of whom became seriously ill after one hair colouring treatment, were evidently receiving a dangerous dose. A number died. There was also the suggestion that the heat and ammonia from perm procedures performed with the dye treatments increased absorption and made it particularly toxic.[82]

Nowadays, commercial hair dyes contain less para-phenylenediamine and para-toluenediamine. Is it still associated with an increased risk of developing aplastic anaemia in addition to leukaemia? Epidemiological research, though limited, suggests yes. A 1992 Italian study found that hairdressers had an increased risk of chronic myeloid leukemia and a severe type of anaemia that can lead to acute myeloid leukaemia. They also noted a particular risk increase for users of dark hair dyes.[83] A 1999 study in Japan also found that hair dye users - particularly regular and long-term users - had an increased risk of myelodysplasia.[84]

Aplastic anaemia and myelodysplasia are both bone marrow failures, but they have subtle differences. Aplastic anaemia patients can't produce enough healthy blood cells, while myelodysplasia sufferers produce too many damaged ones.[85] Patients of both - but particularly myelodysplasia - are at increased risk of developing acute myeloid leukaemia.[86]

A more recent study from China in 2010 showed that people using hair dyes twice a year had an increased risk of developing myelodysplasia.[87] In contrast, a US study did not find a link between myelodysplasia and dyes, but did for acute myeloid leukaemia.[88] It seems significant that Italy, Japan and China all have predominantly - overwhelmingly - dark-haired populations, which correlates to a high use of darker hair dye shades containing the most paraphenylenediamine or derivatives.

Dark-haired populations have the added pressure of grey hairs being more visible. If we take China as an example, we can be confident that the social pressure to dye must be intense because, despite a number of cosmetics health scandals making customers more wary of the products they use, the majority of adults aged 30 plus still colour their hair. In 2013, 73% of Chinese 40-49 year olds coloured their hair, followed by 67% of 30-39 year olds. Concealing grey hair was the most common incentive.[89] The Japanese similarly have a tradition of concealing grey hair,[90] hand, interestingly, have a significantly high interest in semi-permanent formulas (which made up 49% of their retail sales by value in 2014.)[91] Although they are less damaging to the hair, these products would still include para-phenylenediamine or a related compound and need to be applied more regularly at home.

There's no doubt that the risk of leukaemia to personal users of hair dye has decreased since products became more strictly regulated in the 1980s. Yet, long-term exposure to hair dye, and dark-coloured or permanent products, appears to still carry an increased risk of some types of leukaemia and associated conditions for users.

Multiple Myeloma

Myeloma is another cancer of the bone marrow, but this time it is white blood cells known as plasma cells that are the target. These white blood cells make antibodies to fight disease meaning myeloma patients struggle to fight infections. Myeloma can affect different areas of the body at once, like the skull, pelvis and spine, which is why it is often referred to as 'multiple myeloma'. [92] It is the 19th most common cancer in the UK.[93]

On the face of it, the historical evidence suggesting an association between hairdressing and multiple myeloma is debatable. A number of US and Canada-based studies conducted between 1974 and 1994 found hairdressers had an increased risk of developing the disease,[94] but two long-term Scandinavian occupational studies between 1960 and 1990 did not.[95] Why did this research suggest US hairdressers were more at risk?

I think it's down to regulation and genetics. Para-phenylenediamine was restricted from hair dye in Sweden until the 1980s, and the weaker para-toluenediamine was used instead, which is still vastly more popular. This was not the case in the US, where the more potent para-phenylenediamine has always been the most popular primary intermediate. In fact, in 2014, it was estimated that 78% of US hair colourants contain para-phenylenediamine compared to 16% in Sweden.[96] So, the key difference between hairdressers in the US and Sweden appears to be exposure to para-phenylenediamine. It may also be significant that Northern Europe has a higher proportion of naturally fair-haired citizens, who may be using lighter hair products to conceal greys. Significantly, they may also not feel the need to colour their hair as regularly as their dark-haired peers abroad.

I ask Lush HairLab colourist and hairdresser Daisy Evans to talk me through the process for colouring greying fair hair. She explains, "If someone who has blonde or fairer hair wanted to restore their natural tones on grey hairs that have come through, I would use a permanent hair dye that matches their pre-existing shade. This process is very similar for anyone who wants their greys coloured and who wants to restore the shade they already have, from light to dark hair. The dye would be paired with 6% hydrogen peroxide (20 volume), which is just enough to lift the tight resistant cuticle layer of the grey hairs, penetrating the pigments straight into the cortex to give a block coverage."

The process might be the same but there is a key difference: lighter hair colouring products require lower levels of primary intermediates.[97]

The lesser risk to Swedish hairdressers is backed up by a meta-analysis of cancer risk for hairdressers in 2009, which, incidentally, still gave hairdressers a staggering risk increase of 62% for multiple myeloma - the highest out of any considered cancer.[98] But, when I look at the 19 international studies conducted between 1966 and 2009 that contributed to this statistic, I see again that the six studies included from Scandinavia consistently show no, or a very low risk increase. Italians on the other hand have the highest odds, with the US behind them. As discussed, Italy is a grey-fearing, predominantly dark-haired nation, and the US is an avid consumer of para-phenylenediamine-based dyes, with manufacturers allowed to include higher quantities in their products than in Europe. So, it makes sense that US and Italian hairdressers would be exposed to stronger products than their Scandinavians peers.

Research into multiple myeloma risk for personal hair dye users is limited, and seems especially hampered by poor information collection from cases on the types of hair dye used, colours, and duration. Three studies in the 1980s and 1990s, all based in the USA, suggested that female users of dark hair dye had a slight increased risk of multiple myeloma,[99] but further studies in the USA and China have not.[100]

The negative results of the latter study draw my attention, given the preference for dark hair dye in China.[101] However, one serious failing of the study was that women who had not used hair dye in the three years prior to interview were classified as non-users, even if they used hair dye previously. Given that cancer can have a long latency period, the researchers could have missed a number of related cases.

There is also another interesting difference between the behaviour of US and Chinese customers: salon visits. A far higher number of customers have their hair coloured professionally compared to US customers, due to health concerns.[102] This could be limiting their exposure to the dye. I'm also curious about mask-wearing behaviour in China and whether this could have had any kind of preventative effect. Was mask-wearing commonplace in a Chinese salon environment before Covid-19?

I ask colleague and director of Lush Greater China, Annabelle Baker, who spent seven and a half years living in Hong Kong. She says, in her experience, mask-wearing was familiar but not routine. "Mask-wearing in salons before Covid-19 would not be likely, but could occur. If someone had a runny nose, a light cold, or a family member at home was sick then mask-wearing would take place to not seem rude to your hairdresser. Hairdressers would also have worn masks if they had any signs of illness or not feeling quite right. After SARS [a 2003 outbreak of a viral respiratory disease known as Severe Acute Respiratory Syndrome] it was really seen that you should wear a mask at any time of slight illness to protect others."

Further research confirms that while mask-wearing is socially encouraged on high pollution days and when ill socially encouraged in China,[103] it's not ubiquitous and not as commonplace in younger generations.[104] The effectiveness of fabric and disposable masks against airborne chemicals like para-phenylenediamine is also debatable. So is mask-wearing in Chinese salons massively limiting exposure to airborne chemicals? Probably not.

Two more recent but small meta-analyses

(of predominantly US studies) have also noted an elevated risk of multiple myeloma for users of dark permanent hair dye, but both struggled to make conclusions because of the inconsistencies of these findings.[105]

On the basis of this evidence, it seems likely that increased risk of multiple myeloma to hairdressers and possibly personal users is associated with exposure to permanent and dark hair dye over a long period of time.

Lung cancer

Lung cancer is the third most common cancer in the UK,[106] and affects the windpipe (trachea), the main airway (bronchus) or the lung tissue.[107] Over 70% of cases can be attributed to smoking,[108] meaning studies looking into other exposures have to consider the smoking habits of their participants to be reliable.

The little research we have about lung cancer has not found a risk increase for personal hair dye users.[109] But salon-workers performing numerous colouring procedures a day have dramatically higher exposures to airborne salon pollution. A small study of female hairdressers with a career spanning over ten years found they had significantly increased levels of oxidative stress compared to users of hair dye, for example, when saliva samples were analysed.[110] A separate study found that hairdressers had a higher number of damaged cells in the lining of the cheeks and at the back of the lips. The number of these increased with hours worked.[111] The problem is that hairdressers are exposed to a range of chemicals in a salon environment, from perm to relaxer treatments.[112] So, although hair dyes are considered to be one of the biggest sources of airborne pollution,[113] most evidence currently looks at general chemical exposure in salons, and so cannot be pinned down to hair dyes in particular.

Significantly, female hairdresser rates of lung cancer were heightened in American studies in the period 1970 to 1990,[114] around the time female smoking numbers peaked in America.[115] (A Finnish study also reported a significant increased risk of lung cancer amongst female hairdressers during this period[116] in which smoking amongst women also peaked.)[117] A ruthless advertising campaign started in the 1920s targeted the untapped female smoking market by associating cigarettes with weight loss and glamour. "To keep a slender figure no-one can deny, reach for a Lucky instead of a sweet," declared American Tobacco Industry adverts.[118]

Cigarettes marketed to women were as long and slender as the models who advertised them, and given names such as 'thins' or 'slims'.[119] By 1985, the prevalence of female smoking had increased from an estimated 6% in 1924 to 46%.[120] Significantly for us, this period also saw more women entering the workplace,[121] and a swell in the service industry (between 1960 and 1969 the number of barbers, hairdressers and beauticians increased by 20% in the USA alone).[122] Recent research also indicates that female hairdressers are more likely to be smokers than female non-hairdressers.[123]

Two recent meta-analyses on lung cancer and hairdressing have come to different conclusions. One, composed of 16 international studies between 1985 and 2010, found no increased risk of lung cancer in hairdressers once smoking behaviours had been accounted for.[124] But conversely, a meta-analysis of 18 studies published in 2009 suggested that female hairdressers had a significant 27% risk increase for lung cancer even when it only included studies that had adjusted for smoking.[125] However, this study included older research from before hair dye reformulation in the late 1970s and early 1980s - and these studies had higher risk increases. It suggests that hairdressers working before and during this period were more at risk of lung cancer.

While hair dye-derived lung cancer specifically does not appear to be a concern for hairdressers, the research I've read has raised some concerns about the salon environment. Several studies have noted that hairdressers are at increased risk of occupational asthma thanks to exposure to irritants and allergens[126] (as discussed in Chapter 5, para-phenylenediamine has a restrictive action on the airway and has been historically linked to occupational asthma.) Nearly all the studies I read commented on the lack of ventilation in salons, meaning hairdressers would be exposed to these compounds for most of the day.

Breast cancer

Breast cancer, which usually develops in the ducts or tissue of the breast, is currently the most common cancer in the UK,[127] with rates in women known to have increased by 23% since the early 1990s.[128] It is also one of the most common cancers worldwide, with around 1.5 million women (25% of all female cancer cases) diagnosed every year. A number of factors have already been shown to increase a person's risk, most significantly a family history of the disease, but also early onset of periods, later pregnancies and menopause, excessive alcohol consumption, hormone replacement therapy and the contraceptive pill.[129]

While little occupational evidence of significantly increased breast cancer risk amongst hairdressers exists,[130] personal hair dye use has made headlines in recent years for its links to breast cancer. I speak to Professor Kefah Mokbel to find out why. He explains, "There are two ways that chemicals can cause breast cancer. One is what we call direct carcinogenicity, where the chemicals damage the DNA, and we have evidence of that in taking samples from the nipple fluid. We know that aromatic amines damage DNA and we have found these aromatic amines attached to damaged DNA in the breast cells. The substance of particular interest here is para-phenylenediamine, which is most commonly used in hair dyes.

"Another mechanism of action is endocrine disruption. So, breast cancer is very much a hormone-dependent cancer for the majority of patients and many of these aromatic amines can damage DNA and mimic the oestrogen hormone in human tissues. And that's why we call them endocrine-disrupting chemicals, they are external oestrogens that sit on the oestrogen receptor and affect the oestrogen axis in the body, which, as a result, increases the risk of hormone-sensitive breast cancer."

Professor Mokbel published a groundbreaking meta-analysis of breast cancer and hair dyes in 2018, in which he concluded that hair dye users had an 18.8% increased risk of developing breast cancer.[131] He says he was motivated to undertake the research after being questioned by his patients about the safety of using hair dyes during their treatment for the disease.

I'm curious to know about the reaction he received from the industry. "The problem is, as soon as there is a study like this, the cosmetic industry then fills the web with the articles to say the product is safe," he says. "Obviously, they want to sell products; it's a multi-billion dollar industry. In the past, I wrote a paper on underarm cosmetics and I found that there was no evidence that using underarm cosmetics increased the risk of breast cancer. When I published that paper, I had letters from all the cosmetics associations and manufacturers congratulating me, yet when I published this one, I had letters from them telling me, 'We are not convinced. We question this association; it could be other factors that haven't been looked at.'"

Professor Mokbel's findings are not alone. In a 2002 Jordan-based study, 95% of breast cancer patients reported use of hair dye in contrast to 51% of healthy controls,[132] while a 2015 Finnish study of 6,567 breast cancer patients concluded that women using hair dyes had a 23% increased chance of developing breast cancer.[133] This discrepancy may be explained by the popularity of para-phenylenediamine in the Middle East compared to in Scandinavia and the Nordic regions, as well as the higher concentration of para-phenylenediamine required for dark shades on darker hair. Both conclusions, however, are concerning. A very recent meta-analysis involving more than 200,000 women between 1978 and 2019 also found that hair dye usage was associated with increased breast cancer risk - particularly permanent colours and temporary rinses.[134]

Research has posed worrying questions about the use of temporary and semi-permanent hair dyes, previously thought to be less dangerous than their permanent counterparts. Significantly, the previously mentioned Finnish study found the highest risk estimates for women using temporary or semi-permanent dyes (a 32% and 31% increased risk respectively).[135] Interestingly, Finland has higher than average sales of semi-permanent hair dye, - the third highest retail sales by value for semi-permanent hair dyes in 2014. Similarly, a 2018 Egyptian study of 250 breast cancer patients at a hospital in Cairo concluded that the risk of breast cancer increased with use of semi-permanent dye and the use of dark hair dye,[136] while a US study found there was a risk associated with non-professional application of semi-permanent dye to others (though not use itself).[137]

The increasing home use of these products, which are typically available in a foam, rinse or surfactant solution, must be driving the problem. Customers applying semi-permanent and temporary dyes at home surely have more contact with the product than in a salon, from application to rinsing. There is also a suggestion that semi-permanent colour (which does not rely on an oxidation process) may penetrate the scalp more efficiently than permanent dyes (which do) because the oxidation process reduces the skin's absorption of specific amines.[138] Users may also be applying the products more often due to their temporary nature, and from a younger age.

Other significant results thrown up by breast cancer studies are that the risk appears to be increased for African American women. Despite reporting lower frequencies of hair dye use (30% compared to 58% in White women), one study found that African American women using dark shades had a 51% increased risk of breast cancer, and a 71% increase for oestrogen receptor-positive breast cancer.[139] Another study found that Black women in the US using permanent hair dye for one year also had a 45% higher breast cancer risk, compared to a 7% risk increase for White women. This increased to 60% for Black women who used hair dye every five to eight weeks (though it should be noted that all women enrolled in the study had a family history of breast cancer).[140]

"Women of African origin are at higher risk;" agrees Professor Mokbel, "there have been a few studies showing that. And we don't know precisely whether this is due to biology, genetic variation, or, the possibility that women of African origins are more likely to use greater amounts of dark colours."

Horribly, I'm learning that women of colour are more likely to be exposed to hormone-disrupting chemicals in self-care products specifically marketed to them from a young age.[141] It has even been suggested that unborn babies are exposed to these hormones via their pregnant mothers.[142] Interestingly, an analysis of para-toluenediamine-championing Swedish hair market still found that all analysed dyes being marketed to people of colour contained para-phenylenediamine. That's despite it being included in only 16% of products marketed towards the general Swedish population.[143]

It could be that hair dyes are negatively interacting with these products or adding to a risk that is already increased amongst users of hormone-disrupting products. This risk may only be emerging now because people of colour are chronically underrepresented in much of the historical data on hair dyes.

I ask Professor Mokbel for the advice he would give to users of hair dye. "Obviously from a health perspective, natural hair is the safest option," he advises. "If someone really wants to dye their hair, I would say to use natural, even organic products. These products usually only temporarily dye the hair. There are many ingredients that we find in nature that can colour the hair, ranging from chamomile, to beetroot, to coffee, to henna, though the colours for all are limited.

"The issue is that society's views and pressures about beauty and looks have made people resort to dying their hair, and finding ways of hiding grey hair in particular. This is the most common use of hair dye. Women use hair dye because society expects them to look a certain way. So some of my patients do take the risk and say, "I have no option, there's no way I'm going to walk around with my hair looking grey."

He continues, "The use of permanent colours, dark colours, and frequent use are the main risk factors. So this is the first thing to target in public awareness. Women who are using hair dyes and who are over the age of 40 should have annual breast screening with mammography. Younger women dying their hair should also be breast aware although they don't necessarily need any particular screening. It is women over the age of 40 who I tend to see in my clinic and probably 40% of them use hair dyes, though some have changed since our study from the branded synthetic hair dyes to more natural ones."

Hair dye use during pregnancy

Although many pregnant women receive a list of no-goes during pregnancy, including foods to avoid, they are unlikely to receive clearcut guidance on hair dye use.

One problem is that this area is severely under-investigated. Nevertheless, a number of studies have found that hairdressers are at increased risk of miscarriage, of having a baby with low birth weight and, in some cases, birth defects, although these complications have not been associated with hair dyes specifically. Other studies have also not found an association.[144]

Further research has found that hair dye use by pregnant women and, in some cases, their use before conception, is also linked to low birth weight.[145] One study of Jordanian women found that mothers who used aromatic amine-based or lead and cinnabar-based dyes at home during pregnancy were more likely to give birth to children with disabilities. Severity of disability was associated with both frequency of hair dye application and dye use during the early stages of pregnancy. Mothers who did not wash their hair and hands after the dye process were also more likely to give birth to children with physical and mental impairments. Researchers linked the results to the high levels of lead, mercury and phenylenediamines found within regional hair dye products.[146]

Some US studies conducted during the 1970s, 1980s and 1990s found that maternal

Beetroot's versatile staining properties were once well known.

hair dye use during pregnancy increased the risk of Wilms Tumour: a rare neuroblastoma cancer that usually affects young children and develops from immature nerve cells.[147] The most staggering was a study of children diagnosed with neuroblastoma cancer between 1992 and 1994, which found that maternal use of any hair dye during the month before pregnancy or during pregnancy was associated with an almost 60% increased risk of neuroblastoma. Temporary and semi-permanent dyes were the most strongly linked, probably because they were more likely to be applied unprofessionally and more regularly at home.[148]

The key limitation with these studies however, is that they all included mothers who were pregnant before or during the period of hair dye reformulation during the 1980s. Given that the children in the latter study were aged between under one and up to nineteen, the mothers on either end of the scale were clearly exposed to products that contained different levels of carcinogens and mutagens. But no analysis of whether the risk changed with time and reformulation was performed.

Maternal hair dye use has also been related to a significantly higher risk of germ cell cancers (tumours of the reproductive cells) in girls generally, in boys whose mothers used hair dye in the month prior to pregnancy, and for both whose mothers used hair dye while breastfeeding in a US study conducted between 1993 and 2001.[149] But again, over half of the children involved were aged three to 15, placing some mothers' pregnancies prior to or during hair dye reformulation.

Childhood brain tumours have also been investigated in relation to maternal hair dye use. A US study looking at causes of childhood brain tumours in patients diagnosed between 1984 and 1991 acknowledged a twofold risk increase for childhood brain cancers in children aged fifteen to nineteen whose mothers had been exposed to earlier formulations, compared to younger children in the study. They found no clear overall risk increase for use during pregnancy, apart from an association with use of semi-permanent products before or during pregnancy. Whether hair dyeing procedures were performed at home or by professionals was not recorded, but we can probably assume that the semi-permanent products implicated were used at home.[150] A further US study on two common brain cancers in children diagnosed between 1986 and 1989 also found no association.[151]

These results were echoed in a seven-country study published in 2005, which found some evidence of an increased risk of childhood brain tumours in children whose mothers who used hair dye. Interestingly, this association was noted in children born in or after 1980, although the study included patients from 1976. Israeli children who were cautiously concluded to be three times more likely to develop the disease if their mothers used semi-permanent hair dye in the month before or during pregnancy. Given that Israel was the only Middle-Eastern country to take part in the study, it may reflect regional differences and dangers in hair dye products, seen in the previously discussed study conducted in Jordan.[152]

It's very difficult to assess modern-day risk to unborn babies with these (what I'm going to call) 'borderline' studies, clearly inspired by the findings of Professor Ames and his peers in the 1970s, and undertaken around the time of hair dye reformulation. It seems clear to me that dyeing your hair during pregnancy before hair dyes were reformulated was probably dangerous, both to the mother and her unborn child. Has that risk since decreased? Recent work in this area is staggeringly limited.

In 2002, researchers specifically warned

women not to use hair dyes during pregnancy after finding an increased amount of damaged cells in long-term hair dyers.[153] DNA-adducts (a piece of DNA attached to a cancer-causing chemical) have also been found in the breast milk of mothers who had used a permanent hair dye in the previous six months or who used light-coloured hair dyes. The chemical in question was 4-aminobiphenyl: the previously mentioned bladder carcinogen also found in on-sale batches of contaminated commercial hair dye brands in the US. Whether the dye was applied at home or professionally was not assessed.[154]

Childhood leukaemia has also been linked to hair dye use during pregnancy, though inconclusively. A small but multi-state study in Brazil found an increased risk of childhood acute lymphoblastic leukaemia and acute myeloid leukaemia in children under two whose mothers had used hair dyes or chemical straightening treatments during pregnancy and breastfeeding. They did not break this down to consider the risk of dyes or straightening treatments specifically.[155]

Children whose mothers had exposure to hair dye during breastfeeding were also at greater risk of developing leukaemia in a study of 958 children diagnosed with leukaemia between 2008 and 2017 in Zhejiang province, China.[156] In contrast, three studies from Egypt, Iran and the UK (including the study using data provided by Mark's questions) did not find a link between hair dye use and childhood leukaemia.[157]

Given the high number of women who dye their hair worldwide, I'm shocked that there has been no recent, detailed investigation into hair dye use during pregnancy. We are limited to these small-scale, regional studies, when we need something much larger and more encompassing. In an ideal world, the massively wealthy hair dye industry should hand over no-strings-attached funding to epidemiologists to do this research but that seems unlikely. So what do you say to pregnant women who ask that question: is it safe to dye my hair? Mark asks me what advice I would give a friend.

Well, from experience, I know that pregnancy is not only a vulnerable time for mums physically but also mentally. Many expecting women tend to change their behaviour and limit harmful exposures, but it's also a time when you can feel hormonal and self-conscious about your changing body and reach for cosmetic fixes to feel good. At my time of concluding this, I'm 14 weeks pregnant with my second child. A combination of pregnancy hormones (hello teenage skin) and overgrown lockdown hair is not filling me with confidence. I feel pale, nauseous and knackered. I'm certainly not 'glowing'. It's actually a time when I feel very tempted to do something more drastic with my hair in an attempt to feel better about myself - and I'm not a regular user of hair dye.

But, on the basis of what I have learned, and the gaps in that research, dyeing my hair with a synthetic hair colourant is not something I would feel comfortable with during pregnancy, or while trying to get pregnant. If a friend asked me my opinion, I would say the same. We really shouldn't be telling people it's ok to dye their hair in pregnancy because we don't know that it is. I did, however, pick up a Lush Rouge henna brick at the weekend (a bold change from my usual Brun but pregnancy hormones make you do strange things) and I'm loving the results.

Safe or safer? The big hair dye question

For hundreds of years, women have been conditioned to fear growing old and 'losing' our looks. That's allowed a savvy hair colourant industry to make us spend an incredible amount of money and time concealing grey hairs, a completely natural process that we have been told is ugly and devaluing on women. So successful is this social pressure that to be grey at middle age is somehow unnatural for women. It reveals a truth about the female body we are continually told to airbrush. (I'm reminded vividly of a friend telling me that she had to explain gently to her dumbfounded first boyfriend that, yes, women did have body hair - they just dedicated a lot of time to removing it.)

We are paying handsomely in money, time and, for some of us, possibly health, for our investment in this lie. But, simultaneously, a fresh marketing campaign is ensnaring a new generation even younger - making hair dye fashionable, fun and affordable on a pocket money budget. To one generation, it is riding the zeitgeist of self-expression and individuality; to another, charging us to adhere to social expectation.

Are these products as 'safe' as they are advertised to be? In my mind, no, though this will invariably depend on what products you use, the styles you choose and whether you have your hair coloured at a salon or do it yourself. I tackle this in the next chapter.

How about safer than they used to be? Yes, probably. In many cases, cancer risk does seem to have decreased for hair dye users and hairdressers since product reformulation in 1980, but our hair dyeing behaviours have also changed massively in 50 years. People are now being sold hair dye from a younger age, and encouraged to change their colour more. A huge number apply it themselves at home. Manufacturers may provide data on their ingredients but they are not prepared to finance epidemiological research looking at the cumulative effects of hair dye exposure - even when existing evidence links these products to an increased risk of bladder cancer, non-Hodgkin lymphoma, breast cancer and some types of leukaemia. If you have a family history of any of these cancers, I would gently advise not using synthetic hair dyes.

Perhaps the most concerning discovery is the link between temporary and semi-permanent dyes and breast cancer. Permanent hair dyes have been under scrutiny for decades, but temporary and semi-permanent colours have grown in popularity for home use because they are cheaper, perceived to be less harmful, and enable consumers to change their hair regularly.[158] They are also heavily marketed at younger generations. But while semi-permanent dyes are marketed as gentler, many colour molecules are actually also used in permanent formulas at different amounts.

Basic Red 51, for example, an azo dye that can break down on the skin and release aromatic amines, is allowed by the EU in on-head concentrations of up to 0.5% in oxidative (permanent) dyes, and at 1% in non-oxidative (semi-permanent) hair dyes.[159] Yet one fifth of the Basic Red 51 exposure allowed in hair dyes by the EU has led to cell degeneration in a human skin model, although the exposure time was 48 hours - far longer than a patient should be exposed to hair dye. (Given that dye residues have been found in the hair follicle after the product has been washed away, it must also be considered that skin cells are exposed to hair dye remnants for longer than the application time, argued the study authors.)[160] Three common semi-permanent colours including Basic Red 51 have also been shown to have a toxic effect on human cells in lab tests.[161]

Similarly concerning is recent evidence that hairdressers (and indeed hair dyers) could be at risk from exposure to nitrosamines: a group of carcinogenic chemicals formed when by-products of amine dyes become exposed to gases produced from natural sources, tobacco smoke, motor vehicles and other fuel-burning processes.

In 2012, the SCCS acknowledged that oxidative hair dye ingredients could form nitrosamines before and during the hair dying process, and they then restricted materials accordingly. This assessment, however, did not consider nitrosamines that could form after hair dyeing, when colour continues to develop. Evidence has suggested that between 20% and 70% of applied amines or couplers could remain 'unconsumed' on the hair after the procedure, depending on the combination used. "If secondary amines are present on the hair for months, years, even decades through repeated application," wrote concerned researchers in 2013, "the risks are clearly magnified."[162] Questions also remain around the manufacturing safety of hair dyes.The discovery of contaminated batches of hair dye in Turkey, the US and Sweden containing proven bladder carcinogens is alarming,[163] while a second Swedish study also found hair dyes containing the banned (undeclared) substance HC Yellow 5. Some ingredients were also incorrectly labelled, indicating a lack of tight regulation.[164]

Hair dye is not an easy thing to give up, and you may not want to. That's ok. There are ways to minimise your personal exposure to hair dye materials which we'll look at in the next chapter. My main hope is that, with knowledge, comes the power for people to make their own informed decisions regarding their hair and their health.

How hair dyes work and how to make them work for you.

8

Logic suggests that not all types of hair dyeing pose a potential health risk. A customer who gets a no skin contact balayage treatment at the salon, for example, is limiting their exposure to problematic materials significantly in comparison to someone using permanent dye to colour their whole head dark brown at home on a regular basis.

Products that promise to care for the health of your hair aren't necessarily a better option for use when we think about systemic toxicity. The visible health of the hair and invisible effects of hair dye on the body are different things. Bleaching the ends of your hair will be more mechanically damaging than using a colour-depositing semi-permanent hair dye at home. But that semi-permanent product and all-over the scalp application method allows more of the product to penetrate the skin. Even a customer using what we understand to be one of the most problematic products - let's say a black permanent hair dye containing para-phenylenediamine - could limit their exposure to it significantly by having a minimum skin contact service at a salon rather than by applying it themselves.

Similarly, not all types of hair colouring affect your hair in the same way. Hair that has been lifted by a shade or two with a bit of leave-in lightener will feel dramatically different to hair that has been bleached white-blonde, and in some cases these changes to the hair fibre will be desirable. Style and technique can make a massive difference to how your hair feels, as well as how much of the product is available to be absorbed through your skin.

However you colour your hair, knowing how the many varieties of hair dyes work and their effects empowers you to find the option that fits your hair, lifestyle, and any health concerns you may have. It will enable you to decipher the marketing jargon on a product, to read behind the lines on claims like 'ammonia-free', and to realise why temporary colour may not be quite so temporary on bleached hair.

We've already considered whether these materials increase your risk of cancer. What's interesting now is to look at what effect they have on the hair, and how you can continue to use hair dye as safely as possible, if you want to.

Heavy lifting: how bleach works

If you've chosen to lighten up recently, you're not alone. Blonde shades of hair dye and bleaching products have long been bestsellers for White American and European women thanks to the targeted advertising campaigns of the 1950s onwards, and have also become increasingly popular amongst Black American,[1] African American and Asian women.[2]

In 2017, blonde was the colour of choice for 39% of Brits, with 18% plumping for platinum.[3] Extensive bleaching can be damaging to the hair - although the look and feel of bleached hair can also be highly fashionable. It's nuanced: the effects of the product depend on the material you use and the technique applied. Hair that has been lifted by a shade or two with a bit of leave-in lighter will feel dramatically different to hair that has been bleached platinum.

While Iron Age Celts were mucking about with limewater and Venetian ladies were coating their hair in acque, the identification of hydrogen peroxide in 1818 was a breakthrough moment for hair bleaching.[4] When it was publicly applied to the hair in 1867 it signalled a new era of cleaner, more effective, modern lighteners.[5]

Chances are you have products containing hydrogen peroxide at home whether or not you dye your hair. A colourless liquid at room temperature, hydrogen peroxide is a bleaching agent and mild antiseptic that decomposes to oxygen and water.[6] You'll find it in mouthwashes, toothpastes and stain removers, amongst other things. Certain cells in your body also produce it as part of an immune response to fight infection.[7] We absorb hydrogen peroxide in the food we eat (hello instant coffee), produce it internally, and remove excess amounts in our urine and exhaled air.[8] Excessive levels of hydrogen peroxide in your cells has been implicated in the development of disease,[9] but it is not thought to be generally toxic unless strong concentrations are applied directly to the skin or inhaled.[10] Some people drink very low solutions of hydrogen peroxide, though this is not something I'd recommend myself.

The amount of hair lightening you achieve relates directly to the amount of oxygen hydrogen peroxide released from the hair. In the hairdressing industry this is expressed in 'volumes' - terms you may notice if you are using a kit at home. A solution of 6% hydrogen peroxide (a typical home-use amount), for example, releases 20 volumes of oxygen from the hair. A professional in the salon has higher volume products to create more dramatic transformations when required,[11] which will be paired up with an alkali to speed up the process.

Hydrogen peroxide is capable of lightening the hair alone, though not extensively.[12] It's typically used by itself in leave-in products designed to lift the hair by a shade or two. These products became popular during the latter half of the 20th century, when tanned skin and gently tinted hair were suddenly chic: a western 'holiday look' that represented the ability to travel abroad.[13]

Mark is still a keen advocate of highlights for those wanting to lighten their hair in a safer way. "There are two lovely safe things you can do with hydrogen peroxide," he says. "One is highlights and the other is balayage, both properly done by a professional. Neither of them touch the scalp - or if they do it's very minimally. A hairdresser can do highlights by simply lifting with hydrogen peroxide, though it is more fashionable now to add ammonia, use a lifting permanent colour, or a toner afterwards. It might be worth the hairdresser wearing a mask and gloves and not mixing it in a tiny cupboard but with a few tweaks to the procedure, this is a style you can have with minimal risk to your hair or your health."

Balayage is a more recent fashion, taken from the French word 'balayer', meaning 'to sweep'. It's a free-hand technique in which a colourist will apply bleach or a lifting colour without the use of foils to mimic natural hair highlights and lowlights. It's usually applied through the lengths of the hair rather than at the scalp.

These techniques can have other benefits as well as the reduced skin exposure during application. If, like me, you have fine, straight hair that needs regular washing, a little roughening up of the cuticle can be appealing, as Mark explains: "One of the things that highlights do which people may not notice, but they like, is it makes finer hair feel more manageable as long as you use a bit of conditioner. You've then got some damaged hair and some fine hair, and that's very addictive." I occasionally dabble with streaks of leave-in lightener applied to my mid-lengths and ends for this reason.

It's one of the reasons Lush Global Strategic Lead Charlotte Nisbet lightens her hair. "I don't have any grey hair," she says, "so I don't really 'need' to dye it, but bleaching my very straight, very limp hair gives it so much more texture and body so it actually feels more manageable with colour on."

Hair lightening kits give customers the chance to give themselves the 'sunkissed' look at home. You'll still find these on the shelf of your local supermarket or pharmacy, although some now contain violet pigments too, many of which will be coal-tar derived. Wearing gloves and applying a hydrogen-peroxide only product in a well-ventilated space probably poses little risk to your health, especially if you avoid applying close to the scalp. (As hydrogen peroxide can be irritating to the skin, this is sound advice anyway.) It may take a little more time or practice to do at home, but using a brush kit will also mean far less product touches the skin compared to a dye designed to be massaged into the roots and all through the hair.

Bigger transformations, however, whether at home or in the salon, require a little extra firepower. That's why hydrogen peroxide is usually paired with ammonia: a whiffy alkali that speeds up the bleaching process. This colourless gas is composed of nitrogen and hydrogen and dissolves in water to form an alkaline solution. Ammonia is another natural byproduct produced within the body, primarily by gut bacteria as they break down waste food. We also come into contact with it in cleaning products and areas of organic waste breakdown (such as agricultural sites).[14] In low levels, ammonia is considered to be rapidly detoxified by healthy individuals and excreted in our urine as urea, but it can cause burns and respiratory damage if you are exposed to high amounts.[15] That's one of the reasons extensive bleaching practices are best-handled by a colourist.

Ammonia has an important role in bleaching. It swells the hair fibre, enabling the hydrogen peroxide to enter the cortex, and also appears to play a part in rupturing the cell wall of melanin.[16] This enables the hydrogen peroxide to degrade the coloured pigment - 'lightening' your hair.[17]

A consequence of bleaching your hair is that these materials also target the structural proteins and lipids (fats) of the hair - the bricks and mortar that keep each fibre intact.[18] Carefully controlled colour lifting can minimise the changes caused by the bleaching process. Lifting by a few shades and switching up your routine can normally keep your hair looking and feeling healthy. Go from dark to platinum and we're talking about something high-maintenance that may look amazing but will also change the hair fibre irreversibly.

The white-blonde 'bombshell' look of early to mid 20th century screen sirens are a great example. By nature, these were high-maintenance looks at the most extreme end of bleaching. Hollywood actress Jean Harlow's (1911–1937) cool-blonde glamour was maintained with a combination of peroxide, ammonia, household bleach and soap flakes. With such a strong bleaching product being applied weekly by her hairdresser, it's perhaps not a huge surprise that she later resorted to wigs to give her hair a break.[19]

Highly bleached hair needs TLC. That's because, as well as swelling the hair cuticle, the combination of peroxide and ammonia also oxidises and removes some of the precious lipids that give your hair its water-repellent properties. Lipids also have a starring role inside the cuticle, forming a sticky glue rich in amino acids and

“As long as there’s movies, I suspect a rebel is going to bleach her hair and wear a leather jacket with studs and ‘F**K you on the back”

proteins that holds the cuticle cells together - a bit like the jam in a Victoria sponge cake. Known as the delightfully Star Trekky 'cell membrane complex': this labyrinthine interface provides a pathway into the cortex.[20]

18-methylicosanoic acid (18-MEA) is a fatty acid found on the cuticle of the hair and in the cell membrane complex, which coats the overlapping cuticle cells in a water-repellant layer. This key lipid gives the hair its glossy appearance and reduces tangles by decreasing friction between the hair fibres.[21] It's also directly in the firing line when it comes to bleaching processes. A mild dabble with a leave-in lightener may have minimal impact but bigger lifting procedures can eradicate a majority of the hair's 18-MEA. One study found that 80% of the hair's 18-MEA was removed after three bleach treatments - the equivalent of a whopping 480 hours of UV radiation.[22] Hair that has lost its 18-MEA is porous and dry, and more likely to become tangled.[23]

In some cases, this is a highly fashionable look. By the 1970s and 1980s, the polished, platinum styles of Hollywood starlets like Marilyn Monroe (1926-1962) were being replaced with rebel blondes, who let their roots grow out and wore their hair unkempt à la Blondie vocalist Debbie Harry (born 1945) and The Pretenders guitarist and vocalist Chrissie Hynde (born 1951). It was an alternative fashion to the carefully constructed femininity of the silver screen, and part of the counterculture of the time. Today, bleached hair worn in that slightly messy style is still synonymous with rebellion.

Mark has long admired distressed platinum-blonde styles. "Bleached hair can be Marilyn Monroe but it can equally be a tousled rockstar look, and that look comes with that product. You have to have fairly dry hair where the guts have been pulled out of it with bleach - you can't achieve that look naturally. As long as there's movies, I suspect a rebel is going to bleach her hair and wear a leather jacket with studs and 'Fuck You' on the back."

High concentrations of ammonia and hydrogen peroxide also target the tough bridges that hold the protein structures of the hair fibre together. Known as disulphide bonds, these are bridges made of the amino acid cystine[24] that maintain the texture of your hair and give the fibre its mechanical strength.[25]

Just like your follicle shape, the number of disulphide bonds your hair contains is determined by your genes. Their alignment in the fibre also supports your pre-determined hair shape (which is why disulphide bonds are targeted in a perming or relaxing treatment). Place a curly or coily hair under the microscope and you'll see numerous disulphide bonds criss-crossing diagonally between proteins, supporting the hair fibre's shape. Swap it for a straight hair, and you'll see that these are linked horizontally rather than at an angle, and are fewer in number.[26]

When cystine is oxidised during the bleaching process, the disulphide bonds weaken and break. Lifting the hair a few shades can degrade 15-25% of the disulphide bonds in your hair, but extreme bleaching, say from black or dark brown to blonde, can break up to 45%.[27] This makes your hair more susceptible to damage from day-to-day brushing or heat treatments. Increased porosity of the cuticle also means bleached hair needs topping up with moisture.[28] Thankfully, that's where a professional comes in.

If you are having your hair bleached professionally, your colourist will discuss different 'levels' of lift with you. This will enable them to work out the product and time required to take you to your desired shade on a spectrum that ranges from black (level 1) to very fair (level 10). It will also enable them to advise you about the impact on your hair's health. Big jobs are tackled in stages and require a second oxidising agent, known as an 'enhancer' (normally persulfate) which usually comes in a powder form. The enhancer makes the hair more porous, which facilitates better absorption of dye pigments in the toner that will typically be applied between each application of bleach.[29] "When the cuticle has been damaged, there are three key things it needs: protein, moisture and condition," says Lush HairLab colourist Daisy. "At Lush, we use amino acids, hydrolysed wheat protein and aquafaba to provide protein in our products, and these temporarily patch up broken areas of the cuticle and strengthen the hair. Oils and butters soften and moisturise the cuticle to create a more pliable head of hair that is less likely to snap. We then use anti-statics to improve the condition of the hair by smoothing down a raised cuticle, meaning the fibres reflect more light, making the hair easier to de-tangle."

Having a professional bleach your hair is also best practice if your hair has been processed previously by heat treatments, perming or elaxing procedures. Lush HairLab Afro Hair specialist Sarah Sango explains that coily and Afro-textured hair requires especially careful attention before and after bleaching. "The tighter the curls are, the harder it is for the sebum (oils that are naturally produced from the scalp) to travel down the hair shaft," she says. "As a result, Afro hair tends to be relatively drier than other hair types and extra care should be taken when applying bleach to hair.

"Achieving a light shade of blonde will involve applying many applications of bleach and higher processing levels of a developer, so I recommend only going three shades lighter than the client's natural colour to avoid disrupting curl patterns. A wig or extensions are both great options for a client who wants a dramatic change without having to lighten their hair.

"As people with Afro hair often apply a lot of products to keep hair moisturised," she continues, "it's a good idea to clear the hair of any product buildup beforehand, and to apply protein treatments at least once between chemical treatments to help prevent or repair any damage. However, it is also important not to overload hair with protein and ensure moisture and protein levels are balanced. I also advise my clients to wear a satin or silk bonnet at night to retain moisture in the hair, and to use hydrating products to keep it looking and feeling shiny and healthy."

Toning it down: is your hair off-colour?

When you significantly lighten the hair it will also reveal red or yellow undertones thanks to the resistant pheomelanin pigment inside the hair fibre. This may come as a surprise for the inexperienced bleach user at home.

"Home bleaches promise a lot!" says Daisy. "They're marketed in a way that tells people it's easy to go from dark to light, but your surface hair colour has underlying pigments from orange to yellow that are exposed when you bleach. Professional colourists will almost always use a toner in the form of a demi or semi-permanent colourant after a lightening service to conceal any unwanted shades. Toners neutralise unwanted shades by using basic colour theory; if you have orangey hair, you would use a blue-based toner. For yellow, it would need to be violet-based. Toning the hair after a bleach service still needs to be treated in a precautionary manner, as you have already put the hair through a hefty oxidising process and most colourists will use a demi or semi-permanent dye to minimise further damage."

Flaxen undertones weren't problematic for the screen actresses that first popularised the blonde bombshell look. 1930s black-and-white films were insensitive to yellow tones, instead painting that halo of blonde curls in an ethereal light that drew the eye. Against a carefully made-up face, dark eyes and pencilled-in eyebrows, the aesthetic was delicious, if high maintenance.[30]

But product marketing has since presented the yellow tones in bleached hair as unappealing, needing to be countered by toning shampoos and tints. It's a reasonably modern concept as it relies on women being able to use shampoo-based products at home. In the early to mid-20th century, regular shampooing had yet to take off, and sub-standard bathroom facilities at home meant that women who could afford it opted for a regular wash and set at the hairdresser's instead. They opted for high-maintenance styles from the sharp, 'flapper' bob of the 1920s to the bold blonde coiffures of the 1950s, which would be maintained by weekly trips to the salon. As electricity became more widely available, salons could also offer permanent wave machines (first invented in 1906), hair dryers and electric curling tools.[31] Many women didn't have the facilities to dress their hair elaborately at home, let alone use regular toning products.

But several mid-century shifts in behaviour changed this. A post-Second World War emphasis on personal hygiene encouraged improved grooming habits at home, and, significantly for us, an increasing number of family houses became equipped with indoor plumbing. These factors created the perfect conditions for a 'shampoo revolution', encouraging customers to wash their hair - and then also to style it - at home.[32]

This, in turn, gave manufacturers the opportunity to introduce new types of products and formats that have since changed the way we bleach and colour our hair. Affordable cream-based lighteners could be applied in the privacy of a consumer's own bathroom, while semi-permanent dyes in shampoo formats were introduced to tint and wash in one.[33] Consumers switched some of their spending from salons to shops.

Two of my colleagues get their blonde looks created by the hairdresser and maintain them at home. Lush Makeup Category Lead Jess Cerasale began lightening her hair at the age of 13, "because my hair is naturally very mousey and I find it very boring if I am honest." She currently sports a head of pearly blonde hair that is bleached at the salon but toned at home. "I vary from a full head of balayage foils with smudged roots to full bleach around the front of my face and just a toner on my already pre-lightened ends," she says. "I usually use a cocktail of three toning shampoos depending on the effect I want and the condition of my hair."

Fellow colleague Mandi Nicholls, 54, Lush North American Contact and Support, has gone for all colours of the rainbow before but now prefers to wear her bleached hair a silvery grey. "The first time I used hair dye I was 18 or 19, and I started by dyeing my hair black," she recalls. "Now it's highlighted, then toned grey. My hairdresser comes to me and normally bleaches my hair every four months, and I then use a semi-permanent toner to keep it grey every six to eight weeks at home."

As in Jess and Mandi's case, fashion dictates that bleaching is very rarely the only component of hair lifting today. Yet toner is probably where we are getting into a more problematic area of hair dyeing, as we know these products contain aromatic amine derivatives and have a possible link to increased risk of breast cancer. As it's domestic use that has been particularly implicated in these studies, that suggests that the regular use and enhanced skin contact of the dyeing process at home is a contributing factor.

A lasting impression: Permanent hair dyes

The rise of oxidative permanent dyes has been a heady one. So valuable to the customer is a colour that can conveniently lighten and give complete coverage in one step, that the product's popularity vastly outstrips other hair dye formats. In salons too, it's become a staple for colour changes and concealing grey hairs. "People used to use bleach in salons for lifting the hair a lot more than they do now," Mark recalls. "Then they introduced permanent colours that could also lift." But, as it is also the product type most implicated in health concerns, being clever about when, how, and where you use permanent dye is probably advisable.

Permanent dyes give total coverage because they combine bleaching with colour depositing. The combination of peroxide and ammonia opens the hair cuticle and oxidises the melanin, while a combination of colourless chemicals called primary intermediates, precursors or bases (typically para-phenylenediamine, para-toluenediamine or para-aminophenol) react with the peroxide and oxidise, developing colour. This forms the basis of your shiny new shade.[34]

But primary intermediates themselves don't offer an exciting array of colours. Para-phenylenediamine and para-toluenediamine produce dark brown to black shades, while para-aminophenol creates an intense, reddish orange.[35] That's why colourants also contain couplers: compounds that don't produce a great deal of colour by themselves but react with peroxide to enhance the colour created by the primary intermediate. Key couplers you'll find on the ingredients list of your box dye include derivatives of meta-phenylenediamines for blue tones, phenols and naphthols for red, and resorcinol for yellow and green. These are essential to tweaking the shade formed by your primary intermediate, with one or two primary intermediates usually combined with three to five couplers.[36]

The combination of hydrogen peroxide and ammonia in permanent formulas create long polymers of colour that are too large to exit the cuticle. These turn your hair a uniform colour, and do not wash out over time - a big advantage to those who want to maintain a certain colour and cover 100% of grey hairs.[37]

Graphic designer Leanne Coen, 33, relies on permanent dye to colour her hair back to its original black. "My hair was jet black growing up," she says, "but grey hairs appeared quickly. Now, I am completely grey without my hair dye. I class it as an essential not a luxury. I tend to buy mid-range products, spending around £5. Sometimes I'll go cheap because they don't have the conditioner but a hairdresser once told me off for buying too cheap. I personally don't see the difference."

Craft party business owner Katie Bishop, 34, also regularly uses a permanent dye at home to keep her hair glossy black. She says, "I began dyeing my hair from the age of 15 as I started to go grey young due to my thyroid condition. If I didn't have to dye my hair I wouldn't, but if I left it, I would be completely white. I've never experienced irritation but I worked with a professional colourist to work out the best product for my hair type as my hair is very resistant and doesn't take to many dyes."

The convenience of permanent dyes is compelling. On the other hand, they leave an obvious line as your hair grows, meaning regular touch ups are required. Leanne, for example, dyes her hair every two weeks to cover regrowth at her roots, Katie every month. If you don't like the result, changing it will also be a lot of effort and will damage your hair further.

Given the research discussed in Chapter

7, using these products regularly at home, particularly darker colours, appears to be on the riskier end of the spectrum. If choosing to use them, the ideal situation would be to have them applied at a salon with minimal scalp contact. But this is obviously not an option for everyone who wishes to colour their hair. Leanne, who is a mum of two, says, "I have never actually had my hair dyed professionally. I can't afford (and couldn't book) the hairdressers often enough, and I don't have the time or patience. I always use the gloves provided but I get the dye all over my forehead and neck most of the time and I shower it off. I'm more concerned about it staining my bath or tiles than any effect on my skin."

Katie, who also balances running her business with being mum to her four-year-old daughter, reveals, "I colour my hair at home now because of Covid-19. I use gloves so the product doesn't go on my hands but it goes on my forehead and ears occasionally. I tend to wash it off in the shower so it goes all over my body. I don't look at any health claims because otherwise I wouldn't use it - it is my one treat to myself each month."

Regular home hair dye users are clearly unlikely to suddenly switch up their entire routines. But there are ways to minimise your exposure when dyeing at home. Maximising the time between wash days and using less-cleansing shampoos can help to keep your colour in for longer, reducing how often you use these products at home. When applying your dye, keep your bathroom well-ventilated, or, if that's tricky, consider swapping to a space with windows you can open. Apply a barrier cream around the hairline and wear gloves for the entire colouring procedure and rinsing process.

If you can, using a brush to apply the dye more precisely to the roots (avoiding the scalp wherever possible) would also be worthwhile, even if you then switch to massaging through the lengths and ends of your hair. You may also find you don't need to leave the dye on your hair for the entire maximum application time and can remove it a little earlier. I'd also recommend thoroughly removing the product over the bath or shower tray, rather than getting in the shower yourself. This limits how much of the product runs over your body.

If you have a hairdresser friend, relying on their expertise and good nature is also a good plan. Lush HairLab's Gemma Sales says, "I've got a friend who gets me to put her box dye on for her. Normally we just get a tube and a bottle of the peroxide. They expect you to put the cream into it, shake it up and then use the bottle to apply. I never do that, I always apply it properly with a brush. But these bottle formulations often have a nozzle so you can apply it directly down your parting and then I think you are encouraged to massage it through the hair and into the roots to get an even coverage. Obviously, you don't have as much skin contact if you are applying it with a brush. From a home dye perspective, if you could get someone else to apply it to you with a brush, you might expect there to be less skin contact."

Swapping out your permanent dye for a natural alternative is another option. Natural dyes may not offer you the convenience of a fast-working permanent dye, but they have the added benefit of keeping your hair in much better condition. (Leanne has agreed to a henna party once Covid-19 restrictions are lifted.)

I have to admit that (Lush hairdressers aside) salon colourists may not be best-placed to offer henna expertise. Henna has a deeply suspect reputation within the hairdressing industry due to its historical contamination with heavy metals that can make your colour or perm go haywire (as discussed in Chapter 5). Thankfully, you can find a breakdown of henna's best application methods in Chapter 13.

The 'free-from' phenomenon: demi-permanent dyes

Demi-permanent products are a more recent introduction to the market, advertised as being longer-lasting than semi-permanent dyes, but healthier for your hair. They rely on the same chemistry as permanent products but use a lower level of hydrogen peroxide, giving them minimal lightening power and a weaker ability to cover grey hairs..[38] They also rely on a less effective alkali, monoethanolamine, which does not open the cuticle to the same extent, and are useful for those who want to tone their natural hair. They tend to last up to 20 washes[39] and cover up to 50% of grey hair.[40] It's a less damaging procedure on the hair fibre, but colour uptake is not uniform and depends on the texture and condition of the hair being coloured.

Former industry chemist Dr Robert Hefford says, "The problem with demi-permanent systems is that there's far less lightening happening while the colour is deposited, so the final result is more unpredictable. These products are often marketed as a longer lasting semi-permanent option which would still wash out - but they don't always! The level of permanence often varies from shade to shade. Demi-permanent black can often become a muddy khaki colour with washing, and then not fully wash out, meaning the only way to get rid of it is to colour or use a hair colour remover over it."

Demi-permanent products are sold on the basis that they are less damaging to the hair than permanent dyes. Compared to a permanent dye, which uses ammonia, the cuticle is not lifted as significantly by a demi-permanent product, which helps to keep the hair fibre in better condition.

The 'ammonia-free' claim is a common one anyone browsing the shelves of their local beauty outlet will notice. It's a marketing term that's increasingly being found on permanent hair dyes too but Dr Hefford explains that 'ammonia-free' permanent dyes aren't necessarily a better option for your hair. "As well as increasing the pH, the ammonia makes the oxidising mixture more active, opens up the hair cuticle scales, and also seems to disrupt the cell membrane of the melanin in the hair. This is why it's more effective to use ammonia to lighten hair than any other alkali. You need a higher concentration of monoethanolamine to achieve comparable results in the same time frame as an ammonia-containing product."

He continues: "Ammonia is perceived as being harsh because it smells nasty, but the reason you get that smell is that it's evaporating off the head as you do the bleaching. This means the pH on the head will drop faster, so it's actually less harsh to the hair to use ammonia than it is to use monoethanolamine. It's also better for the scalp. From a safety point of view when lightening hair, you need to reduce the pH of the mixture on the client's scalp as quickly as you can by adding acid. Monoethanolamine-based bleaches have a higher alkalinity content which means you have to add more acid and it takes longer."

He believes that users of monoethanolamine-based products are more likely to experience skin irritation, but that's especially true of bleaches. "Sellers of these products always receive more complaints of scalp irritation from the "high-lift" blonde products - the ones designed to lighten the hair very significantly, and in my experience, the worst offenders amongst them are the ammonia-free, monoethanolamine-based variety."

It's a claim backed up by evidence. Hairs treated with higher concentrations of monoethanolamine have been found to sustain significant surface damage, protein loss and a decrease in mechanical strength,[41] and suffer up to 85% extra damage compared to ammonia

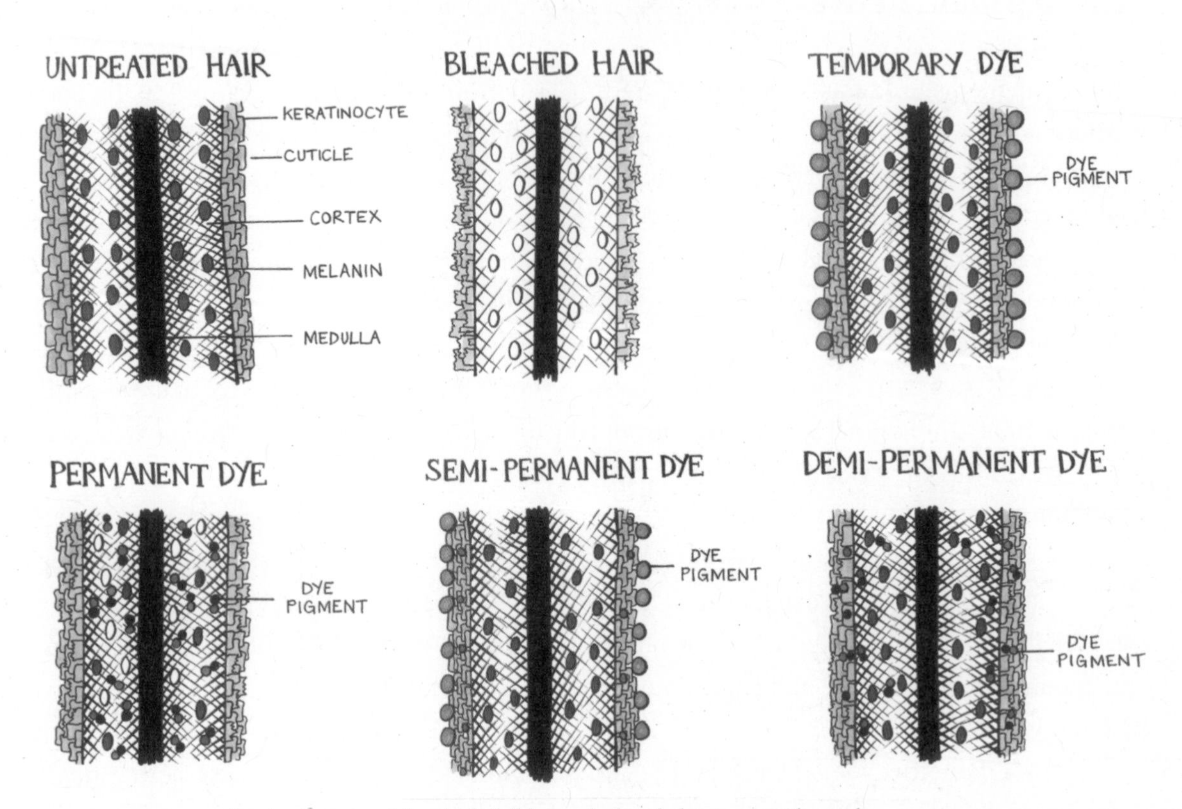

Bleach, colourants and dyes that both lighten and colour the hair penetrate the cuticle to different extents and have different effects on the melanin in the cortex.

formulas.[42] So 'ammonia-free' permanent formulas are not doing much for the health of your hair, despite the marketing hype.

The rise of 'free-from' claims in hair dye manufacturing has been carefully catered to a public increasingly conscious of the health of their hair. But Mark believes that manufacturers are plugging these formulas to divert attention from the health concerns surrounding hair dyes. "Hair dye manufacturers are worried about health concerns circulating about hair dye and they don't want to talk about their use of ingredients like para-phenylenediamines and its derivatives so they talk about ammonia instead. It's a naughty piece of misdirection."

Deposit systems: Semi-permanent and temporary

Many of the oldest herbal tints used to colour the hair gave temporary results, with users desperate to source longer-term recipes and products. Yet, nowadays, modern semi-permanent and temporary products are cleverly marketed as an opportunity for customer experimentation and creativity. They are also commonly presented as damage-free, because they involve no bleaching and deposit colour pigments onto the cuticle rather than into the cortex.

Able to tone the hair rather than introduce dramatic, long-lasting colour changes, nevertheless, these products can still have a very vivid effect on fair and previously bleached or processed hair. Colour uptake can also vary

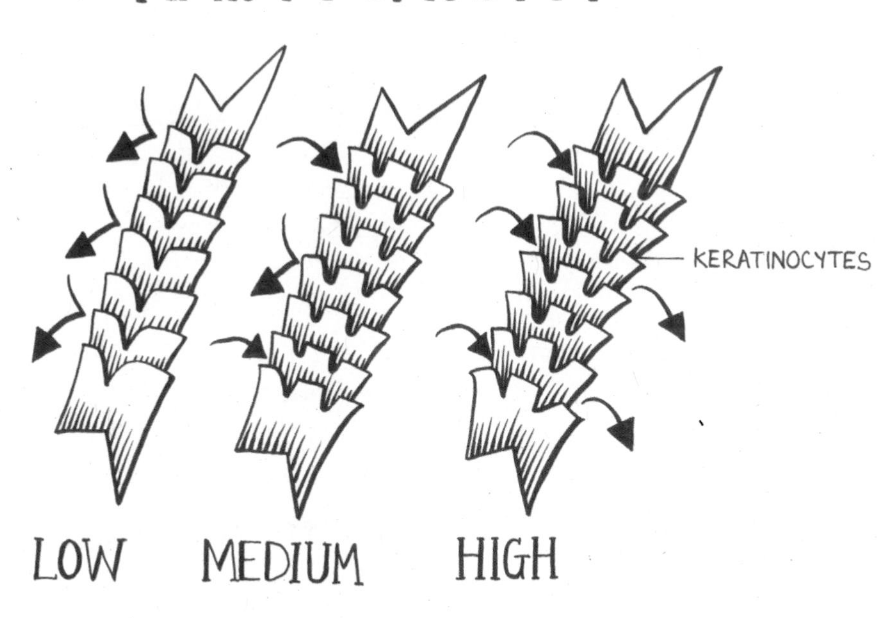

Your hair's porosity determines how well it absorbs and withholds moisture. Hair that has been bleached, dyed with oxidative colour or heat-treated is more likely to be highly porous with a damaged cuticle.

depending on how porous the ends of the hair fibres are compared to the roots.

Semi-permanent colours typically come in lotion and mousse formulas.[43] They contain compounds known as basic or cationic dyes, which have a positive charge that gives them a high affinity to your negatively charged hair, and also aromatic amine compounds that are small enough to penetrate a short distance into the cuticle.[44] Unlike permanent or demi-permanent dyes, however, the compounds do not form larger pigment chains inside, and so typically leave the cuticle between three and six washes.[45]

Temporary dyes usually come in rinse, gel, mousse, and spray formulas[46] and are marketed as 'wash out'. That's because they contain large pigments, often acid dyes, that are characterised by poor wash fastness and minimum penetration into the hair. They are typically used to create bright so-called 'fantasy' or 'fashion' shades on fair and white hair, but will only cover minimal greys.[47] While acid dyes are soluble in water and so, in theory, easily removed by shampooing, on very fair hair, they are not necessarily so temporary. Porous hair will similarly have a longer-lasting colour result because the pigments are able to enter the cuticle.[48]

In terms of hair health, there are benefits of using these formulas, as Sarah explains. "Using semi-permanent colours rather than permanent dyes is a gentler process on Afro hair. All Afro hair patterns (3A to 4C) can be low porosity or high porosity, but low porosity hair that is dehydrated in particular is not the ideal candidate for permanent hair colour because it can lead to breakage. These gaps and tears allow the hair to absorb too much water, which can cause frizz, tangles, and even colour loss on colour-treated hair. In order to fill in the gaps, you need a protein treatment to strengthen your strands. High porosity hair can be good for taking colour. It will lift faster and lighter. However, the cuticle layers do not close back tight enough to retain moisture, leaving hair looking dry."

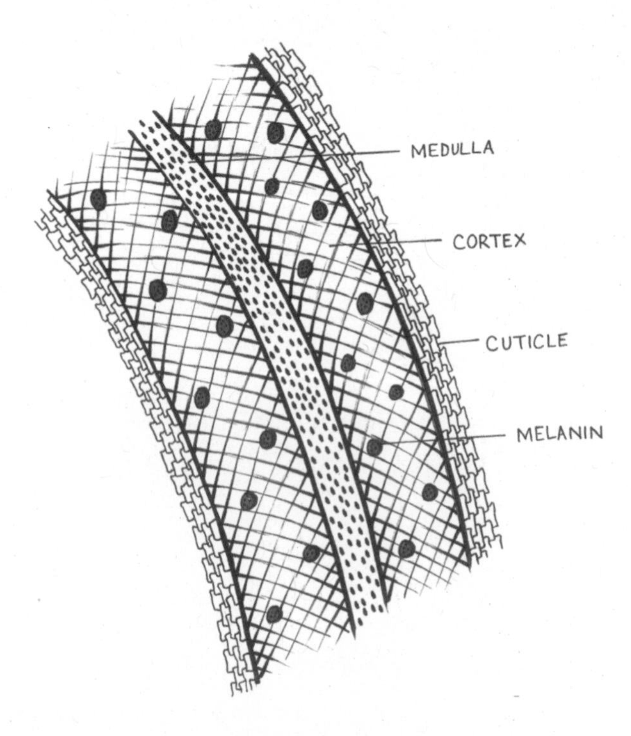

The hair fibre is composed of three main layers: a protective outer cuticle, the large melanin-containing cortex, and the inner, sometimes non-existent medulla.

You can check the porosity of your own hair by taking a few strands from your brush and adding them to a glass of water. If the hair sinks, it is classed as highly porous, whereas if it floats it is determined to have low porosity.

Temporary and semi-permanent products are frequently used for toning the hair - a very fashionable concept nowadays with lots of products designed for home use. However, the less precise, looser formulas of these hair dyes mean more scalp contact, especially when they are applied at home. This is probably what is implicating them in breast cancer risk increases, as discussed in Chapter 7. "At a salon, a toner would be applied at a basin so even though it's runnier it's running off into the basin," says Gemma. "But with a home dye, you're generally doing full-head cover. Many people using home dye just don't want a patchy finish. So they would rub it in, massage it all over, and try and make sure it covers everywhere."

If you want to use a toner at home, limiting skin exposure is key. A balayage style, in which toner is only required at the ends of the hair, rinsed off without body contact would curtail product exposure. If you want to get closer to the roots, applying as precisely as possible with a brush then massaging through the lengths of the hair (wearing gloves of course) would also be better than massaging the product straight into the scalp. Finding a friend to help, a thicker formulation, and using a barrier cream would also help with this type of application.

Progressive dyes

Another member of the temporary and semi-permanent family is the progressive dye, which deposits silver salts, lead and bismuth, rather than colour molecules, on the cuticle. These ingredients react with the sulphur in the hair's keratin and oxidise on the hair surface to gradually darken the hair fibres.[49] It's an ancient form of hair colouring adopted by the Romans with their use of lead combs, and then successfully commercialised in the early 21st century. Typically, these formulas used lead acetate as a main ingredient, but many companies have now moved to bismuth - another naturally occurring metal - as lead has been widely outlawed on toxicity grounds. A quick scoot on a pharmacy website also tells me that a number of Just For Men formulas have now expanded to rinse off para-phenylenediamine-based dyes instead.

The main advantage of progressive dyes is that they offer gradual coverage. Without penetrating the cuticle, they cannot cover 100%

of white hair fibres but instead gradually reduce the overall appearance of grey hair. Because the transformation is subtle and the application easily done in the privacy of your own bathroom, they have been heavily and unapologetically marketed at men for decades. They do, unfortunately however, often go through a greenish shade before they progress to more natural browns and blacks, and the colour progression is not controllable.[50] As Dr Hefford says, "It's what is known as the paint job. The colours can be very flat and to cover grey or light hair you have to put lots of colour down."

The price of a good dye job

With the historical stigma of hair dyeing mostly eradicated now, the main incentive for customers to purchase a home-dye kit rather than pay a much higher price for a salon visit is cost, not secrecy. So, is there a difference between the products being used by your hairdresser or sold by your local pharmacy? Dr Hefford says, chemically, no. "Good results can be obtained from home hair colouring kits (technically the products are the same), however, this does depend upon how complex the treatment is and how 'difficult' your hair is. You tend to get a much better result from going to a professional colourist. It will also cost you a lot more."

Daisy chews the question over thoughtfully. "In my opinion, 'good results' can't really be achieved by anyone who just applies a dye all over their hair," she muses. "Home hair dye brands tend not to supply customers with education or advice on what is really going on when they dye their hair, or how to apply it. This would detract from their main marketing focus of convenience and ease. It takes experience and practical knowledge to know how the different 'zones' of the hair behave, for example, how the heat from the head will alter the power of the dye or bleach and how the ends will be colder and more porous.

"You would need to buy numerous shades from a pharmacy, taking into account the warmer and cooler areas of the hair, consider the level of peroxide emulsion needed, and know whether to use a permanent or demi-permanent colourant. All that and not forgetting the techniques you would need to perform in order to get a 'good' result. Sometimes, you just can't beat a professional choosing what shades and applications would work best for you."

The cost you pay for a salon visit is justified by the expertise of your colourist and the guarantee that you should get the result you want - or be warned that it is ill-advised. Customers with curly, coily, or Afro-textured hair, or hair that has been processed, will also likely reap the benefit of putting themselves in the trusted hands of an expert.

Sarah explains, "You have to be extra cautious when colouring relaxed hair. It's important to know how far you can go, and a hairdresser will be able to examine the hair and know the correct usage that is safe. I personally always advise a two-week gap between using a relaxer and a bleach or an oxidative colour and recommend an ombre style for customers who want to colour relaxed hair. This means that when the regrowth comes through and you need to reapply the relaxer, you are not damaging the roots continuously with both processes.

"If you are applying a darker colour using a semi-permanent or temporary dye or henna, this is something that can be done on the same day, because the colour will be deposited on top of the cortex, preventing hair from going through and chemical change. However, I recommend waiting at least a few days, ideally two weeks, because relaxed hair can be very fragile."

As well as getting a more predictable result,

visiting a good hairdresser appears to be a safer alternative to dyeing your hair at home. An experienced colourist can create styles for you that require less upkeep, and perform procedures with far less skin contact than you'd manage yourself. Having your colour applied by a professional and opting for a low-maintenance style such as balayage can dramatically reduce your exposure to the dye. "If you are going to use materials like para-phenylenediamine, ideally you want them professionally applied because you don't want them touching the scalp," says Mark. "The more that hairdressers can develop looks that don't involve whole-head dyeing, the better."

Having said that, a huge number of people colour their hair at home for a variety of reasons, including cost and convenience. Getting to a hairdresser regularly simply isn't a practical option for everyone who wants to colour their hair. Whatever your situation, the Covid-19 pandemic has also injected the international colourants market with new life. Deprived of hairdresser contact, more and more of us are turning to DIY dye jobs.

In 2020, sales of home hair colourants increased by 10% in the UK and almost 30% in Italy compared with the same period in 2019,[51] while "how to color your hair at home" was the third most searched beauty trend in the US, according to Google Trends.[52] 26% of UK home hair dye users agreed that they had coloured their hair at home more regularly since the Covid-19 outbreak,[53] with UK retailer Superdrug announcing a 76% growth in haircare sales - driven by home hair colouring products - in the weeks of April 27th to May 2nd 2020.[54] This was roughly a month after the UK went into its first lockdown with salons closed - presumably also around the time hair dye users realised salons were not going to open in time for their roots touch-up.

It's unclear whether or not customers will return in the same numbers to the experienced hands of their colourist once the pandemic is over. Some stats suggest not, with consumers swayed by the affordability of home hair dye products.[55] Only time will tell, but hopefully the information in this chapter helps customers who want to colour their hair at home to do it in the safest and most effective way.

Hair dye allergy: are you the sensitive type?

9

When I was on maternity leave in 2017, I declared to my partner that I had decided to treat myself. A local salon was offering a discounted eyelash tint for a limited time. I hadn't so much as had my nails done at a salon before and I decided that this was a luxury I would indulge in. One Saturday, I handed over the baby, and lay back in the small beauty treatment room, preparing for 15 minutes of peace and the promise of up to six weeks of sooty lashes.

Ouch! "Is it meant to sting like that?" I asked my therapist, as she spread a gloopy mix over my eyelashes. "Yes, it can do," she reassured me, fanning my eyes to alleviate the burning. After a few minutes of discomfort, the dye was removed and cooling pads were placed over my eyelids. I emerged a little red but pleased with the results.

It was the third time I had the treatment that things really kicked off. Shortly after returning home, my eyes puffed up like golf balls, bordered by an itchy red rash. When I called the salon, they agreed that unfortunately I had an allergy and I wouldn't be able to have the treatment again. It was only in the course of writing this book that the obvious occurred to me. The salon had never tested me for a pre-existing allergy.

Allergy: a touchy subject

A majority of people will be able to colour their hair without issue. But some will find hair dye causes them problems, with reactions ranging from mild dermatitis and localised irritation, to cases of face swelling and acute chemical burns. On rare occasions, sufferers have been known to go into anaphylactic shock.[1] That's because hair dyes contain a number of potent allergy-inducing materials.

Patch tests are designed to alert you to an existing allergy before your body receives a high dose of the material that causes it. To counteract potential reactions, manufacturers include a warning label on their products instructing customers on how to do a patch test at home before they dye their hair. Yet, according to European market research in 2014, only around half of hair dye users take the time to do this.[2] I ask toxicologist Dr David Basketter, a specialist in hair dye allergy, who has provided toxicology consultation to many major hair dye producing companies, why that is.

"I think that the emotional tie of dyeing your hair is very compelling," he explains. "That's why we don't see people taking patch testing that seriously, even though there are pictures in the press of women who've had such a bad reaction to their hair dye that they've been hospitalised."

Awareness of the potential dangers of hair dye allergy is not widespread, even amongst younger generations that tend to change their hair colour regularly. In France, for example, 57% of hair dye users aged 16 to 24 confessed they did not normally test themselves before using hair dye, compared to 43% of those aged over 55.[3] This opens younger generations with less brand loyalty up to an increased risk of suffering from uncomfortable and even dangerous reactions.

After years of home-dyeing, Lush Global Strategic Lead Charlotte, 29, was surprised when she discovered she had an allergy at the salon. "I experimented with lots of different colours when I was younger without ever having any reaction," she says. "Working in Lush, I moved over to henna, but after a few years I wanted to go lighter again, so I had a patch test at a salon. I was confident that I'd be fine but the little patch behind my ear really burnt, and then, even though I wiped it off as soon as I got home, it actually caused a blister a day or two later. I never realised I had any kind of allergy before that, but maybe I'm only allergic to some dyes and not others. Now it feels like a bit of a risk."

At the age of 27, I was unfamiliar with the concept of patch testing when I had my eyelashes tinted. As someone with no existing allergies (that I was aware of), I had never had to scrutinise labels and I brushed aside my reaction as a one-off. It didn't come up in my mind until a year or so later, when I also reacted to a salon patch test for a balayage service. Still I did not connect the dots until I researched allergy more extensively for this book.

Patch testing: flawed but essential?

Unfortunately, allergy tests performed at home or at the hairdressers are not infallible. In fact, patch test instructions and warnings on hair dye products are not even legally required within the EU - it's instead a voluntary action from the manufacturers. That's because the EU's advisory body, the Scientific Committee on Consumers Products (SCCP), believes home tests are not reliable enough to predict allergy.[4]

Clearly, a dermatologist is best-placed to give a reliable patch test and interpret the results confidently. But advising customers to visit a professional before they use a product you want to sell them hardly makes good business sense. Instead, manufacturers have acknowledged the risk of allergy with hair dye products by adding a warning and patch test instructions to their product labels.

The amount of variation between patch testing instructions is huge. Sometimes manufacturers recommend that the hair colourant should be applied neat, other times that it should be mixed with hydrogen peroxide. Application times can range from 45 minutes to 48 hours. The concentration of the product being applied is also vague ("a small amount"). Perhaps most significantly, customers are advised to check for a reaction within 48 hours, when some reactions can take place up to a week after the material has been applied.[5]

Loft Machinist Darcie Foulger was 17 when she experienced a reaction to a black permanent dye. "I had a mild burning sensation and the glands behind my ears throbbed," she remembers. "It was the first time I had dyed my hair all over from the root. I did do a patch test for the black dye with no reaction, and I used it once more afterwards as the reaction the first time wasn't too uncomfortable and I didn't question it."

For years, authorities and manufacturers have been butting heads about how effective home tests are compared to professional diagnostic tests conducted by a dermatologist. But, despite the reservations of the SCCP, in my mind, pre-testing at home must be better than just whacking the stuff straight on your head and hoping for the best. If you have a severe allergy this could be dangerous. Unfortunately, there are going to be a number of customers who do the patch test like Darcie and get a false negative even if manufacturers improve their procedures. Discontinuing your use of that product is key.

If you do have a positive response to a product patch test, it won't specifically identify which material in the hair dye has made your skin react. There are a number of suspects. In a study of products on the German market, nearly all of the 20 most commonly used hair dye ingredients were potent or very potent contact sensitisers: materials capable of inducing allergy.[6] In the US, 106 of 107 products assessed contained at least one potent sensitiser, and the average product contained six.[7]

Yet, as it did in the early 20th century, para-phenylenediamine is the material that generates the most news coverage. It has been listed as a 'strong sensitiser' by the Scientific Committee on Consumer Safety since 1961,[8] and, in 2006, was even given the dubious honour of being Allergen of the Year by the American Contact Dermatitis Society. Para-phenylenediamine is also estimated to be included in nearly 70% of hair colourants available worldwide,[9] although it is used to a lesser extent and typically in smaller concentrations within the EU.[10]

Such is its notoriety, that, for several decades, para-phenylenediamine has been used as an indicator of general allergy to hair colouring products in region-specific dermatology tests known as the 'baseline' or 'standard' series. This involves a dermatologist applying a small concentration of the most common allergens (substances that cause the immune system to respond in a way that affects the skin) to the back of a person suffering from contact allergic dermatitis, leaving them on for 48 hours, then checking for a reaction over a period of days - usually up to seven.[11]

Your first contact with para-phenylenediamine could elicit no noticeable symptoms whatsoever. However, in a process known as sensitisation, this substance can prime your immune system to respond more violently each time you come into contact with it. "It's known as the induction of a contact allergy," explains Dr Basketter. "However, it's initially completely asymptomatic, so not obvious that anything has happened. But, you can detect that state in an individual by applying a diagnostic patch test for 48 hours. If you see a red skin reaction that occurs between 48 to around 96 hours later, the person has a developed allergy; at this point, we talk about a material eliciting an allergic reaction in the skin."

Sensitisation is the reason some people may be able to use hair dye without problems for years and then find they are beginning to react to it. The ability of materials like para-phenylenediamine to induce allergy has also led to debate about how often people should patch test. But, as Dr Basketter argues, "Whilst patch testing at home must present a risk of inducing allergy to hair dye, it's a tiny dose in comparison to the amount of allergen that would be on your head and on your hands during the hair dyeing process. So, I would argue that the relative risk is still very small compared to the chance of having a really bad allergic reaction on your head."

Dr Basketter does admit that telling customers when to patch test is a hotly debated topic. "I differ from some others in my perspective. I would rather see people perhaps patch testing on an annual basis and just being alert to the fact that if they start to develop an itchy scalp some months later, that should trigger them to patch test again or seek medical advice.

"But, of course, if you're deciding to go from light blonde to dark brown then that represents a considerable shift to a much higher dose of substances like para-phenylenediamine and para-toluenediamine, so that's absolutely when you should be testing yourself. However, in the interest of consistency and safety for the consumer, it's simpler to say that every time you change your dye that's another point where you should test yourself."

Para-phenylenediamine: what's the problem?

We are surrounded by allergens in our day-to-day life, with contact allergy affecting an estimated 27% of the general population in Europe.[12] Yet para-phenylenediamine is recognised as a strong inducer of allergy that can cause patients to react to dyes used for hair, textiles, furs, and leather, printer ink and photographic products.[13] Even dark clothes have been reported as causing a problem in some cases.[14] The thing is nobody really knows exactly why.

What we do know is that para-phenylenediamine itself does not trigger an immune response until it is oxidised.[15] Whether you are dying your hair over the bath or in a salon, the bottled para-phenylenediamine you use is combined with couplers that not only influence the final colour, but also prevent para-phenylenediamine from oxidising before it is used on the hair.[16] When applied to your hair and exposed to air or hydrogen peroxide, para-phenylenediamine then triggers a chemical reaction that generates colour. Most of the dangerous byproducts of oxidising para-phenylenediamine (including the catchily named Bandrowski's Base) are converted into a non-sensitising dye.[17]

But not all of these byproducts are consumed by the dye process.

One 2006 study found that some hair dye products used up to 60% more primary intermediates and couplers than actually required to dye the hair. These are unconsumed by the chemical process and so could remain in contact with the scalp until they gradually disperse.[18] Customers could therefore be exposed to the sensitiser for longer than anticipated by manufacturers. The allergenic component of para-phenylenediamine has also been found to accumulate in the skin when low concentrations are used intermittently, which could be equivalent to receiving a higher dose of the sensitiser.[19]

Despite progress made in this area, the exact nature of what is sensitising consumers remains a mystery. Dr Basketter explains, "What we know from work that I and others have done is that it's not the obvious reaction products like Bandrowski's Base, which is actually a more powerful allergen, because when you test people who are allergic to para-phenylenediamine with Bandrowski's Base, they don't react.

"The problem is that some of these reactive intermediate materials are so short-lived, and also so 'dangerous' that you can't ethically put them onto people to test out whether they are the culprit. In reality, even if they are formed in the skin for a few seconds as part of the overall process, that might be the point where they can just latch on to the nearest protein and cause the allergy problem."

What we do know is that colouring your hair regularly and using darker shades - with a higher concentration of para-phenylenediamine or its alternatives - both increase your risk of becoming sensitised.

Exposure isn't the only factor in sensitisation risk. In addition, much like with cancer risk as discussed in Chapter 7, the speed of the detoxification process in the skin varies between different people. Those with speedy genetic variants of the NAT1 enzyme, responsible for metabolising and detoxifying chemicals in the skin, appear to have reduced susceptibility to sensitisation from para-phenylenediamine as they process the material more quickly.[20] Unfortunately, there is no easy way for people to test this at home.

Stress can also affect a person's chances of sensitisation to allergens. The exact impact of environmental and physiological effects on allergic susceptibility is still to be determined, but stress clearly produces heightened immune activity and an inflammatory response in the skin.[21] Former adviser to the UK Department of Health, National Health Service, and consultant for Lush, Dr John James explains, "Unfortunately, some of the people who are anxious to change their hair colour are under stress, and stress is actually a precipitator to central sensitisation. You can see the impact of this among people whose eczema is worse at exam time, for example. Similarly, in younger women, their cycle can affect potential for reactions, as well."

This relates to patch testing too. Research has indicated that women of menstruating age have a diminished allergic response during ovulation, meaning they are more likely to have false negative patch test results to allergens during this period.[22] In practical terms, this means it's possible that an allergy may be missed if you patch test your hair dye during this time. Then during the latter stage of the menstrual cycle, researchers have observed a heightened response to allergens.[23] Given all these variables, it's clear that no patch test is infallible, and that paying attention to any reactions when you dye your hair is key.

Para-phenylenediamine allergy: what's the scope?

Para-phenylenediamine allergy rates amongst the general public are estimated to be around 0.8% in Europe.[24] Yet, experts are concerned because more people continue to colour their hair from a younger age. In a 2012 study, 41% of 202 interviewed US adolescent girls (average age 14) occasionally used hair colourants,[25] while 11.6% of 567 Saudi Arabian women began dying their hair at age 15 or younger - some as young as age of seven.[26] Danish research similarly reported the average first-time hair dye use to be 16, but shockingly cases from the age of one onwards were also reported.[27]

Hair dye allergy data most often comes from patients suffering from contact dermatitis who undergo patch testing to find the guilty allergen. Sure enough, research published in 2008 (using data from as far back as 1937) suggests that para-phenylenediamine allergy affects 4.3% of sampled dermatitis patients in Asia, 4% in Europe, and 6.2% in North America.[28] Smaller but more recent studies, however, have reported higher and lower rates amongst dermatitis patients in different regions: 11.5% in India,[29] 7.1% in England,[30] 5.8% in Hungary[31] 5% in Germany,[32] and 2.4% in Denmark.[33] A recent study of contact dermatitis sufferers in Japan found that as many as 35.1% of participants were allergic to para-phenylenediamine.[34]

Interestingly, allergy rates appear to peak in darker-haired populations. Patch test centres in southern and central Europe have recorded higher numbers of para-phenylenediamine sensitisation than those in Scandinavian countries. The suggestion is that dark-haired populations are more likely to use dark hair products that contain higher levels of primary intermediates like para-phenylenediamine than their fairer Northern European counterparts.[35] Significantly, para-phenylenediamine has also been mostly swapped out for alternatives in Scandinavia and Germany, which see a lower sensitisation rate.

Similarly, a large 2007 study found that 2.7% of the Thai general public (not dermatitis sufferers) had an allergy to para-phenylenediamine,[36] whereas it was as low as 0.3% in Norwegians.[37] Most studies considering para-phenylenediamine allergy in the general population find rates of between 0% to 1.5% in Europe.[38] Interestingly,

'Black henna' has become a popular but dangerous trend with kits readily available for creating at home henna tattoos.

Containing the allergen para-phenylenediamine, this has led to sensitisation and allergic reactions.

European women are more frequently reported to be sensitised to para-phenylenediamine than men, but in Asia and Middle Eastern countries, the tables are turned. This is suggested to be due to the more frequent beard-dyeing habits of men (often weekly) compared to the women.[39]

Yet it's particularly the rates of para-phenylenediamine contact allergy amongst children and teenagers exposed to hair dyes and temporary black henna tattoos at a young age that are causing concern amongst experts.[40]

Stop right now: the dangerous black henna trend

When Lush Concept Team Producer Lucky Prior, 24, was eight years old she had a black henna tattoo while on holiday in Malta. She experienced no reaction. When she had it reapplied at the end of the holiday, however, it was to leave a lasting impression. "I had a superman-shaped scar on my neck for years after," she remembers. "That one has now faded. I got another in Crete when I was 16 and this became red raw and then scabbed over in the following days. Now if I spend enough time in the sun, you can see the scar reappear."

Authentic henna, which comes in a greyish green powder and stains your skin an orange colour, has low allergenic potential and has been used to tattoo the skin for thousands of years in Asia and North Africa. However, by the 1980s a dangerous trend was hospitalising children in Sudan: the addition of para-phenylenediamine to henna blends in order to make darker and longer-lasting tattoos.[41]

Western demand for temporary tattoos during the 1990s (as seen on celebrities like The Spice Girls)[42] led to a flurry of commercial interest that has facilitated the rise of black henna tattoos: blends of henna adulterated with para-phenylenediamine and other aromatic amines found in synthetic hair dyes like aminophenols. Para-phenylenediamine concentrations as high as 30% have been found in black henna tattoos[43] when on-head concentrations must not exceed 6% in the US,[44] and 2% in the EU.[45] Shockingly, tattoo artists in Spain were found to be using concentrations as high as 64%,[46] when research estimated that 10% would sensitise 80% of people.[47] Other popular additions to black henna include turpentine, lead, nickel and even animal urine..[48] Worryingly, these blends have also entered the hair dye market and can be falsely sold as natural henna hair colourants.[49]

Henna tattoo application is often not regulated, making the black henna trend difficult to police. The tattoos are also often offered at fairs, festivals and beaches where they are popular with tourists - notably children. As a child visiting Turkey aged nine, I also remember having a black henna tattoo - a delicate pattern a lady painted onto the back of my hand at the marketplace. It was a treat from my unsuspecting mum - I had the option between a henna tattoo and elaborate hair braiding with beads, I remember. While I had no reaction at the time, decades later, I suspect it came back to bite me when I had my eyelashes tinted at that salon.

The increasing popularity of these tattoos (as well as young use of hair dye) has been linked to the growing prevalence of para-phenylenediamine allergy in children. A German study of 1,270 children between 1994 and 2004 concluded that the extremely high dose of para-phenylenediamine received from henna tattoos was responsible for the extreme reactions to para-phenylenediamine found in children aged 14 and younger.[50] In 2008, research found that para-phenylenediamine was the second most common allergen in nine to 16 year olds with eczema in Turkey,[51] while 8% of 500 children tested in the UK between 1995 and 2004 were allergic to para-phenylenediamine.[52]

If you have been sensitised by a black henna tattoo, you may suffer from the effects of allergic contact dermatitis - typically blistering and inflammation seven days after the application. Alternatively you may have no symptoms until your next exposure to the offending material - perhaps many years later. This second exposure - typically caused by the use of a synthetic hair dye - will elicit a more severe reaction much sooner, usually within one to three days.

"About the absolute fastest you can develop an allergy from a single contact with the world's most powerful allergens is about a week," says Dr Basketter. "Normally, it takes maybe weeks or months or even years of repeated exposure to create an allergy in somebody. You can't be made allergic by that single contact within a 24-hour time period." He continues, "If you get a skin reaction in the same day or the next few days, that tells you one of two things: either you've already developed an allergy or that you have developed an irritant reaction - in other words, not an allergic reaction to the test. But that is extremely rare diagnostically."

That's where the importance of patch testing comes in - and stopping use of your products if you notice any reactions.

In Lucky's case, her reaction to the second tattoo - which emerged within a few hours - but not the first, indicated she was sensitised when the first tattoo, which must have contained high levels of para-phenylenediamine, was applied to her skin. Unaware that this incident had sensitised her, Lucky has suffered from severe discomfort during later exposures to hair dye. "Once, to salvage my lovely long hair after a bad ombre treatment at a salon, I bought some hair dye to match my natural brown and dyed over the bleached hair," she recalls. "My skin became red and itchy around where I had dyed (luckily I didn't need to dye my whole head) which then spread round my face, down my shoulders and back and my lymph nodes went wild.

"I was scared and went to the doctors. They told me to take antihistamines and use hydrocortisone cream. Since then, I've stuck to two brands knowing that they don't cause me a reaction. Recently, however, I patch tested a different colour on my arm and it didn't affect me. Once I put it on my hair though it caused my neck to become red and itchy again. Back to the hydrocortisone!"

Lucky and I also have traumatic eyelash tinting experiences in common, although hers was far more severe. "The therapist didn't do a patch test," she says, "and I ended up with a severe allergic reaction in and around my eyes which landed me in hospital regularly for over two weeks. I told the therapist I was allergic to hair dye but she said it would be fine since it's all vegan. I trusted the professional in this situation but from now on I will always demand a patch test." I advise her to see a dermatologist, aware that I too should do this (various Covid-19 lockdowns and a second pregnancy have slowed my progress in this area).

In an extensive 2013 study, researchers using data from recorded cases estimated that a minimum of 2.5% of people having a black henna tattoo would be sensitised to para-phenylenediamine by the process. But this statistic was based on evidence from the reported cases - considered by the study author to be "the tip of the iceberg".[53] The best advice? Never have a black henna tattoo. Natural henna should be khaki green in colour and orangey red when it oxidises on your skin. More on that in Chapter 10.

Why hairdressers should always use protection

The old saying goes "You must suffer to be beautiful." But unfortunately if you're a hairdresser, you're more likely to suffer while making others feel beautiful. Hairdressers are significantly more at risk of suffering from contact dermatitis from para-phenylenediamine and other allergens in hair dyes thanks to their daily exposure to these products.

Studies in Italy and Poland have found that 36.8%[54] and 25%[55] of sampled hairdressers respectively (all of whom were suffering from occupation-related dermatitis) were allergic to para-phenylenediamine. This rose to 43% in India,[56] and 46% in Thailand[57] (probably due to the popularity of dark hair colourants once again) when small numbers of similarly affected hairdressers were patch tested. These sensitisation figures are grossly higher than those for contact dermatitis sufferers alone, let alone the general population.

We know that work-related allergy and dermatitis can have a big impact on hairdressers. In fact, a Danish study found that 23% of ex-hairdressers left the trade because of hand eczema and 18% because of allergy.[58] A study in the Netherlands also found that skin disease was the reason 39% of hairdresser apprentices switched careers.[59] The good news is that the most obvious preventative measure - gloves - can provide a physical barrier between the skin and the offending materials. However, their effectiveness depends on their thickness, the material used, and, perhaps most importantly, how effectively the hairdresser uses them. Disposable gloves made of natural rubber latex (0.20mm thick), polyvinyl chloride (PVC) (0.12mm thick), nitrile rubber (0.11mm) , and polyethene (0.02mm thick) were considered to offer 'considerable protection' against permeation of irritant ingredients including para-phenylenediamine, para-toluenediamine, and resorcinol in one study, but these materials still began penetrating the gloves between 32 minutes (polyethene) and 183 minutes (natural rubber). The considerably thicker natural rubber latex was the only glove found to be uncompromised after four hours.[60] In another study of thinner gloves made of the same materials, none were considered to be effective.[61]

A meta-analysis of 44 glove-related studies in 2020 similarly concluded that nitrile rubber gloves with a minimum thickness of 0.1mm provided the best protection for hairdressers, blocking the permeation of para-phenylenediamine, resorcinol, and para-toluenediamine for a minimum of 180 minutes. They did, however, note that natural rubber and synthetic rubber also pose a sensitisation risk of their own. This is because they are produced using accelerators: sensitising chemicals used to speed up the manufacturing process of rubber. 'Accelerator-free' gloves could provide a future solution, but for now no tests have been conducted on their effectiveness against hairdresser exposures. For this reason, polyvinylchloride and natural rubber latex gloves were suggested to be sufficient in most cases, if changed regularly and carefully, bearing in mind hair dye ingredients began to penetrate the polyvinylchloride variety at 40 minutes.[62]

Investigating and standardising the quality and thickness of gloves could significantly decrease hairdressers' risk of developing an allergy to hair dye sensitisers. Until that happens, perhaps the best advice for hairdressers is to source thicker varieties and to change their gloves regularly. Preventing allergic contact dermatitis is certainly better than managing it, while para-phenylenediamine-based dye combined with hydrogen peroxide has been found to permeate polyethylene, polyvinylchloride, and natural rubber latex gloves (average thickness 0.03-0.04mm) between 32 to 90 minutes, gloved allergic individuals can still react to it within as little as 15.[63]

Whatever the glove type, how you use them is key. When disposable gloves are washed and reused, turned inside out, and only worn for part of the dying process - as has been reported - their reliability is severely compromised.[64] Gloves that are too tight can stretch the material thinner, and too big expose parts of the wrist. Improving the training and protocols in salons - cutting the hair before applying colour and wearing gloves for the entire procedure including rinsing - could significantly decrease hairdressers' risk of developing allergy. Removing rings and keeping the nails short allows more effective hand-cleaning so that any dye residue can be washed thoroughly from the skin. This is important when switching gloves: a moist glove will act like a nice little allergy incubator for any dye in contact with the skin.[65]

Are you the very very sensitive type? Decoding the 'Para-phenylenediamine-free' claim

For the unlucky people left with a tell-tale patch of dermatitis where their para-phenylenediamine-containing hair colour was patch tested, there's often one burning question on their lips - can I still colour my hair?

One issue you face is that the 'para-phenylenediamine-free' claims on the label don't necessarily give you a hall pass to using that product safely. Para-phenylenediamine has a similar molecular structure to other hair dye materials that are used to replace it, meaning your immune system can respond to these replacements too. Para-toluenediamine, for example, has been a popular alternative to para-phenylenediamine for over 100 years, but it has not erased the problem.

Both para-phenylenediamine and para-toluenediamine are organic compounds composed of amino groups (ammonia derivatives) attached to a benzene ring (a component of coal tar). Para-phenylenediamine's old-fashioned name (1,4-diaminobenzene) makes reference to this. The 'para' and '1,4' both simply refer to the position of the amino groups on the benzene ring.[66] Para-toluenediamine (also known as 2,5-diaminotoluene) is a tweaked version of para-phenylenediamine, which scientists created in 1877.[67] Adding what is known as a methyl side chain to para-phenylenediamine reduces its potency, but also its effectiveness. This means the material needs to be used in higher volumes to have the same effect in hair dye formulations.[68]

Para-phenylenediamine and para-toluenediamine have the same ring structure, chemists have just modified it to some degree," says Dr James. "Think of family members sitting around the table. They've got some characteristics that are the same, some characteristics that are different. Freddie over there, he's got a bad temper, so he will react more quickly and more vigorously than Tommy who also has a temper but keeps it under better control. Effectively, you can reasonably deduce that if you've got a reaction to one, you will probably have a similar reaction to the other."

Interestingly, when I was looking into my eyelash tint allergy experience a few years ago, I discovered that it was in fact para-toluenediamine I had probably reacted to when I asked the salon for the ingredients list of the product. The para-phenylenediamine in my black henna tattoo all those years ago probably sensitised me, and its chemical cousin para-toluenediamine had triggered a reaction. When I was patch tested at a salon for a balayage service around eight months later using a para-phenylenediamine product, the itchy raised reaction confirmed the allergy was established for both materials.

Para-toluenediamine is a popular alternative to para-phenylenediamine in Denmark, Sweden, and Spain, and is used in as many as 88% of all permanent dyes in Germany.[69] Nevertheless, the material remains under scrutiny, with dyes containing 1.6% of it (within legal EU limits) capable of causing strong inflammation in the skin and triggering an immune reaction in local lymph nodes.[70] While the para-toluenediamine's metabolism route through the body is thought to be similar to its cousin, this has also not been fully mapped out yet.[71]

So how does para-toluenediamine compare to para-phenylenediamine in terms of allergy? Most of the data we have from research conducted on dermatitis-suffering hairdressers shows that para-toluenediamine is a significant sensitiser, but not so much as para-phenylenediamine.[72] For example, a North American study of 66 hairdressers suffering from contact dermatitis found that 7.5% were positive to para-toluenediamine and 46% to para-phenylenediamine.[73] The very strong para-phenylenediamine sensitivity rates could also be explained by the prevalent use of this ingredient in American hair dyes, but the trend generally continues amongst hairdressers and hair dye users in Europe where para-toluenediamine is a popular alternative.[74] Consequently, research indicates that you are less likely to become sensitised to para-toluenediamine than you are to para-phenylenediamine, but not exempt.

As I found out, if you are already allergic to one of the materials there is no guarantee that you will be able to use the other without consequence. In scientific terms, this is what is known as cross-reactivity: an immune response to an allergen you have not encountered before. In the case of hair dyes, para-phenylenediamine and para-toluenediamine are frequent allergens that cross react, either because they produce the same reactive byproducts in the skin or because they are so similar that the immune system can't tell them apart.

Dr Basketter says using a para-toluenediamine-based hair dye if you have been sensitised to para-phenylenediamine is risky. "The great majority of hair dye allergies are being caused by para-phenylenediamine or substances like para-toluenediamine that are very similar and cross react with it. You could have someone who's only ever used para-toluenediamine in their lives and you've got a 90% chance that if you patch-test them with para-phenylenediamine they're going to react to it."

2-Methoxy-methyl-p-phenylenediamine: the industry's new darling

In 2013, Wella introduced what was marketed as a massive breakthrough for the hair dye industry: a less sensitising alternative to para-phenylenediamine and para-toluenediamine that still gave full colour coverage.[75] 2-Methoxy-methyl-p-phenylenediamine is the lovechild of Wella chemists who declared that introducing a side chain of methoxy-methyl into para-phenylenediamine kept its strong hair colouring performance, but weakened a person's risk of sensitisation and allergy induction.[76]

So how does it actually compare to para-phenylenediamine and para-toluenediamine? The risk of sensitisation does appear to be lower when 2-Methoxy-methyl-p-phenylenediamine is put into perspective with its peers. Para-phenylenediamine, for instance, is believed to bind to specific cysteine proteins in your skin,[77] whereas 2-Methoxy-methyl-p-phenylenediamine shows less reactivity towards cysteine, meaning that your immune system is less likely to be triggered by protein changes. It's thought that a much higher concentration of 2-Methoxy-methyl-p-phenylenediamine is needed to trigger an immune response compared to the para-phenylenediamine and para-toluenediamine - markedly higher than a person would be exposed to in regular hair dying conditions.[78]

Good news so far.

Significantly though, 2-Methoxy-methyl-p-phenylenediamine was not developed as an alternative dye for customers already allergic to para-phenylenediamine and para-toluenediamine. It was instead intended to be a replacement from the start. Unfortunately, there is no guarantee that you can swap seamlessly to 2-Methoxy-methyl-p-phenylenediamine if you have a pre-existing allergy. It's currently thought that the material has a cross-reactivity rate of 30% based on small recent studies[79] better than that of para-phenylenediamine and para-toluenediamine but not without danger. Some volunteers also had false negatives, meaning they did not react to a patch test but did react to the full-head coverage. The researchers theorised that the large surface area affected by the full-head application of the dye was enough to trigger the cells that stored a memory of para-phenylenediamine or para-toluenediamine in allergic individuals.[80] Shade was also strongly associated with chances of cross-reactivity in the one study that considered it. In fact, 46% of all positive cross-reactions were found in patients using dark dyes.[81]

So when it comes to that burning question, experts are fairly united on the answer.

"If you're allergic to hair dyes, the core advice is stop using them because perhaps half of the people that are allergic to hair dye will react to any other hair dye product," says Dr Basketter. "Some of them react very strongly, and so they remain at risk of having a bad allergic reaction. It may be that 2-Methoxy-methyl-p-phenylenediamine, this newest hair dye material, is somewhat less allergenic. Whether this actually translates to a big improvement we will only see over a number of years."

Old habits die hard

Hair colouring is extremely socially addictive. So strong is the compulsion that research indicates that many allergic individuals continue to dye their hair.[82] The potential dangers of allergy are also not well publicised to customers, who may believe their reaction is normal and be prepared to deal with some discomfort to use a product they like. Lucky, Darcie and Charlotte, for example, have adjusted their application techniques in order to continue to use dye and bleaching products.

Lucky now solely dyes her hair at home having had too many bad experiences at the salon. "Having been burned before by hairdressers (literally), I prefer to feel in control of what's happening to my hair. I admit I didn't always do a patch test when I started dying my hair at 18, but now I always wear gloves and in the past three years I've always done a patch test. I also wrap a towel around my neck to minimise skin contact but generally I only dye the ends of my hair so I can avoid my skin. I fear another allergic reaction."

Darcie has instead swapped home-dying for the salon. "Now, I only have my hair bleached at the hairdressers once a year and don't have reactions. I would prefer to use a natural lightener if it existed. I am reconsidering using toners though as hairdressers always seem to put them on all over hair, including the scalp. When I used a toning shampoo recently,

I noticed I would sometimes get throbbing behind the ears when it was combined with hot water, especially if a lot of product was used, so I've avoided that since."

Charlotte also still colours her hair though she admits, "I'm always a bit anxious about it. Luckily my sister-in-law is a hairdresser, and she is willing to highlight my hair for me in a way that makes sure very little of the product touches my scalp. I wouldn't dye my hair with anything darker again now. When I'm older and go grey I'll probably go back to henna."

Clearly giving up hair dye is not something many allergic users are prepared to do, despite discomfort and even danger of worsening reactions. So better education on the potential dangers of sensitisation is essential to help prevent its development, which is much easier than managing an allergy. Home patch testing, despite its flaws, seems essential to me before you put a large amount of product on the scalp. This will hopefully catch the most extreme allergies, although, following Dr Basketter's advice, it is advisable to do this at least 96 hours before you use a product, not 48 hours. Off-the-scalp dyeing techniques again are preferable to limit skin contact though, ideally, you should be prepared to stop using a product if you experience any irritation. Seeing a dermatologist will help you identify what exactly you are allergic to and what you could also cross-react to.

While salon procedures are clearly not perfect in this respect, they have improved in recent years thanks to stricter insurance policies, even if hairdressers themselves would benefit from better training and stricter procedures surrounding glove use to protect them from allergy. Still, if a colourist does not insist on a patch test when you have a new colour treatment or are returning after a period of time without one, I would not trust them with your hair.

More than hair dye: the incredible history and science of henna

10

Disclaimer: Mark has a bit of a bias when it comes to henna. It's not actually something he denies. When I gently bring it up over a call, he agrees zealously. "I am fiercely, proudly pro-henna!" he declares with all the feeling of Brian Blessed delivering a soliloquy from the West End. "I've been applying it practically all my life. Compare it to the other stuff we are using to dye our hair, it has such a strong bill of health. No-one will ever convince me otherwise!" Exit stage left.

I have to admit that while I too am a massive fan of henna, Mark and I have butted heads a little over the subject. Having investigated synthetic hair dyes in such detail, I feel compelled to do the same for henna. My verdict? It's not perfect but it's bloody good. I love the healthy feeling it gives my hair, not to mention the shine. There are few instances where it's not safe to use as I'll explain, but as a mum-to-be I feel comfortable using it during my pregnancy. It has a fascinating past but also a very intriguing future as scientists increasingly turn to natural materials to face medicine shortages in different populations.

Lost in migration: henna's forgotten origins

A bride-to-be is having henna applied to her hands in delicate, intricate patterns. She must stay absolutely still while the henna artist - perhaps hired, perhaps a treasured family friend - does her work. It's an intimate ceremony, attended by her closest female friends and family, and the henna being applied has multiple layers of meaning. To some, henna's red stain represents her loss of virginity, to others the duration of the tattoo symbolises the length of the marriage. For centuries, perhaps even millennia, this henna ceremony has been an opportunity to receive wisdom and care from her nearest and dearest, and evoke favour from good spirits before her big day.[1]

The bride herself could be Moroccan, Yemeni or Indian. She could be Jewish, Muslim or Hindu. As henna is grown widely across North Africa, the Middle East and Southwest Asia, this ancient ceremony now unites modern women all over the world. Because many cultures and religions can claim a piece of the henna pie, the plant's origin is fiercely debated. Sweeping statements attribute henna's birthplace to anywhere and everywhere in a growing region from Africa and the Middle East to India.

Many modern scholars now frequently narrow henna's origin down to North Africa, given the genetic variance of the plants found here.[2] In a linguistic study of henna's many names, Professor Luc Renaut suggests that the plant's origins might be a little more southerly, around the Bab-el-Mandeb strait in the southern Red Sea. This covers Ethiopia and Eritrea in Africa, and Yemen in the Persian Gulf, from which the use of henna could have spread across both regions.[3] Cultivation and knowledge of the plant may have spread from either North Africa or the regions surrounding the Red Sea via the sea route to India and China,.[4] rand also by ancient Mediterranean

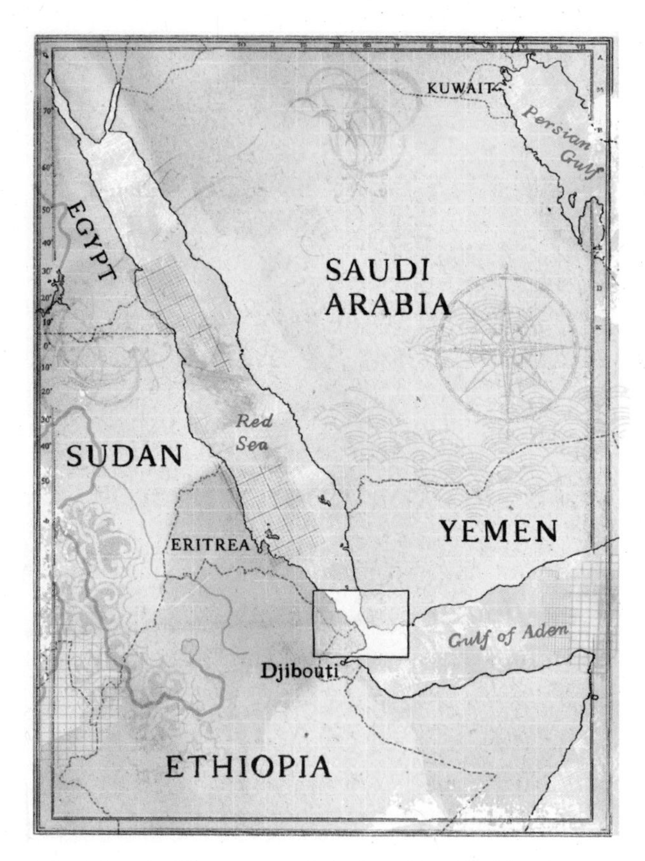

A linguistic study of henna suggests the lands on either side of the Bab-el-Mandeb strait in the southern Red Sea could be where the plant originated from.

trade paths.[5] Is henna mentioned in Ancient Egyptian scrolls dating back to the 16th century BC? When Greek poet Homer waxed lyrical about "rosey-fingered Aurora" and "red-footed Ceres" in his 8th century BC epic The Odyssey, was he making reference to henna staining?[6] How long humans have used henna for is a hotly debated topic.

Our earliest artefacts displaying henna use come in the form of Ancient Egyptian mummies, with hair and fingertips stained yellow and orange.[7] The oldest specimen found so far has dyed false hair that dates back to around 3,400 BC.[8] To try and settle a spirited debate about whether or not Ramses II was a redhead (which still rumbles on), Professor Pierre-Fernand Ceccaldi, the chief forensic scientist at the Criminal Identification Laboratory of Paris in the 1980s, conducted a forensic analysis of Ramses II's hair, part of which had been concealed by a yellow dye. He attributed this probably, but not definitively, to diluted henna or a derivative of the plant.[9]

Offerings of henna have also been found preserved at the ancient cemetery site of Hawara, Egypt,[10] while texts as old as the Ebers Papyrus (an Ancient Egyptian document of herbal knowledge, dated to at least the 16th century BC) also critique what has been translated to refer to seven types of henna from different regions.[11] To some scholars, this is irrefutable proof of early henna usage in the Ancient Egyptian period. To others however, it is a case of wishful thinking: the result of embalming resins that have stained the skin and mistranslations. Professor Renaut says, "The scientific analysis of the Egyptian mummies carried out never delivered the chemical markers to guarantee the presence of henna, and in Egyptian tombs, henna has only been found in the form of flowers, not dye deposits, and only from the Roman period (2nd-3rd centuries AD)." He similarly argues that a gross misreading of the word "cyperus" in the Ebers Papyrus has cultivated the myth of early henna usage in Ancient Egypt, when this word actually relates to a type of papyrus.

"Many people believe that henna has very high therapeutic, aesthetic and even magical-religious virtues," he continues. "In common thinking, the more virtuous a natural product is, the more ancestral it is supposed to be. For our contemporaries, it is appealing and comforting to imagine perpetuating very ancient uses, dating back to glorious civilisations such as the Ancient Egyptians, Persians or Indians. However, the uses of henna we know today only began to reach the Mediterranean regions at a relatively late stage, during the second half of the first millennium BC."

Egyptologist Professor Joann Fletcher has

a different opinion. She identified the use of henna on natural and false hair of an Ancient Egyptian woman whose remains were dated back to around 3,400 BC using a chemical spot test that "was indicative of henna." She concedes this test was "not as conclusive as we'd like, given that in the field we didn't have the luxury of a lab with sophisticated analysis techniques. But there was certainly a red-orange colourant visible on the hair, which was not simply due to the embalming process (since these particular early bodies had not been embalmed), nor was it the result of red ochre (as sometimes found in early burials), since ochre is a mineral which doesn't dissolve in water."[12] After conducting comparative analyses on grey hair and her own hair, and being shown the henna bushes that still grow and are harvested at the site, Professor Fletcher is just as resolute in her conclusion as Professor Renaut is in his.

Despite a strong tradition of henna usage in the Middle East today, references to henna in the pre-Ancient Persian period (the extensive empire founded in 6th century BC) are scarce. One source references several Mesopotamian[13] stone pots said to have stored henna but provides little detail, other than saying that ladies of the period preferred to use a gum resin.[14] Mesopotamian references to a plant known as 'Kamantu' have also been argued to refer to the henna plant, but are disputed on several grounds.[15] If 'Kamantu' did refer to henna, the surviving references mainly refer to the use of its seeds for medicinal purposes. This suggests that the plant was not used as a dye or a perfume like it was in surrounding regions.[16]

Is it possible that the Ancient Persians didn't use henna? It seems strange given the Persian expertise with the plant since then, but I've read numerous papers and scanned countless books for a possible mention with little success. I contact Professor of Ancient History and Persian Studies Lloyd Llewellyn-Jones at my old haunt Cardiff University to see if this ancient dye has in fact left any traces in Ancient Iran. He presents a quite different view to Professor Renaut, believing, for one, Professor Ceccaldi's conclusion that the dye on the hair of Ramses II was indeed henna.

"We know from scientific analysis of Egyptian mummies that henna was used in Ancient Egypt during this time, and given that Egypt was part of an international trade route, I can't see why it wouldn't be in the Middle East too," he says. "They were certainly using indigo in Ancient Persia. Henna is also so omnipresent in the Islamic period, and that can't come out of a vacuum; there has to be some kind of ancestry to it. Given that Persia was the master of the world at its peak in the 5th and 4th centuries BC, and had all these materials at its fingertips, why wouldn't they use it?"

"Part of the trouble is that we have no descriptions of Ancient Persian beauty or beauty products before the medieval period in Persia. We may be missing words for henna because we just don't know them in the lexicography. They may be sitting there behind something we can't transcribe. Until we find a text when it has a specific context, we can't really translate it into words."

While Professor Llewellyn-Jones remains convinced that the Persian word for henna is hidden in the complexities of the language we have yet to fully unravel and that its use pre-dates the Persian Empire, Professor Renaut takes a clinical view. He's traced various terms for henna including 'qwpr' or 'kwpr' in Egyptian, 'koper' or 'kopher' in Hebrew and 'kupros' in Greek back to the triliteral root 'kpr', and argues these emerged in the Near East at 500 BC earliest.

"Kpr is not indigenous to any of these languages. I believe that the term arrived in the Near East at the same time as the plant, around

500-400 BC. The etymology of the Arabic term henna has nothing to do with kpr and, to my knowledge, has not been studied. I believe the Arabic sources mentioning this term are much later than those using kpr and its derivatives."

Despite their differing opinions on when henna was first used by humans, both Professors Renaut and Llewellyn-Jones agree that it was an increasingly familiar commodity on Greek and Roman Mediterranean trade routes during the second half of the 1st millennium BC. Greek botanist and pal of Aristotle, Theophrastus (c. 371-c. 287 BC) mentions the use of henna blossoms in luxury perfumes, manufactured and sold in Ancient Egypt, the Mediterranean and Mesopotamia during this period,[17] and by the 1st century AD, imports of henna from Egypt to Greece are recorded in writing.[18] Greek physician Pedanius Dioscorides (c. 40–90 AD) also describes henna's use as a headache cure, auburn dye and perfumed ointment. He and Roman author Pliny the Elder (c. 24–79 AD) both reference henna plantations in Egypt and Israel.[19]

After the gradual decline and break up of the Western Roman Empire between the 4th and 5th centuries AD, a period of great migration began in Europe, followed by the Islamic expansion out of the Arabian Peninsula and into Western Asia in the 7th century. Given henna's importance in early Islam (see Chapter 3), it is likely the plant was carried to new regions along with the new religion.[20]

Whether or not henna was used by the Ancient Persians remains contentious, but I have an idea I want to pose. Could it be that henna was known in Ancient Persia - the centre of trade during the period we know the plant was circulating - but simply not that popular? Professor Llewellyn-Jones agrees it could be feasible. "Henna is such an obvious cosmetic and we know that the Persians went for major beauty treatments. They had beauticians and imported human hair to be turned into wigs, plaited into beards and used in locs. We also know that they perfumed their hair and beards as well. For Persian men, curled and oiled and set hair was a status symbol. It was a symbol of civilisation: they were taming the uncontrollable.

"But, since ancient times we see references to the hair of the Gods being 'blue-black' like lapis lazuli or 'raven's wings'. A lot of the texts talk about the sheen of the hair. That suggests to me there's a coloured dye going on there. Nudity in traditional Persian art is very rare indeed; it's about the clothed body, the makeup and hair. Hair is everywhere and there's a lot of talk about the tresses being dark. I couldn't find anything that said they were red."

If the Persians simply didn't like the red tones henna gave their hair, then perhaps it provides the reason as to why it wasn't widely used or recorded in what we have managed to translate so far. This would correspond with the pre-Islamic Persian verses that do mention its usage in the hair - and that of indigo.[21] When vibrant red beards became favourable under Islam, it was not drawing on an unknown material, simply a less popular one. This is supported by scrolls from the Tang Dynasty that record henna being imported to China from the Persian Parthian Empire (247 BC–224 AD).[22]

Despite a lack of clarity around henna usage in Persia, use of the plant combined with indigo on the hair to create rich skeins of blue-black has become synonymous with Middle Eastern culture and Persian tradition in particular. Either henna was being used earlier than the current evidence suggests, or something piqued Persian interest.

Perhaps the marriage of Persian beauty culture and Ancient Jewish dye expertise led to the rise of henna in Persia. This ancient Empire

The Ancient Persians were into their hair treatments in a big way, but do not appear to have used henna.

conquered and absorbed numerous territories, including Phoenicia: an ancient Jewish civilisation from the eastern Mediterranean. Tellingly, the Phoenicians were skilled fabric dyers, famed for their use of a very expensive purple dye derived from sea snails[23] (expensive because 10,000 unfortunate molluscs had to be killed to extract one gram of the stuff.) At the time, indigo was considered a less luxurious substitute, but the two dyes are very chemically similar, and indigo and madder (*Rubia tinctorum*) were also illegally combined to create a counterfeit purple.[24]

If the Persian Achaemenid Empire absorbed these dyeing skills along with the Phoenician territories between 539–332 BC, could they have been the ones to discover henna's extraordinary ability to give indigo more staying power on their tresses? It certainly would have been a way to achieve that inky blue-brown shade so revered in their art and literature.

It's also worth revisiting the suggestion that the grandfather of the Prophet Mohammed was advised to use a mixture of henna and an unconfirmed dark plant-based dye on his beard by a king of Yemen.[25] Yemen was a province of the Sasanian Persian Empire between 570–628 AD, with its own long history of textiles industry and dyeing with (imported) indigo. Perhaps the Persians were inspired here too. Whatever the technique's exact origin, it was certainly adopted and honed to perfection by these great lovers of beauty and haircare.

From staining to tattooing: Birth of a custom

Nowadays, the types of henna applications you'll most often find being offered on a sprawling urban street are delicate tattoos. But, while body marking in general has a long and colourful history,[26] creating artistic designs with henna appears to have probably only gained popularity within the last 500 years or so, compared to its longer history as a medicine. Yet modern cosmetic uses of henna have the potential to obfuscate what we know of the plant's origins so they are useful to address first.

Henna-based body art (which is commonly known as 'mehndi' from the Hindi language) has become synonymous with Indian culture in recent decades after a historian claimed it was once known by the same name as 'lac' - a red pigment derived from insects and traditionally used in Indian body decoration.[27] This claim has been fiercely disputed by scholars such as Dr Catherine Cartwright-Jones as "at worst, [...] a cynical political attempt to erase Persian and Arabic influence on Indian culture" after the violent partition of British colonial India into India and new country Pakistan in 1947.[28] Professor Renaut argues, "Just because some ancient sources mention the use of yellow, red or brown body dyes (without specifying the substance used), it does not mean that it is henna. Many colouring substances (especially earth-based) were used in the ancient world before henna became as popular as it is today." He also believes that misinterpretations of a 6th century AD text by Greek physician Aetios of Amida has led to confusion.

"This medical compilation attributes to the 'Indian Barbarians' (insulting today but, in antiquity, all peoples who were neither Greek nor Roman were called barbarians) the storage of henna in powder form and the use of this powder to make a paste applied as a poultice. The 'Indian Barbarians' probably refer to the populations settled on the southern coast of the Red Sea, on either side of the Bab-el-Mandeb strait and not to the inhabitants of India as 'kpr' has no parallel in Sanskrit. These 'barbarians' mastered the use of henna as a colouring paste (for even if the author

The Phoenicians were famed for the expensive purple dye they produced from sea snails.

does not say so, the cataplasms described must certainly have coloured the skin on which they were applied)."[29]

Yet, the enthusiasm for mehndi in India has led to a fresh wave of mythology surrounding henna's origins, as well as what we might call hopeful or simplistic interpretations of Ancient Vedic Hindu texts that have been argued to make reference to the plant. As mentioned, India has a long history of body marking, but whether this traditionally involved henna is hotly debated given the availability of materials such as turmeric and lac.[30]

Although exactly when henna came to India remains obscure, it was probably popularised under the rule of the Islamic Mughal empire (1550 – 1850) according to the work of artists and accounts of travellers to India during this period. By the 18th century, we begin to see paintings that show court-goers with red patterns rather than just stains across their palms,[31] (although whether this references the use of henna or a similar material is unclear).

We have more definite proof of henna's early use in tattoos in North Africa and the Middle East. One of the earliest known accounts comes from traveller Sir John Chardin (1643 – 1713) who observed "[The Persians] paint on the King's horses for distinction sake, a broad tagged lace, with flourishes like those of coronets."[32] A French naturalist writing a century or so later also recorded that Egyptian women had tweaked the hand and nail staining of their ancestors by tying threads around their fingers before applying the paste. "[Whatever their religion,]" he writes, "the women could no more dispense with this daubing than their clothes."[33]

Englishwoman turned Shareefa of Wazan, Emily Keene Keene (1849-1944), who married into Moroccan nobility (a prolific interacial marriage that faced strong opposition from both families), refers to the same techniques. "For the feet, sandals are simulated by first arranging calico straps on the foot and round the base of the big toe. The henna paste is applied with care so as not to mar the symmetry of the straps. [The] coverings are not removed for some hours, when the paste generally comes off with the coverings [...] and a red-brown sandalled foot is presented."[34]

From the 15th century, works document that henna was part of the 'Haft Qalam Ārāyish' - seven 'must-have' cosmetics for Persian women - in which henna was prescribed to 'blacken' the fingers, probably in combination with indigo, lime or salt ammonia.[35] Professor Llewellyn-Jones tells me that by the 16th century, nomadic women were creating patterns with henna while urban women were using block colour - an interesting contrast given the popularity of intricate tattoos in urban centres now. Persian ladies of the Safavid period (1501-1736) were reported to "artfully color with henna their beautiful bodies with odd designs, most often representing trees, birds and other animals, the sun, the moon, or stars."[36]

We see here two different regional techniques forming: the use of lace or string to create patterns in North Africa and more elaborate painted designs in Persia. These regional differences live on today, with henna artists in North Africa personalising geometric shapes and angles, but those in the Middle East and India drawing on more organic, flowing lines. Some of these designs draw on ancient iconography. In the bazaars of Morocco, for example, henna is sold alongside archaic spell books, while the patterns themselves reference iconography from pre-Islamic fertility cults as well as the sciences of Islamic treatises on 'siḥr' (magic).[37] (Layers of meaning, both modern and ancient, are meticulously combined in the lines being inked into the skin.

As these patterns indicate, henna usage

vastly predates monotheistic worship (religions defined by belief in a singular God), although it has become associated with religion over the last millennia or so. Hinduism, an ancient form of worship, which incorporates many indigenous faiths and multiple deities, has a long tradition of body markings, with tattoos used to show social status and to invoke protection from multiple gods and goddesses.[38] Henna tattoos have therefore slotted naturally into the Hindu way of life.

Yet, despite being strongly associated with ceremonies involving henna, both Judaism and Islam both actually forbid tattoos. Henna tattooing is apparently tolerated because it is a painless, bloodless and temporary practice,[39] but celebrated? That seems to be an accommodation of both religions for a practice that was integral to the communities that converted to the faith.

This compromise has not been without tension. The resistance of Catholic Arab women in Israel to abandoning traditional customs like henna tattooing is described in an account from 1865: "The Greek Catholic Church vainly produces anathemas and threatens with excommunication those women who tattoo themselves and use kohl, and henna and rouge," writes English traveller and wedding guest Mary Eliza Rogers (1827–1910). "They will persist in doing so while they believe it adds to their beauty, and to their powers of attraction [...]. Their respect for custom is stronger even than their fear of the Church.

"If the priests persisted in carrying out their threats of excommunication for such offenses, their congregations would soon be scattered; so they are lenient, and thus Greek and Roman forms of Christianity are blended insensibly with ceremonies and practices so ancient that their origin even is unknown."[40]

Protection, medicine, talisman? The origins of a custom

What can alleviate fever, ringworm, chapped skin, headaches and hair loss? Henna apparently.[41] Numerous uses of henna as a medicine are recorded by travelling scholars across North Africa and the Middle East over the centuries. It has even been used in an indigenous medicine for vitiligo in the northern districts of Kerala State, India.[42]

The plant's appeal as a medicine is rooted in its use as a form of ancient spiritual protection. With illness often blamed on demonic forces such as the Evil Eye, (a widespread belief that the envious gaze of relatives, neighbours or malevolent spirits could cause harm),[43] henna was revered as a potent source of divine blessing in North Africa and the Middle East. Its use was believed to avert the attention of supernatural spirits that may cause harm and instead bring the approval and blessing of friendlier ones.[44]

Thanks to its red pigment, henna was also used in life-changing or life-threatening rites of passage associated with the spilling of blood, notably childbirth. Newborn babies amongst the Imazighen (descendants of pre-Islamic people in North Africa) have long been anointed with henna to deter evil spirits, to strengthen and cool the skin, and to protect them from lice or other pests.

Exact practices vary. When an infant of the Moroccan Ait Sadden people is born, the baby is rubbed with butter and oil and sprinkled with henna powder during hot weather to prevent perspiration and consequent chills,[45] while Ait Waryagher infants are smeared across the crown with henna as a protection against fleas, lice and the Evil Eye when they are forty days old.[46] In the city region of Fez, a newborn is rubbed with henna, sugar, alum, marjoram, mint, mastic, water and oil. A pregnant Ait Warain woman is adorned with henna, antimony and walnut root before giving birth to ensure that she is received as a 'bride of paradise' in case she dies during delivery, which must be reassuring.[47]

Henna has also been incorporated into religious customs associated with blood loss. During the Islamic festival of *Eid al-Adha*, a lamb will traditionally be decorated with henna then sacrificed to Allah on behalf of a household, with feast guests also painting themselves with the dye.[48] In strict Jewish and Islamic circles, a henna party that mimics a bridal ceremony takes place before the night of a boy's circumcision to symbolise his transition into adulthood.[49] Among the Hausa people of Nigeria, tradition similarly dictates that the night before a boy's circumcision, he is washed by his father, anointed with henna on his hands and feet and paraded through the streets.[50]

Henna's most famous ceremonial use nowadays is also associated with blood-loss: the bride's (assumed) loss of virginity on her wedding night.

Bloody weddings: marriage and henna

It's the Sunday before the wedding of a young Jewish couple, and the climax of an ancient service known as The Henna. An elaborate dressing ceremony, procession and party have already preceded this special moment: the henna painting of the bride and groom. One after one, family and friends bless the soon-to-be newlyweds and apply a blend of henna, rose water, eggs, cognac, salt and herbs to their palms, prepared by women in the bride's household. It's the most sacred component of The Henna and can take up to five hours.[51]

Known by many different names today, this pre-wedding henna ceremony is a richly symbolic celebration that has been incorporated into many cultures. Today it's often associated with joy and celebration, but its origins are rooted in protection, and practices varied in different regions. A Moroccan bride of the Ait Yusi community, for example, was painted with henna then washed the following morning on a pack saddle, which was supposed to give her power over her husband. Among the Ulad Bu'aziz people, the bride instead was painted with henna while she mounted the ram that was to be slaughtered for the occasion. She then boxed its ears, in order to make herself the mistress of her husband.[52] You may sense a theme.

The henna used by the bride is still believed to hold supernatural significance in some cultures. Algerian mothers may perform a 'henna curse' if their daughters are married at a very early age, by placing a little of the bridal henna into a dish and placing it upside down in the wardrobe. Every night it remains there means a year of sterility for the young wife, saving her from a potentially dangerous childbirth. One woman recounts that her mother accidentally left her henna in the wardrobe for ten days, and she took a decade to conceive a child with her husband.[53]

While historical marital ceremonies often focused on the bride, reaffirming female bonds before marriage and the childbirth that would hopefully follow, henna did also play a pivotal role in male ceremony in many Imazighen societies. Amongst the Algerian Kabyle people, for example, guests would engage in a poetic joust and compete to buy and sell henna for the groom. The husband-to-be would then smash a dish of henna at the end of the night with his heel to symbolise his virility.[54] - a neater antic perhaps than stag night rituals of today. Many of these male ceremonies were more public than those for the bride-to-be, symbolising a young man's entry into society and his dominance and virility before the wedding night.[55]

Traditional Arab Jewish henna ceremonies were impressively lengthy and elaborate affairs that took place over a series of days and served a practical as well as spiritual purpose. In early 20th century Islamic Yemen, marriage was a pragmatic way of uniting an increasingly isolated minority Jewish population. The Henna was meant to symbolise wealth and fertility, but also to give supernatural protection for the young bride entering adulthood who may have been the subject of jealousy.[56]

After the relocation of much of the Jewish community from Yemen to the newly established State of Israel between 1949 and 1950, it took several decades for The Henna to be re-established among a community that had been trying to assimilate into a new Israeli life. Professional henna organisers are now hired to guide bride, groom and guests through the condensed and modified ritual that celebrates Yemenite Jewish identity.[57] This is the case for the number of Jewish communities who relocated from North Africa and the Middle East during a period of religious persecution in the 20th century.

Not all of the henna customs practised nowadays are historically accurate. Traditions have been modernised and some of the more uncomfortable practices designed to accustom a bride to the responsibilities of wifehood have been edited out. "Whereas once the application of henna and even its removal were surrounded by necessary rituals designed to respect the material of henna and appease its associated spirits, today the henna is washed off within the hour if it is applied at all," recounts one scholar at a Yemenite Jewish henna ceremony. "I myself observed a ceremony where the bride put on plastic gloves, received the henna in her palm, and promptly peeled the glove into the garbage."[58] While some of the intricacies and discomforts of pre-wedding henna ceremonies have been forgotten or edited, henna's inherent importance to these communities hasn't been. Its modernisation appears to ensure its survival in future generations.

Lawsone and other naphthoquinones: how does henna work?

Henna is one of few natural materials able to leave a long-lasting stain on the skin and hair without a mordant, thanks to a powerful pigment hiding inside its leaves. Named 'lawsone' by Italian chemist G. Tommasi in 1916,[59] this tiny but mighty dye is a naphthoquinone: a type of natural pigment that forms a chemical defence in plants. Naphthoquinones are believed to be responsible for changing the colour of fertilised fruits and protecting plants against ultraviolet light, dryness and insects.[60]

Lawsone (2-hydroxy-1,4-naphthoquinone) typically comprises between 1 and 2% of the dried leaves of the henna plant,[61] and acts as a dye when natural precursors in the henna leaf respond to mildly acidic conditions. When dried henna leaves are combined with lemon juice and water and applied to the skin, for example, the lawsone binds to the protein in the skin cells and oxidises, creating an orange or red stain. This pigment works primarily in the outer layers of the skin known as the epidermis, and the stain or tattoo fades as these skin cells are naturally shed over a series of weeks.[62] On the hair, henna binds to the protein-rich cuticle like a varnish instead of penetrating the fibre which chemically alters the colour of the melanin. The increased thickness of the cuticle also adds body and shine to the hair.

While henna is approved for use as a commercial hair dye in the EU and the US,[63]

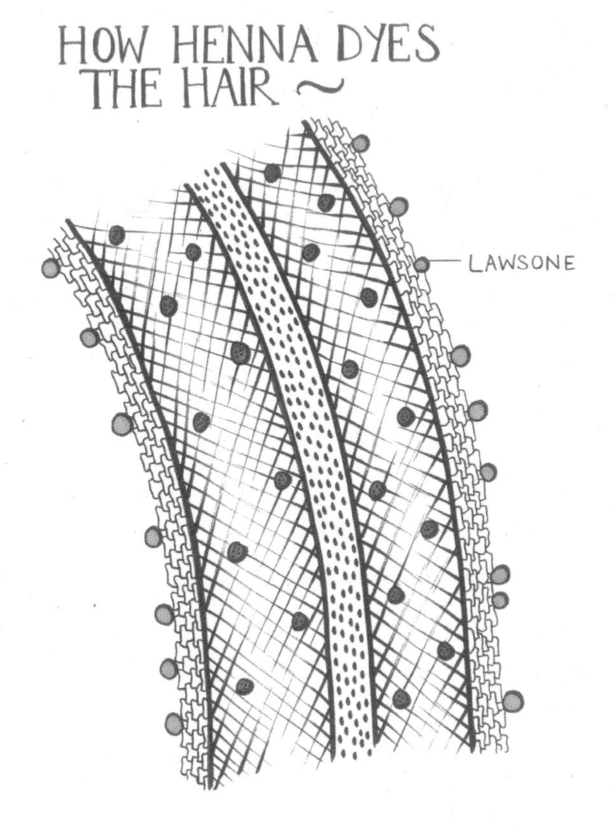

Lawsone within the henna leaves chemically reacts to keratin in the hair fibre, binding to the cuticle.

lawsone isolated from the henna plant has also been of modern interest as a potential dyestuff. This idea has been rejected for now because of lawsone's properties in tests conducted in a lab environment.[64]

Naphthoquinones like lawsone are part of a chemical defence system employed by plants to survive heat and drought, and repel parasites and grazers. They strike a balance between being both brightly coloured to attract pollinators, but wield antibacterial, antifungal and antiparasitic qualities to deter harmful organisms or hungry herbivores.[65] This is believed to be related to their ability to act as both antioxidants (molecules that inhibit oxidation) or oxidants (molecules that trigger oxidation) depending on the conditions of their exposure.[66]

It's a risky game as raising levels of oxidative stress triggers the plant's defence system to fight off attack but can also harm its own cells.[67]

Inside the human body, a recurring cycle of danger and response is also at play.[68] We are continuously exposed to substances that cause us oxidative stress, in the form of the foods we eat or external pollutants. These stressors generate 'free radicals': unstable oxygen molecules that have split into atoms with unpaired electrons and generally maraud around our body causing trouble.[69] Free radicals are important because they help to trigger and maintain our internal defences, but too many can damage our DNA and trigger a number of human diseases. They are also theorised to cause the visible signs of ageing.[70]

To counter oxidative damage from rampaging free radicals, we make and consume antioxidants: molecules that are stable enough to donate an electron to a rampaging free radical and neutralise it. This reduces or minimises the impact of oxidative stress within our body.[71] While we produce some antioxidants internally, we also consume many through our diet by eating foods like berries, tomatoes, broccoli, spinach and nuts, and drinking green tea.[72]

Plants also respond to higher levels of reactive oxygen species with antioxidants, while diverting energy from growth, metabolism and photosynthesis to maximise their survival when under environmental attack.[73] When it comes to peckish herbivores, a snack-sized portion of a plant can be a good thing, encouraging the grazer's immune system to respond to hazardous stimuli with its own defences, but also dissuading the animal from having too much.[74]

When isolated from the henna plant and investigated, lawsone has brought up some interesting results in vitro, primarily mutagenic.[75] However, this is now recognised to be due to its oxidative rather than mutagenic qualities, according to a 2018 review of 12 studies, and researchers believed that positive mutagenicity experiments were a result of the poor antioxidant

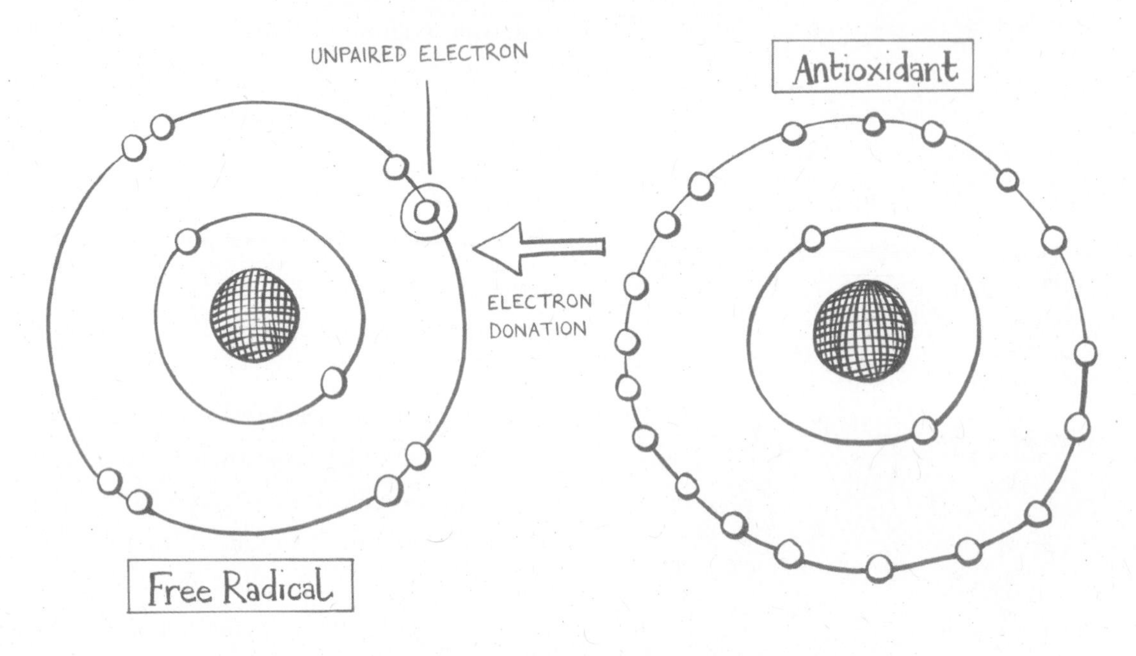

An antioxidant neatly neutralises a rampaging free radical, delaying or preventing oxidative stress to your cells.

defence systems of *in vitro* cells compared to live ones.[76] A number of studies have also found lawsone to have antioxidant qualities, recognised by the communities who have used the plant in medicines for thousands of years.[77]

The amount of lawsone that penetrates the skin in a henna tattoo situation has not been clearly defined, let alone the lesser amount in a hair dyeing scenario. Research in 2007 suggested a majority of the lawsone that entered the skin remained in the outer layer of the stratum corneum after 74 hours when henna paste was applied to *in vitro* skin cells for an hour then rinsed. Between 0.3 and 1.3% lawsone was found to penetrate through the skin and become potentially systemically available.[78] However, as lawsone is known to be one of the weaker naphthoquinones, compared to say, the juglone in walnuts,[79] it is not believed to produce reactive oxygen species at a rate that exceeds the capacity of the body's cells to remove them except in rare circumstances.[80] It is only in those with lowered resilience to oxidative stress that henna is potentially dangerous.[81]

In 2021, Lush commissioned its own further work on henna to test genotoxicity (DNA damage) with animal-free testing lab XCellR8. It involved a pioneering new animal-free experiment - an upgrade on the current BlueScreen method which involves adding test materials to incubated human white blood cells and seeing the reaction. Lush toxicologist Chloé Raffalli explains, "With XCellR8, we have developed a new *in vitro* 3D genotoxic test that combines a very realistic skin model (a reconstructed epidermis) with the BlueScreen method. The advantage of this technique, in comparison with the standard genotoxic assays in 2D, is that it takes into account the protection of the skin barrier as well as the metabolism of the skin enzymes."

Henna (diluted with a little hot water to mimic application methods) was applied to the skin barrier and measured after two hours and 48 hours to see how much had penetrated the epidermis and reached the white blood cells beneath. At both time intervals, henna was found to be non-genotoxic and cell health was not compromised.[82]

A gentle alternative? Henna, allergy and oxidative stress

Most of the time, the only irritating thing about henna will be the act of applying it (ask regular users - it can get messy.) Henna itself has very low allergic potential, when it is not adulterated,[83] and confirmed cases of henna allergy are very rare (although in powder form it can irritate the airways).

Many cases of henna allergy have instead been found to relate to ingredients added to the product - most notably para-phenylenediamine as discussed in Chapter 9, but also high levels of essential oils. Interestingly, we also know that lawsone is not necessarily the problematic component in these cases and the allergenic component of henna remains unknown.[84] However rare, if you experience a reaction whilst using henna, you should immediately stop using it.

Sufferers of a condition known as glucose 6-phosphate dehydrogenase deficiency (G6PD) should also not use henna. G6PD deficiency is a genetic disorder in which the red blood cells don't work effectively, affecting an estimated 400 million people worldwide, and most common in Africa, Asia, the Mediterranean, and the Middle East.[85] Lawsone can be a strong oxidiser of G6PD-deficient red blood cells and induce hemolytic anaemia when applied to the skin.[86] Babies with undiagnosed G6PD deficiency are particularly vulnerable to oxidative stress due to their small size and incomplete skin barrier. Similarly, babies who are daubed in henna adulterated with para-phenylenediamine have become seriously unwell. In fact, the delicate skin of newborn babies means any type of topical cosmetic application is subject to debate.[87]

The study of henna and its chemical compounds reminds us that all materials, natural or synthetic, can be beneficial or harmful to humans, thanks to the complex systems that maintain our health. Dose, lifestyle and genes all play a part in how we interact with stimuli such as food, medicines or hair dyes, and how our bodies are able to deal with oxidative stress.

Some of the experts I have spoken to emphasise this. Professor Bruce Ames tells me, "Every plant gets eaten by insects, so plant evolution is chemical warfare. Every plant has 50 or so toxic chemicals in place to kill the insects and predators. I got very interested in what I call nature's pesticides." Yet, the potential toxicity of natural foods are balanced out by the essential vitamins and nutrition they give to our bodies. A punnet of fresh strawberries brings infinitely more benefits to your body, brain and DNA than a packet of synthetic strawberry sweets. What you put into your body can have a big impact on how you deal with daily exposures. "I spent many years showing that diet is really important," says Professor Ames. "If you don't intake vitamins, you can damage your DNA."

Freshness and natural materials like henna have been at the heart of Lush product invention for so long precisely for their benefits on the skin and hair. Lush Co-Founder and Product Inventor Helen Ambrosen explains, "What we've always done is to make wonderful fresh products with large amounts of natural ingredients. We use minimal preservatives or entirely self-preserving formulations to protect the natural microbiome of the skin, which has a central role in skin health."

Your microbiome is the community of unique and friendly bacteria, microorganisms and their genetic material that live on your skin.[88] Diverse microbiomes are the healthiest, offering better protection against invasive microorganisms that can cause disease.[89] Modern lifestyles, however, have drastically impacted the health of our skin. Populations living in urban western societies show a less diverse and less healthy microbiome than indigenous communities, due to their everyday exposure to synthetics like cosmetics, cleaning products, washing powders and more. Our behaviours and environment are fundamentally damaging the delicate ecosystem of our skin, leading to 'western conditions' such as acne.[90] When it comes to cosmetics, research has also found that products with a high level of synthetics deplete the natural diversity of your microbiome, unlike natural ingredients.[91]

That's why natural ingredients like henna remain at the heart of Lush's ethos.

Ancient remedy, modern medicine

After millennia of multi-purpose use, henna's star shows no sign of fading. The humble plant has been incorporated into modern religions, cultural celebrations and modern beauty regimes around the world, and remains precious to numerous communities spread across rural and urban regions.

Science is also now confirming some long-believed medicinal qualities from henna's use in folk medicine. Powdered henna extracted in water has been shown to be an effective treatment for the Malassezia species (one cause of dandruff), thanks to its antifungal activity,[92] and henna in water and shea butter also cleared 100% of head-lice from sufferers in an Egyptian study.[93] The plant's antibacterial properties on the skin have also been demonstrated, with henna extracted in water and oil found to give a similar antimicrobial performance to some antibiotics.[94] In India, surgeons are known to use henna as a durable skin marker for operations,[95] and, in a cream form, it's been demonstrated to be an effective alternative to hydrocortisone for treating nappy rash.[96] Henna and lawsone are both being tentatively investigated for their antioxidant and anti-inflammatory potential against cancer cells, given the expense of and limited supply of cancer medicines and treatment.[97]

However, despite its many benefits both ancient and modern times, for Mark there has long been one henna application that supersedes all others. That's hair colouring.

A herbal heritage: Lush and henna

11

It's 2001 and Lush Co-Founder and Product Inventor Helen Ambrosen is late leaving her lab at 29 High Street, Poole. As the light outside slowly dims, she's mixing a blend of Iranian henna leaves, herbs, and cocoa butter together for the very first time.

On the shelf above her, a historic form of currency known as a tea brick owned by Mark has held pride of place for a few years. This evening, an absent-minded glance in the brick's direction has resulted in what could potentially be a stroke of genius - if she gets it right. Pressing the creamy henna mixture into an impromptu brick mould, Helen leaves it to set, and heads home.

Nearly 20 years later, Mark still raves about Helen's invention that evening. "Adding cocoa butter to the henna so that it melts when you add water and turns into this lovely creamy base was just sublime. It's unpackaged and unpreserved; the cocoa butter makes it easier to comb and get the henna out. The simplicity, the clarity, the nod to history: all are just exquisite in my opinion."

Letting your hair down: Henna parties and herbal haircare

Nearly five decades ago, it was the lack of synthetic chemicals that fuelled Mark's initial interest in henna. Then, when he met beauty therapist Elizabeth Weir, their shared passion for natural cosmetics flourished into a business: Constantine & Weir. In 1977, The Herbal Hair and Beauty Clinic launched at 29 High Street in Poole, offering a range of beauty services to fellow seekers of natural cosmetics. The eventful background to this chapter of Mark's life and those that followed is recorded in detail only a childhood friend could deliver in Jeff Osment's biography *Dear John: The Road to Pelindaba*.

It was in 29 High Street that the gloves were donned and the henna truly doled out. "We used to host henna parties," Mark recalls, "where we'd put loads of music on, get the clients gowned up, and then we'd dye their hair, steam it, and wash it. I used to charge just about enough to make a living, and it was great fun."

Although sometimes raucous in nature, the parties gave Mark the opportunity to further hone his expertise in herbal hair colour. "I learned there is a real art to dying the hair with henna," he explains, "particularly back then when I was using blends of dry leaves. It's like making a cup of tea; you can make it one way or another. I used the traditional technique of applying henna, and learned to really lay it on the hair, adding loads and loads, so it was nice and heavy. I also tried lots of different blends using coffee and red wine – I used to use a lot of red wine in henna. One glass for me, one glass for it! The smell of spices, clove, and nutmeg as it heated up was beautiful."

The time and attention Mark put into the henna craft was only occasionally sidelined by practical jokes. He recalls, "One of my favourites was to pretend I was a volunteer fireman. I had a bell I used to ring – I still have it somewhere – and I'd apply the henna then go into another room and ring it. Then I'd appear and say to the client, 'Oh, I'm terribly sorry, but I'm a volunteer fireman and the bell's just gone. I'm going to have to leave you here and I'll be back in a couple of hours.' They took it all in very good humour on the most part."

As well as enjoying a hands-on henna service, clients of the time could purchase colour toning products: Saffron shampoo to "brighten and condition blonde hair" and Henna Shampoo "containing 60% henna infusion to give the hair shine and body". "Natural dyes are fun to use", promises a Constantine & Weir services list from the time, "and the effect on the hair can be so pretty and natural (or dramatic and stunning), that you will wonder why you haven't tried them before."

It was Mark's experiments in henna products that gained the attention of Anita Roddick, the businesswoman responsible for the rise of cult 1980s cosmetics brand, The Body Shop. Mark sent her some samples, including, in his words "a henna shampoo that looked a bit like you'd done a poo". Undeterred, she placed an order for £1,572.75 - a princely sum at the time.

Constantine & Weir consequently became both operators of a beauty salon and an R&D hub for The Body Shop, while Mark's first marital home with Lush Co-Founder-to-be Mo in Poole soon became a stockroom for The Body Shop products in development. Mark recalls, "The van used to come secretly in the night to take our wares over to Littlehampton. As each order built up, so the house filled with five litre bottles of Elderberry Conditioner or Henna Shampoo. It was stashed everywhere and once it was gone we would feel a great sense of achievement! Then the next order would come through and it would start all over again."

Mo, who, in slightly Willy Wonka-esque fashion, had a relative with a chocolate factory, quickly took to the practicalities of manufacturing on a larger scale. She remembers, "We've always been conscious of the materials we use and dabbled extensively with natural materials, which, back in the day, was akin to witchcraft! But we realised early on that there are many great ingredients to be incorporated for use in cosmetics. That has been our speciality.

"We took many messages from those large-scale days: make a mistake and you make a big one. Big batches encourage big buying and big storage, and everything bulks up - your filling line is required to do tens of thousands of a single product. Now, we make volume but it suits us to do little and often. This is not the most commercial route, but it works for us and it gives us the edge on competitors."

Back at 29 High Street in the 1980s though, the real competition was in who could bag henna blends most quickly and efficiently. Hauling bags of the stuff up and down the many narrow flights of stairs was also no joke. "We had these massive sacks arriving with 50 kilos of henna inside," recalls Mark. "We'd drop them off at people's houses so they could bag them up. Liz was great. She used to carry massive bags of the stuff down those narrow stairs at 29 High Street. How she did it, I've no idea."

Alan Hopkins, a herbalist who rather innocently rented a room in the building, was soon also roped into the henna business when he proved a valuable bagger. "Alan was like an automaton," remembers Mark, "he just used to just go into a trance as he worked. We got a measuring machine to help out, and discovered he was more accurate than the bloody machine. The really good Persian henna came in little one kilo bags though, and they were really sexy. You really felt as though you were getting something special."

They were, as it turned out, a castor bean

allergy. "The sacks had been used for transporting castor bean husks and then turned inside out," says Mark, "so we were inhaling leftover ricin from the husks of the beans. I didn't develop a severe allergy but some people couldn't get close to it. It was only when we sent the sacks over to Porton Down that we actually realised what the problem was. Thankfully we got that sorted quickly once we knew."

With the henna blends safely shipped via lorry to The Body Shop, Mark would then visit their shops and teach the staff how to henna hair, further imparting his accumulated wisdom. When The Body Shop bought the rights to all products invented by Constantine & Weir in 1992, the agreement also included a contract not allowing the Constantines to open a physical shop for a number of years.

Naturally, they opened a mail-order business instead.

Causing a stir: hair colour and Cosmetics To Go

Cosmetics To Go sold some of their more avant-garde inventions initially rejected by The Body Shop like Mo's shampoo bar and bath bomb inventions. While henna was not initially on the table, as Mark and co still sold it to The Body Shop, customers were introduced to hair products like Waxed And Clam-Baked shampoo bar (made with henna and juniper berries for processed hair) and Dimestore Blonde hair lightening kit "for a 'summery' look".

"Show us an actual photo of someone who's used Dimestore Blonde and I might be tempted to buy it," wrote Michelle from Surrey in one of the cult Cosmetics To Go catalogues. Proud Dimestore Blondes Helen Ambrosen and fellow Lush Co-Founder Rowena Bird promptly featured in the next issue, showing off their shiny, highlighted locks.

The Really Cookin' range of 1993 introduced henna treatments to a new batch of customers, including Cajun Swamp Water, made with red henna for "natural or 'varnished' red locks"; Zydeco, made with henna, coffee and cloves for a "mahogany red-brown sheen"; and Jalapeno, cooked up with red henna, rhassoul mud and lemon juice for "fiery red" locks. These fresh treatments needed to be refrigerated and used within two weeks. Also on offer was Le Soleil highlighting kit: a power and cream kit to lighten the hair on its own, or possibly before use with the red henna treatments.

Sadly, before customers could say "ready, steady, cook", by January the following year Cosmetics To Go was no more, a victim of its own success as detailed in Mira Manga's book, *Danger! Cosmetics To Go: A Company On The Edge!* The

Rowena Bird and Helen Ambrosen show off their highlights alongside Mark.

doors were closed on the veritable Wonka's factory of beauty confectionery - but not for long.

Lush and fresh handmade hair colour

By 1995, the team behind Cosmetics To Go had rallied and were cooking up cosmetics in 29 High Street once more. Restrictions on running a retail shop now lifted, Mark, Mo, Liz, Helen, Rowena and Paul Greeves spent the little money Ro had left on fruits and vegetables from a market stall and returned to their fresh, handmade roots. In 1995, 29 High Street opened its doors once more and was later christened 'Lush': a small-scale business that was to succeed where Cosmetics To Go had faltered.

Henna featured as an ingredient in the very first Lush Times brochure in 1995, in products such as Plantational shampoo: "A smooth blend of powdered seaweed, henna, nettles and rosemary [to] give shine and freshen colour on all red and brown hair." Yet, by 1998, pre-made henna treatments were being sold on the shop floor like bowls of ice cream at a delicatessen.

Mark and Helen had also been hard at work with their formulations, using their wealth of herbal knowledge to create henna-based concoctions that all customers could benefit from - whether that was to colour the hair or simply add body and shine.

Perusers at 29 High Street, and the newly opened Kingston, London shop could choose from Solanna, made with chamomile, rhubarb and red henna, for "dazzling strawberry blonde"; Erborigian Flax, an "intense treatment for blonde hair", made with chamomile and fresh lemon juice; Capella File d'Oro, made with red henna, cloves and coffee "for rich red brown tones"; Al Khanna, a fresh lemon and henna blend, to create "fiery red" base; and Sea Henna, "an intense treatment conditioner for all hair types" made with henna and balsamic vinegar. "Order these fast -" warned the 1998 Lush Times catalogue, "- they smell so delicious our Kingston shop sold out the very first morning they were in stock!"

Bricking it

But the real henna revolution came in 2001, with Helen's cocoa butter breakthrough. It was a moment of genius inspired by the tea brick: a means of currency in China, Siberia, Tibet, Mongolia, Turkmenistan and Russia from the 9th century to the 20th century when tea became a valuable commodity.[1] Merchants compressed loose tea into densely packed bricks, which were much more easy to transport along trade routes and had the added benefit of fermenting further in the heat to give a stronger flavour. [2] Helen used a similar technique to solve the problem of how to sell henna in the Lush shops.

She recalls, "When we first started Lush we used to have hot bain maries with the hot hennas in which was lovely. It made the shop smell beautiful but they didn't sell very well really. I tried to make the henna more visual so I added cocoa butter, swapped the citric acid for lemon juice and pressed it into a mould. Even back then we were on a real mission to make everything that we could solid. I wanted to make it more visual; we'd had so many years of green powders!"

Mark remembers the years of pre-mixed henna formulas less fondly: "That was a rubbish idea, wasn't it?" He was instantly sold on Helen's tea brick-inspired invention, which was more user-friendly and another nod to the historical genius of past civilisations. Together, they decided on four final henna brick recipes, three of which included varying blends of the indigo and henna combination so loved by the Persians to colour the hair darker shades of brown.

Hauling sacks of henna up and down the narrow, winding staircases of 29 High Street was no mean feat.

Future Lush Ethics Director Hilary, who was working in the R&D department at the time, was tasked with designing a mould that celebrated the ingredient's cultural significance. She recalls, "Helen and Mark loved the fact that, in the past, tea was pressed into bricks and used as trading currency in place of money - the idea that simple ingredients like tea and henna were once so very important to people. Instead of looking at tea brick designs, I looked online at the beautiful henna designs used in weddings and adapted some of the recurring leaf themes I saw."

A little bit of Lush naughtiness went into the range of course too. The category name 'Caca' was a play on the fashion for dolling up cosmetics with fancy French names ('Caca' meaning 'shit' à la France). Caca Rouge, for example, literally translates as 'red shit'. According to Mark, this was apt both because of its look, and because "they were and are *the* shit".

Four henna bricks were launched for customers to purchase: Rouge, Brun, Marron and Noir, each using a bespoke mix of ingredients inspired by the Persians and Ancient Egyptians - without the blood of a black cat some contemporaries recommended. Using Iranian red henna in various quantities, combined with ingredients like indigo herb and clove bud oil, not to mention Fair Trade organic cocoa butter, customers could find a range of shades from fiery red to the glossiest darkest brown. A blend for blondes that proved particularly difficult did not quite make the cut ("We decided to give ourselves a quiet life!" quips Helen.)

Because the richest red lawsone is released under mildly acidic conditions, Rouge and Marron included a dash of lemon juice to enhance the warmth and brightness of the colour.
Where the intended colour was darker, like Brun and Noir, Mark and Helen used a combination of henna and indigo (*Indigofera tinctoria*): a technique honed by the Persians, as described in

Chapter 10. Unlike henna, however, indigo does not adhere neatly to the hair's keratin, making it harder to use on the hair.[3] Following in the fine Middle Eastern tradition, Mark and Helen combined differing levels of indigo and henna to create two rich brown shades, one medium, one dark.

Even if you weren't switching up your hair colour, the combination of ingredients within the henna bricks gave them kudos as hair treatments too. Applied to brown hair, for example, Brun would moisturise courtesy of the cocoa butter, while clove and rosemary would treat the scalp, and the lawsone component would add body and shine to the hair fibres. This final point was particularly useful for finer hair. "If your hair is very thick," explains Mark, "henna might not seem to improve the combability because it adds a bit of body. But it would still be improving the overall condition as well as adding shine."

Same henna, new product: a fresh look at a cult classic

Nearly 20 years after their invention and armed with customer feedback, Mark, Helen and Daisy donned their aprons and decided to revisit the henna bricks in 2020 with with fresh eyes. They had three main objectives: improving the coverage provided by the bricks, achieving a wider pantone of warm and cool tones, and having another crack at that pesky blonde shade. All this while delivering the same benefits of the henna brick to the customer: convenience, freshness, limited packaging and self-preserving.

"The henna brick is absolutely brilliant for at home use," says Daisy. "The cocoa butter binds the henna and indigo powders together, cutting out all of the messy parts from the preparation of your henna dye that you would traditionally experience, such as dusty powders that settle all over your home. The bricks are enjoyable to prepare yourself and are great for your hair.

"Still, we looked at the amount of cocoa butter in the brick formulas to see if they could be having a negative effect on the amount of coverage the products can offer. To cover grey unpigmented hairs, for example, you need to give back to them the depth that they are lacking. This means that the dye should deposit more pigment onto the stands.

"A set of experiments I carried out clearly showed the shades gain more depth as we reduce the cocoa butter. But cocoa butter plays an important role in the brick formula, and gives added benefits to the customer in terms of condition and moisture. It also makes the henna much easier to apply! So I have explored other ways that we could keep it present while improving the coverage of the bricks. This includes using solvents to see if we could extract a deeper pigment from the henna and indigo leaves, keeping the solution warm for set periods of time, as well as cooling it down. Some things that I have found is that the powders much prefer a natural-based environment instead of playing around with synthetics too much."

Just to up the ante, Daisy performed most of these henna experiments from her kitchen during the Covid-19 pandemic. "I moaned about the work surface space in my kitchen long before I knew I would be performing henna experiments in here!" she laughs. "It's turned into a home lab by day, and somewhere to cook and rest by night."

In order to create deeper, richer tones on the hair, Daisy experimented with adding other materials into the bricks. For the warmer colours, Rouge and Marron, hibiscus (*Hibiscus rosa-sinensis*) has been a hit, adding extra depth and redness to the tone. Creating cooler tones in Noir and Brun has been trickier. "Indigo doesn't perform well on its own on a canvas as complex

Despite its distinctive odour, noni fruit has a variety of uses in its native Southeast Asia and Australasia, including in traditional medicine.

as hair," explains Daisy. "It absorbs into more porous areas and not so much into healthier areas of the fibre, resulting in a seriously patchy colour job (luckily, these tests were on hair cuttings!). Indigo needs henna to help it evenly develop onto the hair, as well as giving the hair a base colour to work from." The addition of spikenard (*Nardostachys jatamansi*) was promising, but this heavily protected plant proved too complex to source. Noni fruit (*Morinda citrifolia*), however, combined well with indigo to bring inkier tones to the overall shades, creating the cooler palette customers have been asking for.

Excitingly, Daisy has also formulated a brand new brick especially designed for fairer hair. Vénitien is a blend of red henna, cassia (Cassia italica), hibiscus, rhubarb (Rheum palmatum), chamomile (Matricaria recutita) and lemon (Citrus limonum) and is designed to give that much revered Renaissance golden-red tone to light hair. Less intense than Rouge, it's ideal for more subtle strawberry blonde hues. Cassia Italica, a species of many names indigenous to Africa and Asia, is also known as 'neutral henna' for its similar effects on the hair. Hair treated with cassia appears thicker, as it similarly binds to the cuticle (though not as readily as henna) and it can also impart golden colouring to bleached, white and grey hair.[5]

With customers telling us they wanted a brick that was easier to break down and melt, Daisy has also been working with colleagues on a snappable brick. This makes the product easier to break up and heat at home, and Mark is onboard for anything that stops customers resorting to more rudimental measures ("Grating it is just putting yourself through unnecessary hell. Don't do it."). These formulas will feel a little thirstier due to the higher powder content and have a slightly more mousse-like texture.

Over at Lush's innovation hub (aka Unit 1 in Poole), the ever-adaptable manufacturing team has also been hard at work on the practicalities involved in any product reformulation: how to handmake the new and improved product efficiently and to a high standard in larger batches. Mainly this has focused on practical ways to set the reduced cocoa butter bricks, which are drier than the originals and require a little more muscle to press.

Compounder Mirek Smuga reveals, "So far, we have done lots of different trials on henna mixes to check what impact they have on the hair but also to check they are not too dry to press and are still easy to use. Personally, my main goal is to create a recipe that is clear and easy to follow for our manufacturing compounders, so we can make the best quality product in an efficient manner. We have a product that already works very well but our aim is to make it even better! I hope that our customers will soon feel and see an improvement in our lovely henna bricks."

Daisy had better prep herself for a busy year. An injection of fresh enthusiasm into the henna bricks also has Mark reeling off exciting ideas for the future of herbal haircare at Lush, both in terms of product and salon services. But while, for now, his plans remain open-ended, there's one thing he won't be swayed on: where we source our henna from.

How did you put my country into a brick? Sourcing the finest Iranian henna

12

Sistan and Baluchestan Province, Iran. As it has for hundreds of years, the sun dawns over a henna harvest, cultivated amongst fruit and vegetable crops. The climate here is arid and semi-tropical; underfoot, the soil rich in deposits of gypsum, silt, sand and salt.[1] The dry climate in this most southeastern region of Iran is not suited to many plants, and yet it's ideal for the production of lawsone - the material that gives the henna leaf its vibrant staining properties.[2] Hardy plants like henna are an important source of income in this region and also necessary to counteract the soil erosion that has come with overgrazing, drought and deforestation.[3]

Devoted to its high quality, Lush has sourced henna from Iran for decades. One man in particular has remained insistent on that point. "When I was young, I was introduced to Persian henna by a friend, Stephen Smalls, and I've never moved off that because it's the finest henna in the world," Mark declares. "The colour, the quality - I'm not sure how they do it, but no other source comes close."

When I speak to Professor of Ancient History and Persian Studies Lloyd Llewellyn-Jones about Iran's history with henna, he immediately agrees, "Interestingly, it's exactly the same with saffron. Iranian saffron is by far the best quality. Far better than Turkish saffron for the depth of colour it gives. Their rose is the same too - somehow they manage to hold the fragrance better than any other country I've known. I don't know what they do but there is something very unique in the Iranian quality of stuff. It's top end. Maybe it's because Iran has so many climate zones. I've passed fields and fields of roses and they are just burgeoning up. It's such a rich environment for growing things really."

Political conflict, however, has made sourcing this beautiful ingredient infinitely more tricky. Britain and Iran have had a turbulent relationship in recent years. Between 1979 and 2021, diplomatic relations between the two countries have been strained - and severed - on numerous occasions. With embassies in both countries frequently closed, travel insurance was unavailable, and this made visits from Lush impossible. Contact with Lush's henna suppliers, an Iranian family-run business that operates in Germany and Iran, was consequently limited to emails and first-hand reports from Iranian journalists commissioned to visit. After diplomatic relations were tentatively revived in 2015, and travel became possible once more, the Lush buyers were finally able to visit some provinces of Iran. [4]

Lush buyer Mark Rumbell, who was responsible for henna sourcing between 2015 and 2019, explains, "It was the first time that anyone from Lush had been able to visit. Part of what we did was to actually go and show people our final product and say this is what you make, and it goes all over the world."

With limited internet access, and that fact that 'Lush' means 'slime' or 'carcass' in the Farsi language,[5] the suppliers might have expected the worst. So, it was a relief that, when shown a freshly made henna brick for the first time, the company director asked, "How did you put my country into a brick?"

Strong roots

Iran is the eighteenth-largest country in the world, with a wealth of natural resources and a rich heritage of art and science. Stretching from the Caspian Sea in the north to the Persian Gulf in the south, and bordered by countries including Armenia, Afghanistan, Pakistan, Iraq and Turkey, the climate varies in different zones, from mild and fairly wet on the northern coast to arid and hot in the south east.[6] It's in the latter that you will find Sistan and Baluchestan Province: a region home to the finest henna harvest. Much of Sistan and Baluchestan Province is religiously and culturally divided. It is mostly populated by Shia Muslim Iranians and the Sunni Muslim Balochi (a population whose ancestral territory is now divided between Iran and Pakistan), causing conflicts of identity. High levels of poverty have also facilitated the rise of drug trafficking in the area.[7] Much like journalists travelling to conflict zones, Lush buyers undergo specialist hostile environments training to prepare them for buying trips in high-risk regions. However, because the British government still advises people not to travel to this specific region of Iran, Mark Rumbell was once more unable to get the insurance needed to visit on his trip in 2015. Instead, the owners and directors of Lush's henna supplier invited him to travel to other farms they sourced from in the neighbouring Hormozgan Province, so he could still see the henna process from start to finish.

Farmers in Hormozgan Province have been harvesting henna for hundreds of years, though the quality of the crop is not as fine as that of Sistan and Baluchestan Province. The Hormozgan henna leaves are harvested by hand three times a year and dried in the sun. Harvest day is a family affair, with all lending a hand under the experienced eye of grandmother Omina, whose son Mr Ibrahim runs the farm. He explained to Mark that the plants themselves only need replacing every 35 to 50 years, and a henna branch planted in the ground will flourish if given enough water.

While henna tends to fetch a good price, the profit from these crops is still lower than other fruits and vegetables, which can be harvested more frequently and take up less space. Consequently, in many areas, it is treated as a supplementary crop. The farms in Sistan and Baluchestan Province, for example, grow dates as a key source of income. These sticky fruit trees wind-pollinate themselves and so require very little maintenance, and the sweet dates can also be stored for long periods of time.

When the henna crops in both Hormozgan and Sistan and Baluchestan Provinces have been harvested and dried in the sun for several days, they are transported north, to the ancient settlement of Yazd in the midst of central Iran.

A heritage of henna milling

Once an important post on the infamous Silk Road, Yazd has been a major processing centre of commodities including henna for decades. Famed for its rich mercantile history and architecture, Yazd appears in classical geographies from the first and second centuries AD, though is thought to be far more ancient.[8]

The city's location, in the midst of an inhospitable desert, has kept it safe from invasion and modernisation alike many times. It has also preserved a series of 'quanats': ancient systems of underground water canals, reservoirs and watermills that have sustained urban life for

Farms in the Sistan and Baluchestan Province of Iran are arid and rich in silt deposits, making them ideal for henna cultivation.

centuries.[9] Although industry has dwindled, Yazd's inhabitants are still famed for their prowess in the processing of goods including textiles, sugar and henna.[10] Only a few henna mills remain open, but 'mazars' (which means 'to move wheel' in local dialect) still use traditional methods to expertly sieve henna crops, predominantly for export overseas.[11]

Overseeing the milling process of Lush henna at one such mill is henna connoisseur, Mr Turk. His father before him was a miller and Mr Turk himself has over 50 years' experience in the role. Mark Rumbell recalls, "He would use a knife just like one you would use to sample cheese, poke it into each bag and extract a little henna then tell us where it was from just because of the colour and grade. He would say things like, 'This henna is from this town; it's very windy so there's lots of dust in the leaves.'"

Factory owner and henna connoisseur Mr Turk inspects the quality of the leaves.

It is at Mr Turk's factory that initial sieving and quality tests take place. The henna leaves are still flattened by a large 50-year-old stone wheel, though one concession to modernity has been the use of a mechanised wheel rather than one powered by a camel or donkey. These mighty stone wheels can last up to 100 years, and churn out approximately one tonne of henna after 15 hours of work.

For Mr Turk, Lush's henna requirements are a vital source of profit, but only because recent conflicts in Syria and Iraq have so dramatically altered his business model. Whereas once, he could rely on business with neighbouring countries, nowadays, he only exports around 10% of sieved henna to other Arab nations. "If you live in a narrow alley, then you have to have a good relationship with your neighbours," he reflects wryly when asked about how the political situation has impacted his business.

Once processed in Yazd, Lush's henna is then transported to a factory in Kashmar, North East Iran, where it is sieved once more, put through quality control tests, and packaged for a European market. The factory is owned by the three brothers who have run the business since their father's early death.

Company General Manager Ghassem inherited the business at the age of only 23, while studying at university. "It was initially very, very hard," he explains, "because we didn't have any money and we started with very low capacity for work." Their choice of market was key. "Iran has the climate to grow many plants, but Europe has lots of potential to use them. At first, we had no business experience but now we have much more. We can touch this industry now. Because I love my work, I have lots of energy. To supply good quality materials at a good price with a good partner is very important to me."

Standards at the Kashmar factory are extremely high, as Mark realised when his shoes were meticulously machine cleaned before he looked around. Ghassem's younger brother Mohammad, a chairman of the company, explains, "We buy the henna that has been milled, use an instrument to sieve it again, and then package it. We also have a laboratory where we test the henna for colour, quantity of dust, moisture and size, all of which are very important. We can also analyse pesticide use there."

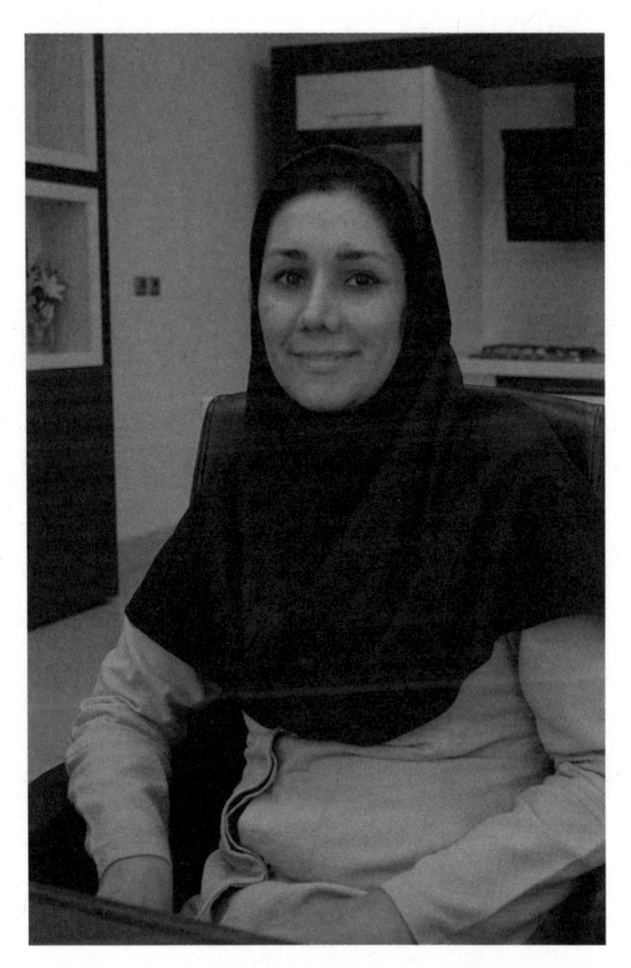

General Manager of the Kashmar manufacturing unit, Azade Zia, is kept busy with the day to day needs of the factory.

A family affair

When I am lucky enough to meet Ghassem and Mohammad at Lush's Dusseldorf factory in Germany, it is initially a terrifying experience. However, that's because, at six months pregnant, I am traveling in what can only be described as a wind-up plane (with a captain who sounds distinctly like someone who's been gifted a fly-your-own-commercial-flight experience). Meeting the brothers and accompanying them on a factory tour is a privilege. Courteous, immaculately dressed and extending their warmest invitations to visit Iran, they are also keen to impress upon me their country's long and proud history of art and culture.

I especially want to quiz them about their business, which is rooted in family life and values. As an employee of Lush (similarly composed of extended family, friends and multiple generations), it seems an interesting parallel. Ghassem explains, "Family is very important in Iran. When you have a business family, you see them every day and you are in connection with them all the time. We like to eat dinner and speak about work; it is very good for us. We enjoy our business all the time."

The motivation for selling to a European market was also based on principles Ghassem learned from his father. "We wanted to grow the business because we wanted to make more jobs for other people," he says. "It was the way of my father to live for other people, so when we started up, I thought about ways we could employ more colleagues."

He continues, "I believe that the world is one country. We have one God, one Earth and so we have one country. I also believe that when we take a thing from God, with the other hand you put it back into the ground. Many farmers in Iran are illiterate. They only know agriculture as corn, but corn growing is from many, many years ago. The world of today is different, and we have new products like liquorice, eucalyptus and mint. So, we pay part of our money to train farmers to grow their knowledge so they can harvest other seeds. Training other people is a very important policy in our company. These people are our friends and family."

In 2020, the business employed 16 new people in farming, accounting, production and quality control roles, and invested in more projects involving corn flowers, tarragon, mallow and fennel. "It is also exceptional that all major leading positions are taken by women," says Sales Manager Nicolas Märgner. "We are doing a good thing here."

A bolt from the blue: sourcing indigo

Lush buyers have been so pleased with the quality of the henna and the business's ethos that in 2019, after Mark Constantine had a good hard look at swatches, they switched Lush's indigo supply to the same company.

Blues and purples are rare in the natural world. The Ancient Mesopotamians mined and traded lapis lazuli for use in jewelry and ornaments,[12] the Ancient Egyptians produced a blue pigment from various combinations of quartz, calcium, copper and alkalis,[13] while Tyrian purple was painstakingly extracted from sea snails by the Ancient Phoenicians.[14] Both processes were costly and painstaking. The discovery of plant-based purple would have been a revelation, though exactly how the ancients discovered the blue staining power of genuses like *indigofera* and *Isatis* remains a mystery, because producing the (initially colourless) pigment is still a reasonably complex double chemical process.[15] *Indigofera tinctoria* leaves, for example, contain dye precursors known as indican. When the leaves are soaked, fermented and then exposed to the air, they form a blue dye.[16]

Since antiquity, India has been the home of commercial production of *Indigofera tinctoria* (also known as 'true indigo'), thanks to its advantages of suitable land and climate, good commercial connections, and large population.[17] (Whether the species is indigenous to India itself remains a slightly contentious issue, though generally accepted.)

Some of our earliest specimens showing human use of the material come from the dyed mummy clothes from Ancient Egypt, reported to date back to c.2,400 BC. These may have been produced from indigo imported from southern Arabia or species of woad (*Isatis tinctoria*) - another blue dye producing plant) indigenous to North Africa.[18] An ancient Babylonian tablet dated to c.600 BC, which gives the world's earliest written instructions for wool dyeing, also describes methods distinctive to indigo. The Yemenites too are believed to have traded blue cloths in the same period thanks to references to the activities of the merchants of Sheba in the Bible. The skills of these nations would have been absorbed into the Persian Empire with the military conquest of Cyrus the Great (c.600 – 530 BC), and indeed we find beautiful silks dyed with indigo in the pre-Islamic Persian Empire.[19]

By early Islamic times, indigo appears to have been widely if not abundantly farmed in Persia. It was an increasingly popular cosmetic for Persian women - one of the seven essential cosmetics (alongside henna) known as the 'Haft Qalam Ārāyish' - to be used as an eyebrow tint and combined with henna to dye the hair inky black.[20] This recipe, known as henna reng (and detailed in Chapter 4), is used by Lush today to create shades of natural hair dye from warm claret to inky brown.

Woad has been cultivated since at least the

Producing a dye from European woad was labour-intensive, time-consuming and quickly lost its appeal after the introduction of indigo from the Middle East and Asia.

Iron Age, and was a thriving industry by the 13th century, with dyeing centres in Toulouse, France, and Thuringia, Germany.[21] The meticulous - and notoriously smelly process of extracting the dye - involved a host of specialists. The leaves of the plant had to be ground in mills and moulded by hand into small balls that would ferment over a number of months. (One endearing 18th century English recipe states woad balls were the size of a 'ferthing luv' - believed to be 'farthing loaf' in a Somerset dialect.)[22] This was a notoriously noxious process. The royal nose of English Queen Elizabeth I was reportedly so offended by the stench that she banned the production of woad within five miles of her royal residences.[23]

Imports of true indigo from the Middle East and Asia were initially met with resistance from European woad cultivators, but by the 16th and 17th centuries trade was highly competitive thanks to the land-grabbing habits of the western powers.[24] European dyers were right to be wary. While imported indigo, which boasted a superior colour and cheaper manufacturing process,[25] was initially added to woad to boost its colour, the superior material eventually replaced it in popularity.[26]

Competition between European powers like the Dutch, Spanish, Portuguese and English for monopoly of the indigo trade facilitated the exploitation of countries with the best growing conditions. The Spanish began producing indigo on an industrial scale using slave labour when they invaded Guatemala in the early 16th century[27] and, in 1631 alone, the Dutch carried an indigo cargo equivalent to five tonnes of gold from Malaysia back to Europe.[28] By the 17th century, commercial indigo was being produced widely across India, although European and Asian merchants recognised that plants from Bayana and Sarkhej were the best quality.[29]

While the British initially focused on the cultivation of indigo in their colony of South Carolina, USA, the American Revolutionary War (1775-1783) soon put a stop to that. They subsequently turned their attention to India.[30] The English East India Company (founded in 1600) established a base in Bengal in the late 18th century and by 1815, Bengal produced nearly all of the indigo required internationally.[31] It was a highly exploitative venture, with indebted farmers forced to grow indigo in the place of food crops after being trapped in debt. The inevitable result was a series of so-called 'Indigo Revolts' by the farmers over the 19th and early 20th century, the latter of which were led by Indian lawyer and renowned anti-colonial activist Mahatma Gandhi (1869 – 1948).[32]

During the same period however, the price of indigo was diminishing, thanks chiefly to the synthesis of a cheap alternative by German chemists in 1882.[33] As manufacturing processes improved, this synthetic 'Pure Indigo' went on to dominate indigo trade across the world, and commercial cultivation of the plant sharply declined.[34]

After a chequered history of exploitation by western powers, indigo remains a prized dye, medicine and cosmetic in communities across North Africa, the Middle East and Asia, and continues to be produced but on a much smaller local scale. In fact, Mark Constantine recalls that sourcing good quality indigo to use with his beloved henna in the early days of Constantine & Weir was 'a huge palaver'. Thankfully today Lush has a trusted source in our Iranian suppliers.

Indigofera tinctoria plants thrive in sandy, clay-rich soil at high temperatures but tolerate more rain than henna, and so Lush's indigo is sourced from both the Kerman and Sistan provinces of Iran. The seeds are planted in spring, then harvested in both early summer and late autumn, sieved multiple times for waste material such as ash and twigs, and processed in Yazd by the same remarkable stone mill.

As Nicolas explains, once the crop reaches the lab in Germany it is sieved and tested again. "We measure by certain parameters, most importantly ash content, the colour it emits and the consistency. Indigo powder should be olive green with a maximum moisture content of 10% and ash content of 25%, and free from insects and foreign materials. It is also crucial that the powder does not trigger itching on the skin."

It is this fine quality indigo that joins henna in Lush's natural hair dyes: both materials grown in Iran and combined in a modern take on a historic Persian recipe.

Back on home soil

In his office in Poole, Mark Rumbell and his colleagues quality check each new batch of henna and indigo for colour, despite the high standards he has seen from first experience. "If you grow tomatoes in your garden," he notes, "you can't expect the same number and the same quality each year."

Hairdressers at the Poole HairLab (both a salon and Lush's in-house R&D department for hair) perform a strand test on virgin hair, using a brick made with the new henna and indigo, and also conduct a filter paper test to see how the colour compares to previous batches. These samples are sent to product inventor and Lush Co-Founder Helen Ambrosen and fellow inventor Wesley Burrage for analysis.

In Helen's lab at 29 High Street, she and Wesley compare these fresh samples to those in what she dubs Wesley's "Library of Hair": a box of dyed hair samples and filter papers. "Some people find it a bit weird when I bring out my box of hair," Wesley says. "But it gives us a master sample that we can visually check each batch against."

Helen adds, "Stan [Krysztal - cosmetic chemist and friend of Lush's co-founders who passed away in 1992] taught me to use this filter paper method. It was more widely used in his day because things like silver nitrate were quite commonly added to the ingredients back then. We're looking for differences. If we see anything odd, we would question it and if there were contaminants in the henna or indigo, we'd be able to see it in the filter paper. We're looking at longevity really."

Henna and indigo also undergo additional checks for contamination, which is a big problem in the industry. In 2007, modified henna products and 'natural' henna products purchased in Turkey were not only found to contain para-phenylenediamine and para-toluenediamine but also carcinogenic materials like 4-aminobiphenyl.[35] Lush's indigo and henna is checked for para-phenylenediamine and 4-aminobiphenyl contamination twice a year and one batch in every five made is also tested for microbial growth, responsibility for which falls under Testing Coordinator Jet Shears. "As we make frequent batches of henna bricks in our production rooms, we test at least one batch a week of each colour," she explains.

The henna brick to be tested is sent to a local microbiology lab, plated up onto a vegetarian agar base and then incubated for five days, before the results are analysed. "We mostly look for bacteria, yeast and moulds," says Jet, "but also we want to make sure there are no potentially pathogenic strains, so we run additional tests for these too. It's quite common to see a fair number of bacteria in the bricks as the powders used are a natural material derived from plants. We don't want to see any counts that are too high though. We keep master samples of all of the batches made for three years too in case we need to check back on any batches for any reason."

A balancing act

Henna sourcing is just one example of the political barriers in place that make buying good quality, traceable ingredients from fairly paid and treated farmers difficult. Yet, there are also wider impacts to consider such as growing demands on the planet and climate change. If resources become finite or crops fail, how does Lush balance its need to satisfy customers with responsibility to the wider world?

Being an ingredients buyer for Lush brings both the opportunity of finding and working with expert producers and farmers, and the challenge of navigating a murky industry made up of increasingly limited resources. In 2020, for example, Lush used 22 tonnes of henna and 13.5 tonnes of indigo, making these ingredients two of the largest quantities of dried herbs sourced by the company. When buying in these volumes, any business decision has the potential to have a massive impact on people, places and ecosystems. It is also important that profits trickle down to the people at the start of the chain: the farmers and communities who are the real experts. That's why price negotiation is always balanced by an understanding of what the people involved in the harvesting and production of the ingredients need to make a living.

Pendle Hill, who has sourced henna for Lush since 2020, explains, "Henna is such an important material in these regions. It's a source of income, but also a crop that stretches back through time and provides a really clear link to the history of a region. Producing quality henna is a point of pride for some of the producers. It's really nice to work with a distributor who ensures the farmers are paid a fair wage for a quality product and is actively working with Lush to introduce new farming principles."

The new principles Pendle refers to are based on agroecology: a farming approach inspired by natural ecosystems. Lush is busy working with suppliers and farmers, like those of our henna, to embrace techniques that are healthier for land and farmers in the long-term. Agroecology consultant for Lush Tarek Soliman explains, "Agroecology is about working with people around food and farming towards understanding the opportunities and limitations of the ecosystem without resorting to chemical agricultural inputs (like pesticides). While the use of pesticides does not affect the quality or the safety of the final product, they can have implications on the health of farmers, biodiversity of the land, and make the agro-ecosystem more vulnerable to pest attacks."

Tarek explains that this isn't the same as organic farming (although the two do overlap), as agroecology also holds a strong socio-cultural element that is missed in third party certification.

"Pesticides are a short term solution for farmers, but there are long-term impacts for the ecosystem. We could simply just use organic suppliers but think that there is more impact in supporting farmers' transition to agroecology, especially when they want it but don't know where to start, or find it too risky, or lack the tools to do it. We have a good mutual understanding with our henna suppliers and will to make it happen, which is very important to have for such a project to succeed. I see it as a powerful co-learning experience and a great opportunity to inspire other businesses to do the same."

With such passionate buyers and suppliers of henna, not to mention Mark Constantine's never-ending zeal for Iranian quality, all that's left is to know how to get the best results on your hair. Thankfully, Mark has a thought or two on that.

Plant Life: your definitive guide to using Lush henna

13

It's May 2021 and Mark and Daisy are in the middle of a very nerdy hairdresser discussion in the Lush HairLab, Poole.

As Mark touches up the Rouge henna at my temples with a tinting brush ("Were you blonde as a child? It'll take more at the temples, if so"), Daisy is reflecting on the difference between applying henna and synthetic dyes, or bleach. Having had the pleasure of both Mark and Daisy applying my henna, their different approaches are fascinating. Daisy is meticulously precise with each strand, while Mark layers henna down on the hair with practised speed.

They are currently comparing application methods. "I've always been taught to apply dye from the top down," says Daisy. "You get taught the hot cross bun method where you divide the hair into four sections. Any hair that I handle I am very thorough with."

"Everything you do is technical, everything I do is hippy," explains Mark. "I'm trying to get the best result from something that's a bit weak compared to oxidative dye. Let's face it, I'm applying a load of mashed up leaves to the hair in my marigold gloves, so I want to get it on as many hairs as possible to get the maximum effect. If I was to use these techniques with bleach or a permanent dye, bloody hell, it would be a disaster."

Daisy agrees, "It's not like oxidative hair dye which is very powerful and swells, so if you miss a bit you might be ok. You need to be really generous with henna."

"Generous is a lovely word to use," agrees Mark. "I would imagine most people self-apply but I would still recommend they get someone else to do it for them to get the best results. Henna parties are my favourite things. It's a great luxury to have someone do your henna and it's a friendly act."

As Daisy knows only too well from her time before Lush, most hairdressers are not familiar with using henna. It's not part of standard training and, thanks to its frequent contamination with materials that do not mix well with oxidative dye or perm procedures, it doesn't have a good reputation. Many hairdressers will have heard horror stories about perms going haywire and unpredictable results when aromatic amine dyes are applied to hennaed hair.

Very high levels of para-phenylenediamine in adulterated hennas can also make you susceptible to a severe allergic reaction when using synthetic colour (see Chapter 6). So, understandably some hairdressers can get a bit twitchy around the subject.

"As a hairdresser, I was having to deal with people who hennaed their hair but I was never taught what it was and how it worked," Daisy reflects. "It was this big scary thing." Thankfully, three years at Lush, and working up close with the material and Mark has given her new-found knowledge, confidence and appreciation of the herbal dye.

Mark too has been impressed with the finesse Daisy brings to her work, and they are beginning conversations about new henna techniques Lush could offer. "All of your technical skills leave me absolutely in awe," he confesses, "I just love the work you do."

After a long Covid-19 lockdown, having my somewhat neglected hair in the capable hands of Mark and Daisy is a treat, especially as I'm six months pregnant. This is somewhere between a masterclass and a lovely salon experience as he and Daisy try Lush's newly reformulated Rouge brick on my hair and discuss different techniques. Both Daisy and I are interested to hear where Mark first learned to apply henna. Was he self-taught?

"Hhmm," he pauses, expertly coiling my henna-slathered hair into a crown at the top of my head, "I took the traditional technique of applying henna which I must have learned somewhere between 1973 and 1978. I was buying Egyptian henna at the time and it was very orangey and then my colleague Stephen Smalls got this marvellous Persian henna. That immediately put me above other people applying henna because I had a redder colour.

"At the time, there was a group of us building The Body Shop's business. Me, Anita and Gordon Roddick, Janice Paskin [formerly Raven], Eric Helyer, who was the UK Production Director and another lady who was Iranian. Her name escapes me. She taught me this method of applying henna. She's probably where my belief that the Iranians care most for henna comes from because you really couldn't get much past her about henna. They want to get the best results. I also read every book - I was nerdy. There was a big old book that had the technique in it too; I can see a series of diagrams in my head."

While Mark may be an old hand at henna application, there's no denying that customers used to synthetic dyes will find the material requires a little more effort and understanding. For the converted however, the benefits of henna outweigh the advantages of aromatic amine-based dyes. "We are offering people a safer alternative that requires more effort, education and experimentation, but doesn't affect the hair or health the way that synthetic dyes do," says Mark, who estimates that he has hennaed 10,000 heads (and counting) during the course of his career.

One of the most common questions asked by customers is what specific shade a certain henna brick will turn their hair. From my time on the shopfloor in Lush Cardiff and Bath, I vividly remember being asked specifics ranging from, "Will it definitely cover the greys at my temples?" to "What precise shade of maroon will my stepsister's hair go? Here's a dimly-lit picture of her at a wedding."

But experience of using henna and knowing how it works (see Chapter 10) teaches you that a brick of Rouge will not turn everyone's hair the same shade. On one blonde, it might result in a vibrant red, on another, in rich copper tones. Taking stock of your hair, your lifestyle, and conducting a strand test is essential homework to getting a beautiful result, as is a generous application. Like many a good long-term relationship, henna requires loyalty, but the benefits are incredible.

How To Use Henna

Here's exactly what you'll need:

- Your chosen henna brick (more than one if your hair is very long, thick, curly or coily)
- A friend with a steady hand (having someone else apply your henna will give the best results)
- A kettle
- A bain-marie/heatproof bowl and stirring spoon
- Wide brush to apply henna (recommended)
- A pair of marigold gloves
- A protective balm, like Ultrabland, to apply to your hairline if you're the messy sort
- A shower cap if you'd like a warmer, redder result
- Clips to section your hair if preferred
- Shampoo and conditioner or co-wash

Have everything to hand. Optional extras (not pictured but encouraged) include a book and cup of tea.

1. Break up your brick and add to your bowl, gradually stirring in freshly boiled water. Mixing in a bain-marie is the easiest way to melt your brick as the added layer of hot water keeps it nice and toasty to release the dye pigment. You're aiming for the consistency of melted chocolate.

The reformulated henna bricks are snappable, making them easier to prepare. A fancy bain-marie like Mark's is great for mixing your henna and keeping it toasty, though a heatproof bowl or saucepan also works.

Mark whips the henna into shape and demonstrates the perfect consistency: melted chocolate.

2. Comb and section your hair, check your henna is a comfortable temperature, and apply to the roots of the hair, working from the nape of the neck up to the crown, back and sides. Use a brush for extra precision at the roots and temples.

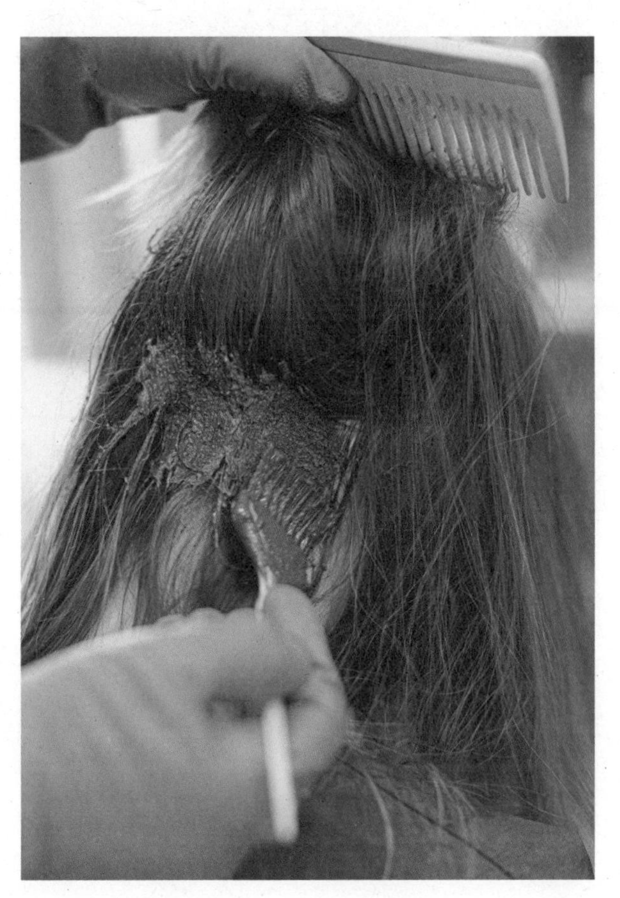

3. Once the roots are covered, smear abundantly through the lengths and ends of the hair with (gloved) hands and pile on top of the head. A really generous application is key.

Working upwards in sections to the crown of the head, he makes sure my roots are fully covered. "Your hair is quick and easy for a henna application," says Mark. "If you had longer hair, I would have separated the lengths and ends into more sections.

4. Cover with a shower cap for a warmer result, leaving on for up to two hours.

Top with a shower cap or wrap for a redder result (it keeps the henna warm). Leave for up to two hours to develop (we leave mine on for one hour and 20 minutes). "You can use a brush or your hands," says Mark, "personally, I like to use a brush. The ends of the hair are more porous and take up the colour quicker, so applying to the roots first enables a more even application. It's also much tidier."

5. Rinse thoroughly (we recommend a co-wash or conditioner to initially lift the henna, followed by shampoo and conditioner).

6. Turn heads.

You can prepare and apply another brick as soon as your hair is dry if this is part of a two-step henna application, or wait a while. Both henna and indigo will continue to develop over a few days and so your end result may be subtly different from your first rinse away.

Before

You can see where I've applied Rouge previously because it picks up on the lightened ends of my hair.

After

Ta-da! After using the reformulated Rouge brick, my colour is deeper, redder and more intense. My hair appears glossy and in better condition too (and I swear it's not just because Daisy's blow dried it for me).

ABOUT THE BRICKS

What colours does Lush henna come in?

Lush henna comes in five shades, based on the finest Iranian henna. Marron, Brun and Noir also contain Iranian indigo to create varying shades of glossy brown.

Rouge
This brick has the highest henna content for fiery shades of copper red on fair and red hair, and adding warm tones to brunettes. Dazzling on fair hair, it's also an essential base shade if you want to apply Brun, Marron or Noir to light, white or twinkly grey hair.

Marron
Gives rich shades of claret brown with plenty of warm hues. Adds depth to red hair and warm tones to brunettes.

Brun
For a cool brunette result, also ideal for adding lustre and depth to dark hair.

Noir
Our darkest cool-toned shade, also perfect for adding gloss and inky depth to dark hair.

Vénitien
Our latest introduction to the range, designed to give warm strawberry blonde tones to blonde, white or grey hair.

Why does Lush henna come in a brick rather than a powder?

Henna leaves are traditionally crushed, added to water and something a little acidic, like lemon juice, then used as a paste. It's been an effective process for thousands of years, though the airborne dust is renowned for its ability, much like sand, to settle everywhere. It may also prove irritating to some people. Adding cocoa butter removes that inconvenience for the customer and creates an easier-to-use solid product, inspired by

Brick by brick. This beautiful new packaging is made from 100% recycled material and is completely recyclable. Four of these packaging designs were inspired by traditional North African and Middle Eastern henna tattoo designs, and the packaging design for Venitien was inspired by Venetian lace from the Renaissance era.

an ancient Asian form of currency: the tea brick.

"The cocoa butter replaces things like eggs or binders you might add in to henna," says Mark. "It's holding it together so you get this really cohesive dye instead of loads of stuff that's dropping everywhere." It also adds gloss and condition to the hair, and makes the product easier to remove, as well as reducing the need for packaging.

In 2021, we reduced the amount of cocoa butter within the bricks to increase the depth and vibrancy of the colour on the hair whilst maintaining all of the benefits. You can read all about the evolution of henna within Lush in Chapter 11.

What other effects will henna have on my hair?

Some people use henna as a treatment for hair health rather than for colour. Mark explains, "Henna adds body, thickness, and shine. The extra body is particularly nice if you have fine hair. If you have thick hair, it won't appear as sleek but the shine will be so much better."

APPLICATION

Do I need to do a strand test on my hair?

Yes, it's a good idea to check you are happy with the colour, especially if you are going from light to dark. Follow the previous application steps to apply a small amount of henna to a lock of hair, bearing in mind that if you are looking to cover grey hairs they should be included in this test.

How much henna do I need for one application?

Each brick is designed to be enough for one head of shoulder-length hair, but if your hair is very thick, curly or coily, you will need more than one. You want to be able to apply generously rather than get stingy towards the end so if in doubt, get more!

Can I apply henna to my own hair?

Of course. You should still focus on the roots first but you may want to adjust your application technique slightly to find a method that works for you, such as working from the top down and clipping your hair up as you go. If you are looking for very thorough coverage, however, having a friend help out is the best way to go.

Can I use henna on my skin?

Our blends have not been created for this purpose. Pure, high quality powdered body art henna (not 'black henna' adulterated with para-phenylenediamine) is a neater option.

Can I use henna on my beard?

Yes, henna has been used for thousands of years to colour beards (see Chapter Two) so you are following in a fine tradition. Beard hairs are coarser than scalp hair fibres and so may require further applications. You'll get the best result if you thoroughly cleanse your beard beforehand and you may wish to apply Ultrabland around the beard line.

Can I use henna on my eyebrows or eyelashes?

Lush henna bricks have been designed for use on thicker scalp hairs and so we do not recommend using them on the very fine eyebrow and eyelash hairs.

Can I combine henna bricks to tailor my colour?

Yes, absolutely.

Can I add other materials to my henna?

You can, but we've already done that for you.

Can I freeze henna?

Henna is best used fresh so we don't advise freezing the bricks or paste.

COLOUR AND COVERAGE

Is henna permanent?

It's as good as. Over time, you can expect natural fading of the henna but if you have very fair or white hair, the majority of the pigment will stay visible. Darker shades like Noir and Brun contain higher qualities of indigo and you may lose some of their cooler tones with regular shampooing. Mark explains, "Indigo doesn't have the same affinity with the hair so it fades more quickly than henna. That's why you may notice warmer tones coming through your henna after a while. You can reapply if these bother you."

Will henna lighten my hair?

Henna does not have the power to lighten your hair, although it picks up on the natural highlights and lowlights beautifully, rather than dyeing the hair a uniform colour.

How can I go darker if my hair is fair, bleached blonde or white?

We're going to have to be strict here: if you are planning to dye your fair hair darker, you must start with a red base. Indigo does not adhere to the hair without the help of henna, so applying a base of Rouge (the brick with the highest henna content) is crucial to avoid khaki tones and potentially patchy coverage. Apply a base of Rouge first, and follow up with your preferred colour on dry hair, whether that's Brun, Noir or Marron. Even if it's Rouge once more, a second application will make sure your coverage is even and more vivid.

If your desired shade is very dark or your natural hair is very fair, additional applications may be needed, but your colour will continue to oxidise over a couple of days and will subtly darken by itself.

Will henna cover my grey hairs?

Henna has a stunning effect on greys. Grey hair is an impression we form of hair composed of fibres that have lost their melanin and turned white, and fibres that still retain their natural dark colour. That's why blondes and redheads tend to go fairer as melanin production decreases when they age. You can read more about hair greying in Chapter 2.

Henna will not fully cover greys, which tend to be coarser than pigmented hairs, but coats them in a dazzling, twinkly way that looks healthy and natural. On a smaller number of grey hairs, this creates a highlights-esque effect. To achieve deeper coverage on hair that has more than a sprinkling of grey, you should follow the same procedure for colouring white and blonde hair, using Rouge as a base and then following with your chosen colour. Re-apply your henna as often as you like to keep the coverage fresh and your lighter hairs extra twinkly. Topping up with a Rouge base followed by your chosen brick regularly, will provide the best coverage.

HENNA AND AFRO HAIR

Is henna suitable for Afro hair?

Yes, henna can have a lovely protective effect on curl patterns 3A to 4C, especially if they are high porosity. The lawsone adheres to the cuticle, sealing any broken or open parts of the cuticle, and is a gentle alternative to synthetic permanent dyes. You may notice that the combability of your hair is not improved when using henna (that's because you are slightly increasing the density of the hair fibre) but the shine is fantastic.

Lush HairLab Afro hair consultant Sarah Sango says, "Henna is a lovely way to colour your hair if you don't want to damage it with a permanent dye. It may also give your curl pattern more definition. Based on feedback I have had from clients, the weight of the product can slightly loosen the tightness of the curls, which may or may not be desirable. Using henna on high porosity hair can also help fill open cuticles."

You may find it a little trickier to apply henna evenly to curly or coily hair, so allow yourself plenty of time and product, and rope in a friend if possible. "If you have very curly or coily hair, henna can be a big job because it becomes harder to wash all of the particles out," says Mark. "The cocoa butter helps with that. A conditioner or co-wash will also create more slip on the hair when rinsing away."

Can I use henna if I am transitioning from relaxed to natural hair?

Yes, and what a lovely treat to give your hair! Just bear in mind that you are working with different textures. Relaxed ends are likely to be very porous and accept the colour more quickly than natural roots. If your hair is dark, this is unlikely to show but bleached or blonde hair may have a very bright result at the ends. This can actually give a rather lovely balayage effect. Multiple applications will be key if you wish to build coverage.

Can I apply henna to braids or a similar protective style?

Yes, though it's advisable to only apply henna when your hair is loose to ensure that you have a thorough and even result (and are able to remove the henna successfully).

Can I use henna on my locs?

Henna can have a lovely effect on locs but it does take extra work to apply and rinse away. The main difficulty is removing the henna, so we advise removing with a co-wash to aid slip in the hair. Strand-testing is the best way to judge the scale of your job and your aptitude for it.

Can I use henna on my extensions?

Henna can be a great option for human hair extensions (not synthetic) to add depth or change colour without inducing damage. Just make sure to do a strand test on both the extensions and your own hair to ensure you have a colour match you are happy with.

HENNA AND SYNTHETIC COLOUR OR CHEMICAL TREATMENTS

Can I use henna on bleached hair?

Yes, henna can give beautiful colour and care to bleached hair, though it is not suitable if you lighten your hair regularly. Some customers choose to lighten their hair and then apply henna rather than using a synthetic permanent dye, so that the protective action of the henna will counteract some of the impact caused by extensive bleaching. You could choose to have highlights then henna over the top for a beautifully vibrant result.

There are some points to bear in mind though. Bleached, porous hair is especially susceptible to very bright results so be extra vigilant with the strand test and always apply a base of Rouge before using Marron, Brun or Noir. You may need to use further applications to reach your desired colour. Vénitien may be used directly on bleached hair without the base of Rouge.

Henna is not suitable to use before a bleaching process, however, as the alkaline conditions open the cuticle and push the lawsone deeper into the hair fibre. (For this reason, you should also not try to bleach henna out of your hair!) Wait for visual fading of the colour and do a strand test if you want to bleach hennaed hair.

Am I able to use henna if my hair has been coloured with synthetic hair dye?

Generally speaking, henna is not the best option for you if you wish to change your hair colour regularly, but it can be used alongside synthetic dyes in some circumstances.

The good news is that you can usually apply henna straight over the top of synthetic colour without any issues, though you should make sure you complete a strand test to check the result.

Colouring over the top of henna with a permanent or demi-permanent product is a trickier task. This is because the dye will find it harder to penetrate the cuticle and the bleaching action of the product will be less effective or push the henna deeper into the hair fibre. If you wish to use a permanent or demi-permanent dye over the top of hennaed hair, wait at least one month or better still, until your henna has recognisably faded, and then rely on a strand test to predict the results. You may need to wait longer, depending on how well the henna has taken to your hair and how dramatic a change you are making. (You may be able to use dye on hair coloured with Vénitien earlier due to its lower henna content.) It is also important to not use shades that are lighter than your hair colour as they will try to lift the colour like bleach does. Instead opt for shades at the same depth or darker.

If you are using a semi-permanent or temporary colour, which deposits colour on the cuticle and has no lightening power, you can usually apply this after using henna without any issues. Be aware that these products do not induce dramatic colour changes on the hair however, (except in the case of fair, white or grey hair) so you may not get your desired effect.

Can I use Lush henna on relaxed or permed hair?

Despite the rumours, yes, you can, with a bit of forethought. Henna has a dodgy reputation when it comes to perms, as the metallic compounds historically added to henna played havoc with the permed coiffures of many women in the 1930s (see Chapter 5). You won't find any of these in Lush henna. Both relaxer and perming chemicals need to penetrate the cuticle to induce structural changes in the hair however, so using henna beforehand (which adds a layer to the cuticle) will reduce the effectiveness of your treatment.

Using henna after your treatment is a lovely way to bring condition, shine and strength to hair damaged by the process. Mark advises waiting at least three days after relaxing or perming the hair to allow the structural changes to solidify, while Sarah suggests allowing a couple of weeks for Afro hair that is particularly fragile after being relaxed.

If you both henna and perm or relax your hair regularly, you may not quite achieve the desired structural changes, but your hair will look in much better condition. It's also natural for a little of the henna colour to come away from the fibre during a perm or relaxer so don't be alarmed.

ALLERGIES, HEALTH AND HENNA

Do I need to do a skin patch test before using henna?

Pure henna has very low allergenic potential and most reactions come from additives to the product such as para-phenylenediamine or even essential oils. However, if you are concerned, you can easily do a patch test at home. Simply whip up a small amount of Lush henna paste with hot water and apply it to your inner elbow (this is where your skin is thinner.) Cover with a plaster or wrap, rinse clean after two hours, and keep an eye out for any redness or irritation in the skin over the next 96 hours (aside from the natural staining of the skin). If you notice any irritation, do not proceed with a head application.

Is henna suitable for me to use if I have an allergy to synthetic hair dye?

Yes! Lush henna does not contain any of the materials that induce allergy in hair dye-allergic individuals (normally para-phenylenediamine and its derivatives). Read Chapter 9 for information on hair dye allergy and Chapter 12 for more on our henna sourcing and quality testing.

Are there any medical reasons I should not use henna?

Very few. Henna is not suitable for individuals who have glucose-6-phosphate dehydrogenase deficiency (G6PD). You can read about this in Chapter 10.

Is henna safe to use during pregnancy?

This is a very personal decision. Henna's incredibly long use gives it good safety credentials, and a lot of women choose to use it during pregnancy as a safer alternative to synthetic dyes. Many ancient customs that involve direct skin painting of a mother-to-be with henna during late pregnancy are still popular today. But research into all hair colouring while pregnant is shockingly low (you can see some of the risks associated with the use of synthetic hair dyes during and before pregnancy in Chapter 4). If dying your hair is important to you, it seems clear that henna is inherently safer than these dyes, given its incredibly long history of use. The results from the experiments Lush has undertaken with animal-free testing lab XCellR8 to test the genotoxicity of henna should also be reassuring (see Chapter 10). However, if you have any concerns about your pregnancy, avoiding all hair colourants while trying to conceive and at least during the first trimester appears to be the safest option.

A little henna self care? Don't mind if I do

I once asked Mark if creating a perfume was like putting together pieces of a jigsaw. He responded that, no, it was instead like putting nice complementary materials together for a dress. I can't help but feel that this attitude extends towards henna too.

Unlike using a synthetic dye, henna is not

like painting by numbers. There are certain steps you have to follow to get the result you want (applying a Rouge base before you go darker, for one) but there is so much scope for creativity and joy, and so much beauty in preparing and using the product.

Although messy, I personally love the heritage steeped in each application. Historically, henna applications have been bonding experiences between family and friends; an act of kindness and care towards your kin. The henna parties at Constantine & Weir embodied that spirit.

Today, I think henna applications also remind us of the importance of self-care. This is not a beauty treatment to be rushed, but savoured. For Persian women, henna applications were a practically essential but luxurious beauty treatment they were encouraged to indulge in while relaxing in the bathhouse. Men too took the time to colour their beards, relax and exchange news. The friends and family of Moroccan women who had just had a baby would pattern their skin with intricate henna designs to encourage them to put their feet up after childbirth. With henna applications comes permission to invest time in yourself - not always easy given the busy lives we lead. Having my hair coated in the reassuring weight of henna leaves and cocoa butter feels like time well spent - especially when it's being applied by my friends, Daisy and Mark.

Going green or targeting genes: What is the future of hair dye?

14

Is a future without hair dye possible?

As early as five decades ago, manufacturers argued 'no'. This was at the height of the mutagen scandal in the late 1970s, when they insisted that women were socially addicted to hair dye and that attempts to ban it would lead to a lucrative - and more dangerous - black market. They reformulated instead, removing the prominent animal carcinogens from their products, and choosing to rely on a dwindling stock of still problematic ingredients rather than abandon them altogether.

Despite these steps however, research has continued to find associations between aromatic amine-based hair dyes and cancer. The same can be said of allergy. Questions over the safety of hair dyes have not been answered by the work in the 1970s and 1980s and continue to grow. So too has consumer appetite for the products, and manufacturers' bank balances.

The profit generated by the hair dye industry, the ingratiation of these products in a third of women's beauty regimes across the world,[1] and the power of the industry lobby maintains the status quo. That's despite numerous experts agreeing aromatic amine-based hair dyes would be unlikely to be licensed if brought to the table now. "If manufacturers came in with para-phenylenediamine, or para-toluenediamine, or possibly even 2-Methoxy-methyl-p-phenylenediamine now and said they want to people to start dyeing their hair with these chemicals, I suspect they wouldn't get through the regulatory system," says Toxicologist Dr David Basketter. "They would be seen as too problematic. But, given the status quo, it's very difficult to take these products off the market."

With this in mind, it feels like this pivotal period in the 1970s and 1980s was a crucial missed opportunity to change the industry. Instead, manufacturers stuck doggedly to their aromatic amines, reiterating that hair dyes were less of a danger than habits such as smoking and stressing the importance of customer choice. Neither of these two points I disagree with incidentally. (Neither does Mark.) It's undoubtedly true that smoking is a bigger threat to people's health, but consumers buying cigarettes are also provided with information about the implications on their health. A majority of consumers buying hair dyes will have little awareness regarding their sensitising potential, or the potential links to some cancers.

Hair dye manufacturers relied heavily on animal testing data they produced during the 1970s and 1980s to argue that their products were safe. These experiments were criticised by scientists at the time as being inherently flawed,[2] as were some of the manufacturer's in vitro Ames' Test experiments they put forward as further evidence. Manufacturer reluctance to acknowledge the findings of the recent epidemiological studies into the long-term effects of hair dyes, let alone to fund more of this research, seems significant. I suspect many are working quietly behind the scenes desperately trying to find alternatives to the aromatic amine dyes causing so much trouble, but they are unwilling to disclose this and admit the problems with the current materials in use. Instead, they plough a lot of money into marketing.

In the UK alone, hair colourant advertising expenditure within the first 10 months of 2020 reached £27 million, most of which was focused on selling home-use permanent dyes (the same products with the most pronounced links to increased risk of some cancers) to a locked down population. The value sales of home hair colourants subsequently increased by 9.5% to £334 million.[3]

In the writing of this book, I was disappointed to find the pressure of the hair dye industry lobby still loomed ominously. Interviewees asked to speak off-the-record. Infinite lab research papers were paid for by the big players. Numerous contacted insiders did not respond to requests to talk. One contact confided that they had been told confidentially by a contract lab scientist that data showing mutagenic effects of hair dye ingredients was withheld by the hair dye companies who commissioned and so owned the data. Another recounted that they actually created a topical product that would reduce a person's chance of sensitisation and offered it to a range of major hair dye companies. It was roundly rejected. Why? They said something along the lines of "it admits that hair dyes are an allergy problem, and we don't want to do that."

"Are hair dyes a health risk?" I ask the experts who have generously given me their time. "Undoubtedly," says allergy expert Dr Basketter. "You can have an argument about what proportion of hair dye users get an allergic reaction of some significance, is it 1% or 2% or 4% or 5%, but it is there. On the other hand, you could argue that as long as consumers bother to do a patch test at least from time to time and take note of any evidence that they may be developing an allergy, then you can mitigate those risks because, as with nearly all allergens, if you avoid exposure, your symptoms go away. However, you will be allergic for the rest of your life."

Former Head of Colour Chemistry at Leeds University Professor David Lewis takes a stronger line. "In my opinion, all aromatic amines are suspect," he states. "The papers I have read indicate that bladder and breast cancers are prevalent in hairdressers and hair dye users – the literature is very large. Most startling is the fact that the aromatic amines can be detected in the urine up to 48 hours after the colouration procedure. Semi-permanent hair dyes are equally suspect as sometimes they are amines applied without peroxide. The current hair dyeing industry is surely on borrowed time unless serious efforts are made to eliminate the dreadful practice of developing colour from colourless aromatic amines by oxidative procedures."

There's another problem the industry would rather not discuss: the health of our ecosystem. Large numbers of colour molecules unconsumed by the dye process, as well as mutagenic byproducts, have been detected in hair salon wastewater, which are not believed to be adequately removed from our water systems.[4] These may bioaccumulate and could have a long-term impact on the health of aquatic eco-systems as well as humans.[5] Untreated textile dyes in water systems, for example, have been found to impair the photosynthesis process in plants and enter the food chain.[6] Professor Lewis states, "Effluent controls are completely lacking in the hair colouration industry and dumping potentially carcinogenic amines into our water supply really requires investigation. In contrast, the textile dyeing industry pays significant money to water authorities for control of its effluent."

With many manufacturers choosing not to

address the health concerns of these products, some hairdressers have taken matters into their own hands. A cleaner solution is proposed by one such salon owner, Nanette Barter, who believes her work in the hairdressing industry has had a big impact on her health. She established her Green Salon after a series of long-term illness and uses acid dyes (water soluble pigments developed for wool dyeing) rather than aromatic amines as an alternative colouring option for clients. This is an approach also endorsed by Professor Lewis.

"Our principles are that not everything organic is good, and not everything synthetic is bad," Nanette explains. "It's just really important to know the chemistry behind ingredients, and people are becoming more and more aware of that as time goes on. Acid dye systems are never promoted in the same way, despite being a safer alternative, because they just don't sell like oxidative colour. Imagine trying to promote something like this in the shops alongside oxidative colour systems, while telling everyone that it won't pre-lighten your hair and won't fully cover your grey, etc. People don't want it because the education isn't there yet."

Acid dyes are water soluble and so less damaging to the water systems they enter, and this is part of the reason Nanette and her team proudly call themselves 'environmental hairdressers'. "We need provisions in the hair and beauty industry for those who are also very conscious of their health and the environment," she says, "and our vision is to be leaders in that field. It's not easy though - we're doing what a lot of other salons won't. It can be costly in the short term, and we have a team of fantastic, experienced stylists who have all had to go back to basics completely to learn about colouring hair in a totally different way. I truly believe the industry needs to change, and it all starts with educating hairdressers while they're still students. They need to know there's a choice."

Nanette's adventurous spirit is admirable; her salon uses no oxidative aromatic amine-derived dyes, performs no bleaching procedures that come into contact with the scalp, and offers no perms at all in her bid to put customer health first. All this requires a great deal of explaining to new clients used to quick results. "I would say we've managed to convert 98% of the people we've had through the door here away from oxidative colour," she reflects, "but they just have to understand that it's a process. The hair is damaged so it takes time to build that condition back up, but it will happen! We spend maybe half an hour with each new client explaining what a Green Salon is, what we can and can't do. It's all about education!"

Green Salons like Nanette's are a really welcome approach to safer hairdressing, although there is still work to be done in assessing the safety of some of these materials, notably a form of acid dyes known as azo dyes. Lush toxicologist Chloé Raffalli explains, "Acid dyes are generally considered safe but when the azo type, which are used in some temporary and semi-permanent hair dyes, are metabolised by skin enzymes they can potentially form genotoxic aromatic amines."[7]

Given the recent associations between temporary and semi-permanent hair dye use and an increased risk of breast cancer (see Chapter 7), this warrants further investigation.[8] However, any risks are likely significantly reduced by professional application and permanent results, minimising the number of exposures a client would normally have to these materials when used in the form of temporary or semi-permanent products at home. The approach Nanette's salon takes is undoubtedly a big improvement on the current aromatic amine-based system, and her determination to find alternatives to the status quo is refreshing and much-needed.

Another more sci-fi-esque option tentatively posed is the future possibility of a drug that targets the melanocytes or even the genes that control them. "People have been trying to target the melanocytes for various reasons for a while now," says statistical geneticist Dr Kaustubh Adhikari, "because once the hair is produced in the scalp, it's dead and then you can only target it through dyes or bleach or so on. If you want to make your hair blonde from a darker colour, or your melanocytes have stopped producing melanin and you want to revert that, then you have to target the melanocytes specifically.

"But, if you did want to do something biologically (unlike dyeing which is chemical), then it's probably much better to target the melanocytes topically and specifically in the scalp rather than taking drugs that could affect melanin production in your entire body. Most of these genes work quite broadly, and if you take a medicine that stops melanin production generally, then you could start to lose melanin in your skin and develop vitiligo. Whatever drug or intervention you develop has to be very specific biologically, both in terms of the place that you apply, the cells that you target, and within those cells, the cellular mechanisms that you target."

Professor of Dermatological Science Desmond Tobin is sceptical that anything targeting the genes that control hair colour would be realistic, and agrees that a drug would need to intervene on a more practical level. "There is no guarantee that improving the function of a single associated genetic variant could significantly make a difference to actual hair colour because we may not know what all the other modifying genes are. Fundamentally, could you influence the entire scalp of 100,000 individual hair follicles in this way? If each hair follicle is largely operating on its own, how do you correct it for all the array of hairs that you have on the scalp?

"Most researchers would take the view that it's really not at the gene level that we could intervene, but probably more at the protein level. My best bet would be to find out what the best supporting influences are that you can provide, so that the pigmentation machinery of the hair follicles can have as long a viable life as possible. So, it's more about supportive intervention, rather than a reversal."

Will this type of biological cosmetic surgery for hair colour ever be a possibility? Will we all be swapping permanent dyes for melanocyte-targeting creams in the future? Or will a healthy fashion for natural hair - and the beautiful shades of grey that come with time - take hold? It seems clear that even this high-tech, futuristic 'solution' wouldn't be able to keep up with the fashion for changing hair colour now: hot pink one week, pastel blue the next. I also suspect that while grey hair will become more acceptable and desirable over the next few decades, the industry will adjust its marketing appropriately - targeting grey-haired customers with toners and rinses.

A future without hair dye seems impossible. People love the opportunities it offers for fashion and self-expression. People rely on current formulas to quickly hide the natural signs of ageing that are still stigmatised in the 21st century.

There is also an established precedent for selling products with a far greater associated cancer risk. Cancer kills 166,000 people per year in the UK - 450 every day.[9] That's more than Covid-19, for which we have accepted extensive restrictions on our lives, and has been attributed to 130,894 deaths in the UK between January 3rd 2020 and August 16th 2021.[10] If tobacco - a widely known leading cause of lung cancer - is not banned, hair dyes are not going to be either. But a future with informed customers savvy to the risks and taking steps to minimise them? That's within grasp.

Advice to go: what you should know about hair dye and what you can do about it

15

Three key things that hair dye users and hairdressers should know have become clear in the researching and writing of this book. I have tried to prioritise them.

One: Hair dyes are not as safe as customers may believe. (This warning does come with a caveat. They are not as dangerous for you as, say, cigarettes or skydiving without checking your equipment. But they are not harmless.) Hairdressers have increased risks of bladder cancer, non-Hodgkin lymphoma, some types of leukaemia (specifically chronic lymphocytic and chronic myeloid leukaemia) and multiple myeloma. Personal users of hair dyes have increased risk of breast cancer, non-Hodgkin lymphoma, lymphocytic leukaemia (as well as some conditions preceding leukaemia) and possibly multiple myeloma.

These risks appear more pronounced in cases of long-term use of dark hair dye or products or regions that use higher concentrations of para-phenylenediamine. Black women are noted to be at increased risk of breast cancers compared to White women. The takeaway? Hair dye users priced out of a professional colour service may be paying for it in other ways.

Two: Hair dye allergy remains worrying but is not clearly articulated to or understood by customers and even hairdressers. Manufacturers need to align on clear instructions for testing and the information on what to do if you have a reaction to a product needs to be more readily available. Claims like 'para-phenylenediamine-free' just aren't cutting it when it's possible to cross-react to materials in hair dye. The effect of allergy on hairdressers too is not being taken seriously, even though high numbers of salon staff are dealing with painful symptoms and large numbers are leaving the profession as a consequence. Better staff training and safety measures are desperately needed.

Three: Aromatica amine-derived hair dye is having an as of yet undetermined effect on the environment. Salon waste is a problem, but the increasing use of home dyes too mean these materials are being washed into our water system ever more frequently. We don't yet know the consequences of this on aquatic life, and potentially even our own health.

These are three pretty big causes for concern, yet we have to be realistic. The current alternatives to aromatic amine hair dyes are not half as convenient or quick. They do not offer the full range of shades and options that customers are accustomed to and are harder to fit into our busy lives. In an increasingly convenience-driven world, we respond to quick fixes because of our hectic lives. When it comes to hair dye, this has driven the rise of products that promise quicker results and more expansive options, over materials like henna and indigo that we once took the time to meticulously prepare and accepted came with shade limitations.

People are not going to stop dyeing their hair. From putrefied leeches to iron shavings and boot polish, we've established that the desire to change our hair colour can be traced back thousands of years. But where is the civilising influence that balances that desire with public health?

Even if it is too late to turn the clock back on aromatic amine hair dyes, we can instead change the way we use them by minimising our use of the riskiest at-home products and choosing styles that limit our contact with these materials. If we understand that the quick permanent results we are accustomed to come with certain health risks, we can then take steps to mitigate them. This would surely add a whole new spin on how to talk to your hairdresser.

Ideally, you would have hair dye applied by a professional and ask for a minimal scalp-contact service and a low-maintenance style that requires fewer root touch ups. Consider asking for a para-phenylenediamine-free product, and remain aware that the main alternatives are still derivatives and not risk-free.

If salon trips are not an option for you, see if a friend with a tinting brush can help apply your product so you are not massaging these materials into your scalp. Pick thicker formulas that give you more control, wear gloves and protect your hairline with a barrier cream. Opt for a well-ventilated space to apply. You may even find you don't need to leave the dye on for as long as stated on the packet. Remove your dye over the bath or with the shower head so that it does not run all over your body.

Whether you're heading to the salon or the supermarket for your colour, you should patch test yourself for an allergy ideally 96 hours before having a treatment, and pay attention to any irritation that can develop, even with a product that you have used before without problems. Generally speaking, lighter shades contain a smaller concentration of aromatic amines than dark colours. If you regularly dye your hair dark, you may wish to consider switching to less convenient but safer options like henna. You'll find more information on making hair dyes work for you in Chapter 8.

Lush too is adapting. As a company, we have always favoured naturals - specifically the powerhouse of henna and indigo - but recent conversations have also turned to what other hair colouring products and services we can offer customers safely. We face a question: as a company, do we stay well away from synthetic hair dyes or do we try to offer customers the safest options possible? It's a conversation that's instigated exciting new human cell testing on dyes with animal-free testing lab, XCellR8.

Recently, the scientists at XCellR8 tested an in-development Lush temporary dye product using the same pioneering *in vitro* 3D genotoxic test used to test our henna (as discussed in Chapter 10). XCellR8 scientists applied this product and a number of other popular commercial tinting shampoos and temporary colourants to reconstructed human skin for different periods of time to see how much penetrated through the skin to become systemically available to the body.

Given that Lush's product contained only one dye component and had a far higher level of natural ingredients, the results were surprising. Lush toxicologist Chloé Raffalli explains, "We were surprised to find that the tinting shampoo led to a drastic diminution of the cell viability, and turned on the genotoxic signals when left on the skin for 20 minutes. We observed the same results with all other brands tested, bar one. Based on this result, the decision was made to discontinue work on the product."

Not all of these competitor products were designed to be left on the skin as long as 20 minutes, although one suggested applying for even longer - up to 30. But the findings are concerning when we consider how easily available these products are from a young age and how often they may be being used.

The research in this book has also instigated testing in other areas at Lush, namely azo dyes: a class of dyes that, according to some research, are able to form genotoxic aromatic amines on the skin. Many azo dyes are completely legal and considered safe by numerous health authorities including the EU. Although we prefer the use of naturals where possible, Lush uses some azo dyes in our products. They too are being tested with the *in vitro* 3D genotoxic test and the results, combined with all the epidemiological research and interviews with experts that went into this book, will inform our own product formulations and offerings in the future. Fresh Lush hair salon services too are in development, informed by what the science tells us about the synthetics and the business's passion for natural materials.

Mark is excited about the future of hair colour at Lush, but, make no mistake, henna remains his obsession. Well, henna and birdsong.

From the evolution of human hair to the advancement of hair colouring methods, the next chapter in hair dyeing is still to be written. The past cannot be undone and it feels unlikely that aromatic amine hair dyes will be replaced in the near future by the current alternatives we have. But perhaps we can move out of the dark ages of dyeing into a new era of health-conscious colouring, one driven by innovative hairdressers and educated customers with their wellbeing in mind. Creativity in how we colour, and ensuring that it is an informed choice not a response to the stigma of hair greying, will be key. We need fashions that are fun but informed, and techniques that are flattering but low-maintenance.

More than that, we need consumers that are empowered through education and driven to seek better from the industry. We hope we've contributed in some way to that goal through the writing of this book, and that we can all demand and seek better solutions to what appears to be a very basic human desire.

Will you highlight, home-dye, henna or balayage in future? Will you even embrace your natural colour? The choice is yours.

Acknowledgements

This book would not exist without the help, support and expertise of copious contributors, colleagues and friends who have been so generous with their time. Here are the many, many people who deserve a thanks, in no particular order.

Suzie Hackney for her incredible creative vision and our wonderful designers, Dani Dixon and Tamsin Thomas for turning pages of dense text into lovely-looking chapters.

Lili Thomas for artworking the front cover and making the final artworking changes.

Paige Jones for making extra artworking changes.

Rachel Norden for her work designing the book's covers, endpapers and patterns within.

Molly Morris for bringing the pages to life with her beautiful illustrations, and Katie Williams for her initial illustration inspiration.

Sam Baggette for the last minute photography.

Grace Cohen and Natalie Denton, our proofreaders, for their scrutiny and diligence. Not to forget our indexer Lyndsay Marshall for saving me a massive job - thank you!

Dr Jarek Bryk for being my first interviewee and drawing me into the wonderful world of evolutionary genomics with such enthusiasm.

Professor Nina Jablonski for giving me her valuable time amidst a relocation whilst on a sabbatical!

Dr Gillian Westgate for her incredible insights into the biology of curly hair and for introducing me to like-minded trichologists across the field.

Dr Kaustubh Adhikari for breaking down complex genomic findings into language I could understand.

Professor Ian Jackson for a fascinating discussion on hair and skin colour.

Dr Selina Brace for showing us where the dead things are kept behind the scenes at the Natural History Museum and for introducing us to Cheddar Man with so much enthusiasm.

Professor Hannes Schroeder who shared his findings and theories about Lola the hunter-gatherer with me.

Professor Michael Dannemann for busting some key Neanderthal myths and for being so willing to answer follow-up questions.

Professor Desmond Tobin for the captivating conversation on hair colour. I could have chatted for hours!

Dr Robert Hefford for delving into the complex history and chemistry of hair dye with me.

Andrew Browning for the highly recommended chemistry lessons (and to his wife Jo for the lovely homemade flapjack).

Iain Sallis for answering my queries on hair loss and for hosting an excellent series of trichology seminars that made Thursday evenings far more enjoyable during lockdown.

Professor Joann Fletcher for discussing mummies, hairpieces and henna in

Ancient Egypt.

Professor Kelly Olson for her warmth and fascinating discussion of hair bleaching in Ancient Rome.

Professor Ahmed El Shamsy for his invaluable information about the relationship between henna and Islam.

Professor Maria Montserrat Cabré for illuminating me on cosmetics and Medieval misogyny.

Professor Michelle Laughran, firstly for sharing her expertise in Venetian hair dye practices, and secondly for going above and beyond to give me valuable extra information and feedback.

Professor Mary K. Gayne for guiding me through the complex world of wigs, politics and privilege in revolutionary France.

Professor Morag Martin for her detailed knowledge on the very precise shades of fashionable hair colour in the same period.

Dr David Basketter for an incredibly informative interview, being the fastest respondee by email ever, and answering a number of follow-up questions.

Professors Bruce Ames and Giovanna Ferro-Luzzi Ames for the fascinating personal recollection of events of the 1970s.

Dr Carol Treasure for her time in discussing alternatives to animal tests with me and her ongoing work at XCellR8.

Professor Kefah Mokbel for talking me through his academic findings on breast cancer, and also his personal experiences as a breast cancer surgeon.

Dr John James for the interesting introduction to allergy and sensitisation - one of the few pre-Covid-19 in-person interviews possible!

Professor Luc Renaut for offering an insightful and alternative view to henna's history.

Professor Lloyd Llewellyn-Jones for the fascinating introduction to Ancient Persia and for his kind encouragement.

Professor David Lewis for fearlessly sharing his opinion and expertise on hair dyes with me.

Nanette Barter for taking me through the rewards and challenges of running a Green Salon and for sharing the personal circumstances that led her there.

Dr Stan Venitt for being as kind and generous with his time as Mark recalled, despite my abrupt disruption of his retirement. (And for inviting us to his home for an interview - a real highlight in the writing of this book).

The friends, family, colleagues and more who allowed me to ask probing questions about their hair dye habits: Leanne Coen, Katie Bishop, Jess Cerasale, Mandi Nicholls, Darcie Foulger, Charlotte Nisbet, Lucky Prior, Debbi Allen, Naomi Rankin, Maria Feast and Sue and Ella-Mae Bolton.

The academics and colleagues who took the time to respond to my questions: Professor Julian Peto, Professor Carl Phelpstead, Dr Nazanin Dooghaee Moghadam, Dr Alexandra White, Professor Fatema Soudavar Farmanfarmaian, Dr Catherine Cartwright-Jones, Ahmed Salah and Janis Paskin.

The wonderful farmers and suppliers of Lush's henna and indigo, including but not limited to Ghassem and Mohammad, Mr Ibrahim, Mr Turk, Azade Zia and Nicolas Märgner.

Former Lush buyers Mark Rumbell and Jo Bridger for sharing their experiences and images of visiting Iran with me.

Current Lush Buyers Pendle Hill and Cadi Pink for their fact-finding, fact checks and feedback, and Tarek Soliman for sharing the principles of Agroecology with me.

Annabelle Baker and Alessandro Commisso for providing me with personal experience of salon and hair dye culture in Hong Kong and Italy.

Jet Shears for talking to me about Lush's microbiology testing (and for subsequently testing a range of new henna formulas).

Chris Grey and Dayfold Ltd for actually finding a way to print this book with ink made with henna.

Chloé Raffalli for her toxicology expertise and for answering my many, many questions!

Elise McKenna for being a goldmine of Lush information and for delving through the company archives on numerous occasions with only the smallest clue to go on.

The wonderful Lush HairLab team for supporting the project. Special thanks to Sarah Sango for her expertise on Afro hair, Gemma Sales for her product knowledge, and last but not least to Daisy Evans for her incredible work on the henna bricks from her kitchen, and the reading of, and responding to, numerous drafts and questions. Bonus mention to the incredible Manufacturing staff at Unit 1, especially Mirek Smuga for speaking to me about the process of reformulating the henna bricks.

The A-Team of Lush co-founders, directors and colleagues who kindly gave me their time, especially Hilary Jones, for talking to me about the design of the original henna bricks; Wesley Burrage for showing us his box of hair (and the reformulation help); and Mo Constantine and Rowena Bird for giving permission for me to use their images.

Helen Ambrosen, firstly for inventing the henna brick all those years ago, but also for keeping that stash of documents Mark had forgotten all about, and for her incredible memory.

Mark Constantine for writing that very first book back in the 1970s, for giving me the opportunity to take on a project so personal to him, and for his unswerving support of working mums.

Matt Fairhall for not panicking when I told him I was pregnant with baby number two and simply slotting it into the schedule. And for the many hours of editing, support and guidance to turn this book into a reality!

Ryan for listening to me rabbit on about hair for the last two and half years, helping with the sciencey stuff, and for always being my rock. To Matilda for putting up with Mummy working late with reasonably good grace and for all the cuddles.

Milly Ahlquist

Milly joined Lush as a sales assistant in 2011 while studying for a Master's Degree in English Literature at Cardiff University. She worked as Trainee Manager in Lush Bath Spa before joining the brand team in 2014 as a writer, researcher and editor.

Previous projects include working on the Lush Times, The Self-Preserving Handbook and creating content for events such as the Creative Showcase and Lush Summit. A mum of two, past-times include drinking too much coffee, dragging her family outdoors for fresh air and a long soak in the bath with a good book when the kids are in bed.

Mark Constantine

Mark co-founded Lush with five friends and creative confidants in 1995 after the collapse of previous mail order business Cosmetics To Go. Mark has been a key driving force behind the business for 25 years and also works as part of the product development team creating hair, skincare and body creams as well as decadent Lush spa treatments.

Challenging the business to create fresh, innovative and anarchic cosmetic products, some of Mark's beliefs have become the backbone of the company. Lush's stringent and pioneering 'against animal testing policy' is just one example of how his strong beliefs have transformed the cosmetics industry.

Credits

Cover design by Rachel Norden with inspiration supplied by The Design Library

Cover artwork by Lili Thomas

Book Design by Dani Dixon, Lili Thomas, Paige Jones and Tamsin Thomas

Page 9 © Simon Plades c/o Debut

Page 16 © Tina Zellmer c/o Debut

Page 29 © Molly Morris

Page 30 © Molly Morris

Page 31 © Molly Morris

Page 34 © Marieke Nelissen c/o IllustrationX

Page 35 © Molly Morris

Page 45 © Débora Islas c/o IllustrationX

Page 48 © Molly Morris

Page 50 © Molly Morris

Page 63 © Natalie Foss c/o Illo Agency

Page 70 © Molly Morris

Page 76 © Molly Morris

Page 78 © Simon Plades c/o Debut

Page 87 © María Jesús Contreras c/o Illo Agency

Page 93 Photo sourced from Wkimedia Commons

Page 97 © Professor Bruce Ames

Page 99 © Dr Stanley Venitt

Page 107 © Lush Ltd

Page 108 TBC

Page 122 © Molly Morris

Page 131 © Jael Makelemi \ Nubiart c/o Illo Agency

Page 138 © Molly Morris

Page 139 © Molly Morris

Page 140 © Molly Morris

Page 149 © Rachel Winter c/o IllustrationX

Page 159 © Tina Zellmer c/o Debut

Page 162 © Bob Venables c/o IllustrationX

Page 164 © Molly Morris

Page 170 © Molly Morris

Page 176 © Lush Ltd

Page 178 © Molly Morris

Page 180 © Molly Morris

Page 185 © Michael Frith c/o IllustrationX

Page 186 © Lush Ltd

Page 187 © Lush Ltd

Page 189 © Molly Morris

Page 196 © Lush Ltd

Page 197 © Lush Ltd

Page 198 © Lush Ltd

Page 199 © Lush Ltd

Index

Page numbers in italics refer to illustrations. Chemical names are filed alphabetically rather than by numerical prefix.

Citations

Chapter 1

1 **Ridder, M** 2020. *Global hair coloring market size 2019 & 2025*, Statista, <https://www.statista.com/statistics/972997/global-hair-color-market-value/>.

2 *Hair Colourants: UK January 2020*, Mintel <https://reports.mintel.com/display/1001408/>.

3 **Morris, D** 1967. *The Naked Ape*, Penguin Vintage, London.

4 Varki et al clarify that the oft-cited figure of '99%' shared DNA in fact refers to shared amino acid sequences. See **Varki, A et al** 2005. 'Comparing the human and chimpanzee genomes: Searching for needles in a haystack', *Genome Research*.

5 **Diogo, R et al** 2017. 'Bonobo anatomy reveals stasis and mosaicism in chimpanzee evolution, and supports bonobos as the most appropriate extant model for the common ancestor of chimpanzees and humans', *Scientific Reports*, Volume 7.

6 **Wei-Haas, M** 2019. 'Controversial new study pinpoints where all modern humans arose', *National Geographic* <https://on.natgeo.com/2LM9PAu>.

Maslin, M 2014. 'East African climate pulses and early human evolution', *Quaternary Science Reviews*, Volume 101.

7 **Yesudian, P** 2011. 'Human Hair – An Evolutionary Relic?', *International Journal of Trichology*, Volume 3.

8 **Gray, R** 2016. 'The real reasons why we walk on two legs not four', BBC <https://bbc.in/2JBW9Yk>.

9 **Morris, D** 1967. *The Naked Ape*.

10 **Jablonski, N** 2006. *Skin: A Natural History*, University of California Press, Berkeley.

11 **Jablonski, N** 2006. *Skin: A Natural History*.

12 **Gray, R** 2016. 'The real reasons why we walk on two legs not four'.

13 **Wang, W et al** 2005. 'Stride lengths, speed and energy costs in walking of Australopithecus afarensis: using evolutionary robotics to predict locomotion of early human ancestors', *Journal of the Royal Society*, Volume 2, Issue 5.

14 **Lieberman, D** 2015. 'Human Locomotion and heat loss: an evolutionary perspective', *Comprehensive Physiology*, Volume 5.

15 **Lieberman, D** 2015. 'Human Locomotion and heat loss: an evolutionary perspective'.

16 **Jablonski, N** 2006. *Skin: A Natural History*.

17 **Schulkin, J** 2016. 'Evolutionary Basis of Human Running and Its Impact on Neural Function', *Frontiers in Systems Neuroscience*, Volume 10.

Rogers, A.R et al 2004. 'Genetic Variation at the MC1R Locus and the Time since Loss of Human Body Hair', *The Wenner-Gren Foundation for Anthropological Research*.

18 **Lieberman, D** 2015. 'Human locomotion and heat loss: an evolutionary perspective'.

19 **Yesudian, P** 2011. 'Human Hair – An Evolutionary Relic?'.

20 **Baker, L et al** 2019. 'Physiology of sweat gland function: The roles of sweating and sweat composition in human health', *Temperature*, Volume 6, Issue 3.

21 **Kamberov, Y et al** 2018. 'Comparative evidence for the independent evolution of hair and sweat gland traits in primates', *Journal of Human Evolution*, Volume 125.

22 **Baker, L et al** 2019. 'Physiology of sweat gland function: The roles of sweating and sweat composition in human health'.

23 **Lieberman, D** 2015. 'Human locomotion and heat loss: an evolutionary perspective'.

24 **Holmes, A et al** 1991.'The evolution of sweat glands', *The International Society of Biometeorology*, Volume 35, Issue 3.

25 **Porter, A et al**, 2001. 'Why do we have apocrine and sebaceous glands?', *Journal of the Royal Society of Medicine*, Volume 94, Issue 5.

26 **Lieberman, D** 2015. 'Human locomotion and heat loss: an evolutionary perspective'.

27 **Lieberman, D** 2016. 'Being Human: Born and Evolved to Run', *The Leakey Foundation and the Baumann Foundation* <https://www.youtube.com/watch?v=cSQl5wZ4g6I>.

28 **Lieberman, D** 2015. 'Human locomotion and heat loss: an evolutionary perspective'.

29 **Holmes, A et al 1991**.'The evolution of sweat glands'.

30 **Jablonksi, N** 2006. Skin: *A Natural History*.

31 **Holmes, A et al** 1991.'The evolution of sweat glands'.

32 **Porter, A et al** 2001. 'Why do we have apocrine and sebaceous glands?'.
Lieberman, D 2015. 'Human locomotion and heat loss: an evolutionary perspective'.

33 **Liebenberg, L** 2006. 'Persistence Hunting by Modern Hunter-Gatherers', *Current Anthropology*, Vol. 47, Issue 6.
See also **Liebenberg, L** 2013. The Origin of Science: *The Evolutionary Roots of Scientific Reasoning and its Implications for Citizen Science*, CyberTracker, Cape Town.

34 **Rogers, A.R et al** 2004. 'Genetic Variation at the MC1R Locus and the Time since Loss of Human Body Hair'.

35 **Corani, A et al** 2014. 'Superior Photoprotective Motifs and Mechanisms in Eumelanins Uncovered', *Journal of the American Chemical Society*, Volume 136, Issue 33.

36 **Jablonski, N** 2006. Skin: *A Natural History*.

37 **Harding, R et al** 2000. 'Evidence for Variable Selective Pressures at MC1R', *The American Society of Human Genetics*, Volume 66.

38 **Westgate, G et al** 2017. 'The Biology and genetics of curly hair', *Experimental Dermatology*, Volume 26, Issue 6.

39 **Byrd, A and Tharps, L** 2014. Hair Story: *Untangling the Roots of Black Hair in America*, St. Martin's Publishing Group, New York.

40 **Li, S et al** 2014. 'Genetic variation reveals large-scale population expansion and migration during the expansion of Bantu-speaking peoples', *Proceedings of the Royal Society*, Volume 281, Issue 1793.

41 **Lin, M et al** 2018. 'Rapid evolution of a skin-lightening allele in southern African KhoeSan', *Proceedings of the National Academy of Sciences*, Volume 115, Issue 52.

42 **Choudhury, A et al** 2018. 'African genetic diversity provides novel insights into evolutionary history and local adaptations', *Human Molecular Genetics*, Volume 27, Issue R2.

43 **Jahangir, R** 2015. 'How does black hair reflect black history?', *BBC* <https://bbc.in/2PFyzLE>.

44 **Byrd, A and Tharps, L** 2014. *Hair Story: Untangling the Roots of Black Hair in America*

45 **Harvati, K et al** 2019. 'Apidima Cave fossils provide earliest evidence of *Homo sapiens* in Eurasia', *Nature*, Volume 57.

46 **Li, Y et al** 2015. 'Discovery of the Fuyan teeth: challenging or complementing the out-of-Africa scenario?', *Dongwuxue Yanjiu*, Volume 36, Issue 6.

47 **Parry, W** 2011. 'Lock of Aboriginal Man's Hair Unlocks Secrets of Human Migration', *Live Science* <https://www.livescience.com/16182-australian-aborigine-genome-human-dispersal.html>.

48 **Westgate, G et al** 2017. 'The Biology and genetics of curly hair', *Experimental Dermatology*, Volume 26, Issue 6.

49 **Kenny, E** 2012. 'Melanesians blond hair is caused by an amino acid change in TYRP1', *Science*, Volume 336, Issue 6081.

50 **Tobler, R et al** 2017. 'Aboriginal mitogenomes reveal 50,000 years of regionalism in Australia', *Nature*, Volume 544.
Kenny, E 2012. 'Melanesians blond hair is caused by an amino acid change in TYRP1'

51 **Chen, F et al** 2019. ' A late Middle Pleistocene Denisovan mandible from the Tibetan Plateau', *Nature*, Volume 569.

52 **Sawyer, S et al** 2015. 'DNA sequences from two Denisovan individuals', *Proceedings of the National Academy of Sciences*, Volume 112, Issue 51.
Hyun Ko, K et al 2016. 'Hominin interbreeding and the evolution of human variation', *Journal of Biological Research-Thessaloniki*, Volume 23, Issue 17.

53 **Darwin, C** 1859. **On the Origin of Species by means of Natural Selection**, John Murray, London.

54 **Bryk, J et al** 2008. 'Positive Selection in East Asians for an *EDAR* Allele that Enhances NF-κB Activation', *PLoS One*, Volume 3, Issue 5.

55 **Bae, J et al** 2017. 'On the origin of modern humans: Asian perspectives', *Science*, Volume 358, Issue 6368.
Goebel, T et al 2008. 'The Late Pleistocene Dispersal of Modern Humans in the Americas', *Science*, Volume 319, Issue 5869.

56 **Bryk, J et al** 2008. 'Positive Selection in East Asians for an *EDAR* Allele that Enhances NF-κB Activation'.

57 **Naidoo, N et al** 2011. 'Human genetics and genomics a decade after the release of the draft sequence of the human genome', *Human Genomics*, Volume 5, Issue 6.

58 **Bryk, J et al** 2008. 'Positive Selection in East Asians for an *EDAR* Allele that Enhances NF-κB Activation'.

59 **Tan, J et al** 2013. 'The adaptive variant EDARV370A is associated with straight hair in East Asians', *Human Genetics*, Volume 132.
Kimura, R 2009. 'A Common Variation in EDAR Is a Genetic Determinant of Shovel-Shaped Incisors', *The American Journal of Human Genetics*, Volume 85.

60 **Hlusko, L et al** 2018. 'Environmental selection during the last ice age on the mother-to-infant transmission of vitamin D and fatty acids through breast milk', *Proceedings of the National Academy of Sciences*, Volume 115, Issue 19.

61 **Kimura, R** 2009. 'A Common Variation in EDAR Is a Genetic Determinant of Shovel-Shaped Incisors'.

62 **Park, JH et al** 2012. 'Effects of an Asian-specific nonsynonymous EDAR variant on multiple dental traits', *Journal of Human genetics*, Volume 57.

63 **Pelto, B et al** 2018. 'Oceanographic and Climatic Change

in the Bering Sea, Last Glacial Maximum to Holocene', Paleoceanography and Paleoclimatology, Volume 33, Issue 1.

64 **Raff, J** 2018. 'What the ancient DNA discovery tells us about Native American ancestry', *The Guardian* <https://www.theguardian.com/science/2018/jan/03/what-the-ancient-dna-discovery-tells-us-about-nati ve-american-ancestry>.

Moreno-Mayar, J et al 2018. 'Terminal Pleistocene Alaskan genome reveals first founding population of Native Americans', *Nature,* Volume 553.

65 **Tackney, C et al** 2015. 'Two contemporaneous mitogenomes from terminal Pleistocene burials in eastern Beringia', Proceedings of the National Academy of Sciences, Volume 112, Issue 45.

66 **Hlusko, L et al** 2018. 'Environmental selection during the last ice age on the mother-to-infant transmission of vitamin D and fatty acids through breast milk'.

67 **Graf, K et al** 2018. 'Human Dispersal from Siberia to Beringia: Assessing a Beringian Standstill in Light of the Archaeological Evidence', *Royal Society of Open Science,* Volume 5, Issue 6.

68 **Jakobsson, M et al** 2017. 'Post-glacial flooding of the Beringia Land Bridge dated to 11,000 cal yrs BP based on new geophysical and sediment records', *Climate of the Past,* Volume 13, Issue 8.

69 **López, Saioa et al** 2016. 'Human Dispersal Out of Africa: A Lasting Debate.', *Evolutionary Bioinformatics Online,* Volume 11, Issue 2.

70 **Gibbons, A** 2015. 'How Europeans evolved white skin', *Science,* <https://www.sciencemag.org/news/2015/04/how-europeans-evolved-white-skin>.

71 **Jablonski,** N 2006. *Skin: A Natural History.*

72 **Schæbel, L K et al** 2015. 'Vitamin D-rich marine Inuit diet and markers of inflammation - a population-based survey in Greenland', *Journal of Nutritional Science,* Volume 4, Issue 40.

73 **Janif, J et al** 2015. 'Are Preferences for Women's Hair Color Frequency-Dependent?', *Adaptive Human Behavior and Physiology,* Volume 1.

74 **Guenther, C et al** 2014. 'A molecular basis for classic blond hair color in Europeans', *Nature Genetics,* Volume 46.

75 **Katsara, M et al** 2019. 'True colors: A literature review on the spatial distribution of eye and hair pigmentation', *Forensic Science International: Genetics,* Volume 39.

76 **Tobin, D** 2008. 'Human hair pigmentation – biological aspects', *International Journal of Cosmetic Science,* Volume 30, Issue 4.

77 **Frost, P** 2014. 'The Puzzle of European Hair, Eye and Skin Colour', *Advances in Anthropology,* Volume 4.

78 **Frost, P** 2014. 'The Puzzle of European Hair, Eye and Skin Colour'.

79 **Frost, P** 2008. 'Sexual Selection and Human Geographic Variation', Journal of Social, *Evolutionary, and Cultural Psychology,* Volume 2, Issue 4.

80 **Frost, P** 2008. 'Sexual Selection and Human Geographic Variation'.

81 **Frost, P** 2014. 'The Puzzle of European Hair, Eye and Skin Colour'.

82 **Hrdy, S** 1997. 'Raising Darwin's Consciousness: Female Sexuality and the Prehominid Origins of Patriarchy', *Human Nature,* Volume 8, Issue 1.

83 **Harari, Y** 2015. *Sapiens: A Brief History Of Humankind,* Penguin Vintage, London.

84 **Krizman J et al** 2012. 'Sex differences in auditory subcortical function', Clinical Neurophysiology, Volume 123, Issue 3.

Sorokowsk, P et al 2019. 'Sex Differences in Human Olfaction: A Meta-Analysis', F*rontiers in Psychology,* Volume 10, Issue 242.

85 **Laeng, B et al** 2007. 'Why do blue-eyed men prefer women with the same eye color?', *Behavioral Ecology and Sociobiology,* Volume 61.

86 First Brit: Secrets of the 10,000 Year Old Man, Channel 4, 18th February 2018.

87 **MerveKılınç, G** 2016. ' The Demographic Development of the First Farmers in Anatolia', *Current Biology,* Volume 26, Issue 19.

88 **Baird, D et al** 2018. 'Agricultural origins on the Anatolian plateau', *Proceedings of the National Academy of Sciences,* Volume 115, Issue 14.

89 **Vigne, J** 2011. 'The origins of animal domestication and husbandry: A major change in the history of humanity and the biosphere', *Comptes Rendus Biologies,* Volume 334, Issue 3.

90 **Vigne, J** 2011. 'The origins of animal domestication and husbandry: A major change in the history of humanity and the biosphere', *Comptes Rendus Biologies,* Volume 334, Issue 3.

91 **Hole, F** 2007. 'Agricultural sustainability in the semi-arid Near East', *Climate of the Past,* Volume 3.

92 **Harari, Y** 2015. *Sapiens: A Brief History Of Humankind.*

93 **Harari, Y** 2015. *Sapiens: A Brief History Of Humankind.*

94 **Harari, Y** 2015. *Sapiens: A Brief History Of Humankind.*

95 **Curry, A** 2019. 'The first Europeans weren't who you might think'.

96 **Schroeder, H et al** 2019. 'A 5700 year-old human genome and oral microbiome from chewed birch pitch', *Nature Communications,* Volume 10, Article 5520.

97 **Storhaug, C et al** 2017. 'Country, regional, and global estimates for lactose malabsorption in adults: a systematic review and meta-analysis', *The Lancet Gastroenterology &*

Hepatology, Volume 2, Issue 10.

98 **Wells, J et al** 2020. 'Life History Transitions at the Origins of Agriculture: A Model for Understanding How Niche Construction Impacts Human Growth, Demography and Health', *Frontiers in Endocrinology,* Volume 11, Article 325.

99 **Itan, Y et al** 2009. 'The origins of lactase persistence in Europe', *PLoS Computational Biology,* Volume 5, Issue 8

100 **Curry, A** 2019. 'The first Europeans weren't who you might think', *National Geographic* <https://www.nationalgeographic.com/culture/article/first-europeans-immigrants-genetic-testing-feature?loggedin=true>.

101 **Flegr, J et al** 2019. 'Skin fairness is a better predictor for impaired physical and mental health than hair redness.', *Scientific reports,* Volume 9, Issue 1.

102 **Lalueza-Fox, C et al** 2007. 'A melanocortin 1 receptor allele suggests varying pigmentation among Neanderthals', *Science,* Vol. 318, Issue 5855.

103 **Dannemann, M et al** 2017. 'The Contribution of Neanderthals to Phenotypic Variation in Modern Humans', *The American Journal of Human Genetics,* Volume 101.

104 **Martínez-Cadenas, C et al** 2013. 'Simultaneous Purifying Selection on the Ancestral MC1R Allele and Positive Selection on the Melanoma-Risk Allele V60L in South Europeans', *Molecular Biology and Evolution,* Volume 30, Issue 12.

105 **Moffat, A** 2013. *Britain: A Genetic Journey,* Birlinn, Edinburgh.

106 **Jackson, I et al** 2018. 'Genome-wide study of hair colour in UK Biobank explains most of the SNP heritability', *Nature Communications,* Volume 9, Article 5271.

107 **Collis Harvey, J** 2015. *Red: A Natural History of the Redhead,* Allen & Unwin, London.

108 **Jackson, I et al** 2018. 'Genome-wide study of hair colour in UK Biobank explains most of the SNP heritability', *Nature Communications,* Volume 9, Article 5271.

109 **Robles-Espinoza, C et al** 2016. 'Germline MC1R status influences somatic mutation burden in melanoma', *Nature Communications,* Volume 7, Article 12064.

Chapter 2

1 **Sandel, A** 2013. 'Brief Communication: Hair Density and Body Mass in Mammals and the Evolution of Human Hairlessness', *American Journal of Physical Anthropology,* Volume 152, Issue 1.

2 **Foitzik, K et al** 2006. 'Human Scalp Hair Follicles Are Both a Target and a Source of Prolactin, which Serves as an Autocrine and/or Paracrine Promoter of Apoptosis-Driven Hair Follicle Regression', *American Journal of Pathology,* Volume 168, Issue 3.

3 **Kamberov, Y et al** 2018. 'Comparative evidence for the independent evolution of hair and sweat gland traits in primates', *Journal of Human Evolution,* Volume 125.

4 **Sandel, A** 2013. 'Brief Communication: Hair Density and Body Mass in Mammals and the Evolution of Human Hairlessness'.

5 **Stenn, K** 2016. *Hair: A Human History,* Pegasus Books, New York.

6 **Carnaby, T** 2009. *Beat about the Bush: Birds,* Jacana Media, Johannesburg.

7 **Stenn, K** 2016. *Hair: A Human History.*

8 **Breed, M et al** 2011. *Animal Behavior,* Elsevier Science.

9 **Solano, F** 2014. 'Melanins: Skin Pigments and Much More—Types, Structural Models, Biological Functions, and Formation Routes', *New Journal of Science,* Volume 2014, Article 498276.

10 **Jablonski, N** 2006. *Skin: A Natural History,* University of California Press, Berkeley.

11 **Tobin, D et al** 2001. 'Graying: gerontobiology of the hair follicle pigmentary unit', *Experimental Gerontology,* Volume 36, Issue 1.

12 **D'Alba, L et al** 2019. 'Melanosomes: Biogenesis, Properties, and Evolution of an Ancient Organelle', *Physiological Reviews,* Volume 99, Issue 1.

14 **Cichorek, M et al** 2013. 'Skin melanocytes: biology and development', *Postępy Dermatologii i Alergologii,* Volume 30, Issue 1.

15 **Praetorius, C** 2014. 'Sun-induced freckling: ephelides and solar lentigines', *Pigment Cell and Melanoma Research,* Volume 27, Issue 3.

16 **Gola, M et al** 2012. 'Melanocyte stem cells: biology and current aspects', *Medical science monitor: international medical journal of experimental and clinical research,* Volume 18, Issue 10.

17 **Mull, A et al** 2015. 'Understanding Melanocyte Stem Cells for Disease Modeling and Regenerative Medicine Applications', *International Journal of Molecular Sciences,* Volume 16, Issue 12.

18 Neuromelanin - a third pigment that colours regions of the brain - is derived mostly from dopamine. See **Haining,**

R et al 2017. 'Neuromelanin, one of the most overlooked molecules in modern medicine, is not a spectator', *Neural Regeneration Research,* Volume 12, Issue 3.

19 **Jablonski, N** 2006. *Skin: A Natural History.*

F. Solano 2014. 'Melanins: Skin Pigments and Much More—Types, Structural Models, Biological Functions, and Formation Routes', *New Journal of Science,* Volume 2014, Article Number 498276.

Baran, R (ed) et al 2010. *Textbook of Cosmetic Dermatology,* Informa Healthcare, London.

20 **Wu, X et al** 2014. 'Melanosome transfer: it is best to give and receive', Current Opinion in Cell Biology, Volume 29.

21 **Ando, H et al** 2012. 'Melanosomes Are Transferred from Melanocytes to Keratinocytes through the Processes of Packaging, Release, Uptake, and Dispersion', *Journal of Investigative Dermatology,* Volume 132, Issue 4.

22 **F. Solano** 2014. 'Melanins: Skin Pigments and Much More—Types, Structural Models, Biological Functions, and Formation Routes'.

D'Orazio, J et al 2013. 'UV radiation and the skin', International Journal of Molecular Sciences, Volume 14, Issue 6.

23 **Brenner, M et al** 2008. 'The protective role of melanin against UV damage in human skin', *Photochemistry and Photobiology,* Volume 84, Issue 3.

24 **Brenner, M et al** 2008. 'The protective role of melanin against UV damage in human skin'.

Tadokoro, T et al 2005. 'Mechanisms of Skin Tanning in Different Racial/Ethnic Groups in Response to Ultraviolet Radiation', *The Journal of Investigative Dermatology,* Volume 124, Issue 6.

25 **Brenner, M et al** 2008. 'The protective role of melanin against UV damage in human skin'.

26 **Praetorius, C et al** 2014. 'Sun-induced freckling: ephelides and solar lentigines', *Pigment Cell & Melanoma Research,* Volume 27, Issue 3.

27 **Praetorius, C et al** 2014. 'Sun-induced freckling: ephelides and solar lentigines'.

28 **Breathnach, A et al** 1964. 'Electron Microscopy of Melanocytes and Melanosomes in Freckled Human Epidermis', *Journal of Investigative Dermatology,* Volume 42, Issue 5.

29 **Praetorius, C et al** 2014. 'Sun-induced freckling: ephelides and solar lentigines'.

30 **Praetorius, C et al** 2014. 'Sun-induced freckling: ephelides and solar lentigines'.

31 **Wade, M et al** 2002. 'Disorders of Hair in Infants and Children Other Than Alopecia', *Clinics in Dermatology,* Volume 20, Issue 1.

32 **Verhave, B et al** 2021. 'Embryology, Lanugo', *StatPearls Publishing LLC.* <https://www.ncbi.nlm.nih.gov/books/NBK526092/>.

33 **Yamaguchi, N et al** 2004. ''Evolution of the mane and group-living in the lion (Panthera leo): a review', *Journal of Zoology,* Volume 263, Issue 4.

34 **Davis, A et al** 2010. 'Sexual Differences in Hair Morphology of Coyote and White-Tailed Deer: Males have Thicker Hair', *Annales Zoologici Fennici,* Volume 47, Issue 6.

35 **Benjamin, M et al** 2018. 'Androgens trigger different growth responses in genetically identical human hair follicles in organ culture that reflect their epigenetic diversity in life', *Federation of American Societies for Experimental Biology,* Volume 32, Issue 2.

36 **James, W et al** 2011. *Andrew's Diseases of the Skin: Clinical Dermatology,* Elsevier Health Sciences.

37 **Kajiura, Y et al** 2006. 'Structural analysis of human hair single fibres by scanning microbeam SAXS', *Journal of Structural Biology,* Volume 155, Issue 3.

Piérard-Franchimont, C et al 2010. 'Mechanobiology and cell tensegrity: the root of ethnic hair curling?', *Journal of Cosmetic Dermatology,* Volume 10, Issue 2.

38 **Loussouarn, G et al** 2016. 'Diversity in human hair growth, diameter, colour and shape. An in vivo study on young adults from 24 different ethnic groups observed in the five continents', *European Journal of Dermatology,* Volume 26, Issue 2.

39 **Cichorek, M et al** 2013. 'Skin melanocytes: biology and development', *Postepy dermatologii i alergologii,* Volume 30, Issue 1.

40 **Cichorek, M et al** 2013. 'Skin melanocytes: biology and development'.

Tobin, D (ed) 2007. *Hair in Toxicology: An Important Bio-Monitor,* Royal Society of Chemistry, Cambridge.

41 **Chou, W et al** 2013. 'Direct migration of follicular melanocyte stem cells to the epidermis after wounding or UVB irradiation is dependent on Mc1r signaling', *Nature Medicine,* Volume 19, Issue 7.

42 **Borges C,** 2001. 'Relationship of melanin degradation

products to actual melanin content: application to human hair', Analytical Biochemistry, Volume 290, Issue 1.

43 **Wakamatsu, K et al** 2011. 'Diversity of human hair pigmentation as studied by chemical analysis of eumelanin and pheomelanin', Journal of the European Academy of Dermatology and Venereology, Volume 25, Issue 12.

44 **Borges C,** 2001. 'Relationship of melanin degradation products to actual melanin content: application to human hair'.
Wakamatsu, K et al 2011. 'Diversity of human hair pigmentation as studied by chemical analysis of eumelanin and pheomelanin'.

45 **Wakamatsu, K et al** 2011. 'Diversity of human hair pigmentation as studied by chemical analysis of eumelanin and pheomelanin'.

46 **Velasco, M et al** 2009. 'Hair fiber characteristics and methods to evaluate hair physical and mechanical properties', *Brazilian Journal of Pharmaceutical Sciences,* Volume 45, Issue 1.

47 **Tobin, D et al** 2005. 'Hair Pigmentation: A Research Update', *Journal of Investigative Dermatology Symposium Proceedings,* Volume 10, Issue 3.

48 **Slominski, A et al** 2005. 'Hair follicle pigmentation', *The Journal of Investigative Dermatology,* Volume 124, Issue 1.

49 **Cichorek, M et al** 2013. 'Skin melanocytes: biology and development'.

50 **Malkud, S et al** 2015. 'Telogen Effluvium: A Review', Journal of clinical and diagnostic research, Volume 9, Issue 9.

51 **Burg, D et al** 2017. 'Promotion of anagen, increased hair density and reduction of hair fall in a clinical setting following identification of FGF5-inhibiting compounds via a novel 2-stage process', *Clinical, Cosmetic and Investigational Dermatology,* Volume 10.

52 **Guinness World Records,** 2019. '10 of the world's biggest hair records' <https://www.guinnessworldrecords.com/news/book/2019/9/10-of-the-worlds-biggest-hair-records-589 939>.

53 **Malkud, S et al** 2015. 'Telogen Effluvium: A Review'.
Van Neste, D et al 2007. 'Exogen hair characterization in human scalp', *Skin Research and Technology,* Volume 13, Issue 4.

54 **Malkud, S et al** 2015. 'Telogen Effluvium: A Review'.

55 **Hsiang, E et al** 2017. 'Seasonality of hair loss: a time series analysis of Google Trends data 2004 to 2016', *British Journal of Dermatology,* Volume 178, Issue 4.

56 **Randall, V et al** 1991. 'Seasonal changes in human hair growth', *British Journal of Dermatology,* Volume 124, Issue 2.

57 **Courtois, M et al** 1996. 'Periodicity in the growth and shedding of hair', *British Journal of Dermatology,* Volume 134, Issue 1.

58 **Kunz, M et al** 2009. 'Seasonality of Hair Shedding in Healthy Women Complaining of Hair Loss', *Dermatology,* Volume 219, Issue 2.

59 **Kunz, M et al** 2009. 'Seasonality of Hair Shedding in Healthy Women Complaining of Hair Loss'.

60 **Blume-Peytavi, U (ed) et al** 2008. *Hair Growth and Disorders,* Springer Science & Business Media, Berlin.

61 **Stenn, K et al** 2007. 'Bioengineering the hair follicle', *Organogenesis,* Volume 3, Issue 1.

62 **Stough, D et al** 2005. 'Psychological Effect, Pathophysiology, and Management of Androgenetic Alopecia in Men', *Mayo Clinical Proceedings,* Volume 80, Issue 10.

63 **Dinh, Q et al** 2007. 'Female pattern hair loss: current treatment concepts', *Clinical interventions in aging,* Volume 2, Issue 2.

64 **Maymone, M et al** 2021. 'Hair Aging in Different Races and Ethnicities', *The Journal of Clinical and Aesthetic Dermatology,* Volume 14, Issue 1.

65 **Rosenberg, A et al** 2021. 'Quantitative mapping of human hair greying and reversal in relation to life stress', *eLife,* Volume 10.

66 **Nordlund, J (ed) et al** 2008. *The Pigmentary System: Physiology and Pathophysiology,* John Wiley & Sons, New Jersey.

67 **Harris, I et al** 2011. 'Fertility and the aging male', *Reviews in Urology,* Volume 13, Issue 4.

68 **Johnson, J et al** 2012. 'Delayed Child-Bearing', *Journal of Obstetrics and Gynaecology,* Volume 34, Issue 1.

69 **Delton, A et al** 2006. 'The Mating Game Isn't Over: A Reply to Buller's Critique of the Evolutionary Psychology of Mating', *Evolutionary Psychology,* Volume 4, Issue 1.

70 **Delton, A et al** 2006. 'The Mating Game Isn't Over: A Reply to Buller's Critique of the Evolutionary Psychology of Mating'.

Chapter 3

1 **Noetling, F** 1909. 'Red Ochre And Its Use By The Aborigines Of Tasmania', *Papers and Proceedings of the Royal Society of Tasmania.*

2 **Sagert, K** 2010. *Flappers: A Guide to an American Subculture,* Greenwood, Santa Barbara.

3 **Dabiri, E** 2020. *Don't Touch My Hair,* Penguin, London.

4 **Sherrow, V** 2006. *Encyclopedia of Hair: A Cultural History,* Greenwood Press, Westport.

5 **Yusuf, M et al** 2017. 'Natural Colorants: Historical, Processing and Sustainable Prospects', *Natural Products and Bioprospecting,* Volume 7, Issue 1.

6 **Samanta, P et al** 2018. 'Fundamentals of Natural Dyeing of Textiles: Pros and Cons', *Current Trends in Fashion Technology & Textile Engineering,* Volume 2, Issue 4.

7 **Robins, G** 1999. 'Hair and the Construction of Identity in Ancient Egypt, c. 1480-1350 B.C.' *Journal of the American Research Center in Egypt,* Volume 36.

8 **Fletcher, J** 2001. 'Reviewed Work: The Remarkable Women of Ancient Egypt by Barbara S. Lesko', *Journal of Egyptian Archaeology,* Volume 87.

9 **Watterson, B** 2013. *Women in Ancient Egypt,* Amberley, Stroud.

10 **Fletcher, J** 1995. 'Ancient Egyptian Hair: a study in style, form and function', University of Manchester.

11 **Fletcher, J.** 2002. 'Ancient Egyptian hair and wigs', *The Journal of the Egyptian Study Society,* Volume 13, Issue 2.

12 **Lucas, A (ed) et al** 1999. *Ancient Egyptian Materials and Industries,* Dover Publications, New York.

13 **Renault, L** 2009. 'Ancient Henna Research', *Journal of Near Eastern Studies,* Volume 63, Issue 3.

14 **Renault, L** 2009. 'Ancient Henna Research'.

15 **Roia, F** 1966. 'The Use of Plants in Hair and Scalp Preparations', *Economic Botany,* Volume 20, Issue 1.

16 **Desroches-Noblecourt, C et al** 1985. *La Momie de Ramsès II: Contribution Scientifique a l'Egyptologie,* Editions Recherchesur les Civilisations, Paris.
Smith, G 1912. *Catalogue General Antiquites Egyptiennes du Musee du Caire: The Royal Mummies,* Imprimerie de L'institut Francais D'archeologie Orientale, Le Caire.

17 For more on the nature of Cleopatra's relationships with both men, see **Fletcher, J** 2009. *Cleopatra the Great: The Woman Behind the Legend,* Hodder & Stoughton, London.

18 **Fletcher, J** 2009. *Cleopatra the Great: The Woman Behind the Legend.*

19 **Watterson, B** 2013. *Women in Ancient Egypt.*

20 **Cooney, K** 2018. *When Women Ruled the World: Six Queens of Egypt,* National Geographic, Washington.

21 **Jackowski, C** 2008. 'Common and Unexpected Findings in Mummies from Ancient Egypt and South America as Revealed by CT', *Radio Graphics,* Volume 28, Issue 5.

22 **Taylor, J** 2010. *Journey Through the Afterlife: Ancient Egyptian Book of the Dead,* Harvard University Press, Cambridge.

23 **Mojsov, B** 2005. *Osiris: Death and Afterlife of a God,* Blackwell Publishing, Oxford.

24 **Najovits, S** 2003. *Egypt, Trunk of the Tree: The Contexts Volume 1,* Algora Publishing, New York.

25 **Hammer, J** 1940. 'Beauty Culture in Ancient Rome', The Classical Outlook, Volume 18, Issue 2.

26 **Olson, K** 2008. *Dress and the Roman Woman: Self-Presentation and Society,* Routledge, Abingdon.

27 **Hammer, J** 1940. 'Beauty Culture in Ancient Rome'.

28 **Smith, W (ed)** 1848. *A Dictionary of Greek and Roman Antiquities, Taylor, Walton, and Maberly,* London.

29 **Pitman, J** 2003. *On Blondes,* Bloomsbury, London.

30 **Bresson, A** 2019. *The Making of the Ancient Greek Economy Institutions,* Markets, and Growth in the City-States, Princeton University States, Woodstock.

31 **Blundell, S** 1995. *Women in Ancient Greece,* Harvard University Press, Cambridge.

32 **Harris-Cline, Diane** 2003. 'Women and Sacred Property: The Evidence from Greek Inscriptions', *Women and Property in Ancient Near Eastern and Mediterranean Societies,* conference proceedings ed. Lyons, D et al, Harvard University's Center for Hellenic Studies, Washington.

33 **Pitman, J** 2003. *On Blondes.*

34 **Pitman, J** 2003. *On Blondes.*

35 **Collis Harvey, J** 2015. *Red: A Natural History of The Redhead,* Allen & Unwin, London.

36 **James, S (ed) et al** 2012. A *Companion to Women in the Ancient World,* Blackwell, Chichester.

37 **Olson, K** 2008. *Dress and the Roman Woman: Self-Presentation and Society.*

38 **Riley, H** 1893. *The Heroïdes, Or Epistles of the Heroines; The Amours; Art of Love; Remedy of Love; And, Minor Works of*

Ovid, Bell & Daldy, London.

39 **Pitman, J** 2003. *On Blondes.*

Rowan, C 2012. *Under Divine Auspices: Divine Ideology and the Visualisation of Imperial Power in the Severan Period,* Cambridge University Press, Cambridge.

40 **Pitman, J** 2003. *On Blondes.*

41 **Kline, A (trans)** 2001. *Juvenal: The Satires,* Satire VI: 'Don't Marry' <https://www.poetryintranslation.com/PITBR/Latin/JuvenalSatires6.php>.

42 **Morris, D** 2004. *The Naked Women,* Jonathon Cape, London.

43 **Aeterna Press,** 2016. *Clement of Alexandria Collection,* London <https://www.google.co.uk/books/edition/Clement_of_Alexandria_Collection_3_Books/zXYkDwAAQBA J?hl=en&gbpv=>.

44 **Arbesmann, R et al (trans)** 1959. *Tertullian: Disciplinary, Moral, and Ascetical Works,* The Catholic University Press, Washington.

45 **Delphi Classics,** 2015. *Delphi Complete Works of Pliny the Elder,* Hastings.

46 The exact life expectancy of the ancients is obscure. A modern excavation of 2,000 working class Romans found that the average life expectancy was 30 - early for grey hair and given the prevalence of arthritis and bone trauma, probably not a huge concern. See **Ruggeri, A,** 2018. 'Do we really live longer than our ancestors?', *BBC,* <https://www.bbc.com/future/article/20181002-how-long-did-ancient-people-live-life-span-versus-long evity>.

In contrast, influential men, who would have had access to better diets, more hygienic living circumstances and medical care, were given more than double that life expectancy. See **J D Montagu, J** 1994. 'Length of life in the ancient world: a controlled study', *Journal of the Royal Society of Medicine,* Volume 87.

47 Although historical sources used in this book may use the Greek term 'Persian' to refer to people of Iranian nationality, my use of the term refers to the ancient Iranian empire established by Cyrus the Great (c.600-530 BC), who came from Pars: the Fars Region of modern Iran. (Following the Arab Muslim conquest in the 7th century AD, many Persian words beginning with 'P' were re-fashioned with an 'F' due to the absence of the former in the Arabic alphabet.) At its greatest extent under Darius I (r. 522–486 BCE), the (Achaemenid) Persian Empire held sway over territory stretching from the Indus River Valley to southeastern Europe and from the western edge of the Himalayas to northeast Africa. This legacy has confused Persian ethnicity with Iranian nationality in the west and led to Iran being referred to as Persia in the west for thousands of years. In 1935, Iran was adopted as the nation's formal name and today, the choice of term between 'Persia' or 'Iran' is often a personal preference which can refer to an Iranian person's ethnicity and also have political connotations.

See **Ansari, A** 2014. *Iran: A Very Short Introduction,* Oxford University Press, Oxford and **Waters, M** 2014. *Ancient Persia: A Concise History of the Achaemenid Empire, 550–330 BCE,* Cambridge University Press, Cambridge.

48 **Llewellyn-Jones, L** 2013. *King and Court in Ancient Persia: 559 to 331 BCE,* Edinburgh University Press, Edinburgh.

49 **Llewellyn-Jones, L** 2013. **King and Court in Ancient Persia: 559 to 331 BCE.**

50 **Najmabadi, A (ed) et al** 2003. *Encyclopedia of Women & Islamic Cultures: Family, Body, Sexuality and Health,* Volume 3, Brill, Leiden.

51 **Horne, C (ed)** 1917. *The Sacred Books and Early Literature of the East: Volume V, Ancient Arabia, Parke,* Austin, and Lipscomb, New York and London.

See **Juynboll, G** 1986. 'Dyeing the Hair and Beard in Early Islam: A Hadīth-analytical Study', *Arabica,* Volume 33, Issue 1.

52 **Juynboll, G** 1986. 'Dyeing the Hair and Beard in Early Islam: A Hadīth-analytical Study'.

53 **El Shamsy, A** 2020. 'The Curious Case of Early Muslim Hair Dyeing' in Sijpesteijn, P (ed) 2020. *Islam at 250: Studies in Memory of G.H.A. Juynboll,* Brill, Leiden.

54 **Shuraydi, H** 2014. The Raven and the Falcon: Youth Versus Old Age in Medieval Arabic Literature, Brill, Leiden.

55 **Shuraydi, H** 2014. *The Raven and the Falcon: Youth Versus Old Age in Medieval Arabic Literature.*

56 **Burnaby, F** 1877. *On Horseback Through Asia Minor: Volume II,* Sampson Low, Marston, Searle, & Rivington, London.

57 **Milliken, R (ed)** 2019. *A Cultural History of Hair in the Middle Ages: Volume 2,* Bloomsbury, London.

58 **Bartlett, R** 1994. 'Symbolic Meanings of Hair in the Middle Ages', *Transactions of the Royal Historical Society,* Volume 4.

59 **Brewer, D** 1955. 'The Ideal of Feminine Beauty in Medieval Literature, Especially "Harley Lyrics", Chaucer, and Some Elizabethans', *The Modern Language Review,* Volume 50, Issue 3.

60 The Iberian Peninsula (modern-day Spain) had a diverse Medieval population composed of Jewish, Muslim and Christian peoples, thanks to the Umayyad conquest of Hispania in 711, followed by centuries of Christian 'reconquest'. See **Lowney, C** 2005. *A Vanished World: Muslims, Christians, and Jews in Medieval Spain,* Oxford University Press, Oxford.

61 **Da Soller, C** 2005. "The Beautiful Women in Medieval Iberia: Rhetoric, Cosmetics and Evolution,' *University of Missouri-Columbia* <https://mospace.umsystem.edu/xmlui/bitstream/handle/10355/4175/research.pdf?sequence=3>.

62 **Stephens, J** 2019. 'Becoming a Blond in Renaissance Italy', *The Journal of the Walters Art Museum,* Volume 74.

63 **Green, M** 2002. *The Trotula: An English Translation of the Medieval Compendium of Women's Medicine,* University of Pennsylvania Press, Philadelphia.

64 **Caballero-Navas, C (ed)** 2004. *The Book of Women's Love and Jewish Medieval Medical Literature on Women: Sefer Ahavat Nashim,* Kegan Paul, London and New York.

65 **Milliken, R (ed)** 2019. *A Cultural History of Hair in the Middle Ages: Volume 2.*

66 **Milliken, R (ed)** 2019. *A Cultural History of Hair in the Middle Ages: Volume 2.*

67 **Cabré, M** 2014. 'Beautiful bodies', in Kalof, L (ed) 2014. *A Cultural History of the Human Body in the Medieval Age,* Bloomsbury, London.

68 **De Lorris, G et al.** 'Le Roman de la Rose' in Milliken, R (ed) 2019. *A Cultural History of Hair in the Middle Ages: Volume 2.*

69 **Shahar, S** 2004. *Growing Old in the Middle Ages: 'Winter Clothes Us in Shadow and Pain',* Routledge, London.

70 **Shahar, S** 2004. *Growing Old in the Middle Ages: 'Winter Clothes Us in Shadow and Pain'.*

71 **Shahar, S** 2004. *Growing Old in the Middle Ages: 'Winter Clothes Us in Shadow and Pain'.*

72 **Green, M** 2002. *The Trotula: An English Translation of the Medieval Compendium of Women's Medicine.*

73 **Jouanna, J et al** 2012.'The Legacy of the Hippocratic Treatise The Nature Of Man: The Theory of the Four Humours' in Van der Eijk, P (ed) 2012. *Greek Medicine from Hippocrates to Galen: Selected Papers,* Brill, Leiden and Boston.

See also **Cavallo, S et al (ed)** 2017. *Conserving Health in Early Modern Culture: Bodies and Environments in Italy and England,* Manchester University Press, Manchester.

74 **Laughran, M** 2006. 'A Man Must Not Embelish Himself like a Woman: The Body and Gender in Renaissance Cosmetics', *15th Annual Medieval, Renaissance and Baroque Interdisciplinary Symposium,* University of Miami.

75 **Spicer, J** 2014. '"A Fare Bella": The Visual and Material Culture of Cosmetics in Renaissance Italy (1450-1540)', *The University of Edinburgh* <https://era.ed.ac.uk/handle/1842/14161>.

76 **Rocke, M** 2014. 'Gender and Sexual Culture in Renaissance Italy' in Brown, J et al (ed) 2014. *Gender and Society in Renaissance Italy,* Routledge, Abingdon.

77 **Rocke, M** 2014. 'Gender and Sexual Culture in Renaissance Italy'

78 **Strocchia, S** 2014. 'Gender and the Rites of Honour in Italian Renaissance Cities' in Brown, J et al (ed) 2014. *Gender and Society in Renaissance Italy,* Routledge, Abingdon.

79 **Chojnacki, S** 2014. 'Daughters and Oligarchs: Gender and the Early Renaissance State' in Brown, J et al (ed) 2014. Gender and Society in Renaissance Italy, Routledge, Abingdon.

80 **Chojnacki, S** 2014. 'Daughters and Oligarchs: Gender and the Early Renaissance State.

81 **Spurling, J** 1999. *Convents and the Body Politic in Late Renaissance Venice,* University of Chicago Press, Chicago and London.

82 **Chojnacki, S** 2014. 'Daughters and Oligarchs: Gender and the Early Renaissance State.

Gender and Society in Renaissance Italy, ed. Judith C. Brown, Robert C. Davis

83 **Child, T** 1895. *Wimples and Crisping Pins: Being Studies in the Coiffure and Ornaments of Women,* Harper and Brothers, New York.

84 **Collis Harvey, J** 2015. *Red: A Natural History of The Redhead.*

85 **Mazokopakis, E** 2018. 'Is Vaginal Sexual Intercourse Permitted during Menstruation? A Biblical (Christian) and Medical Approach', *Maedica: A Journal of Clinical*

Science, Volume 13, Issue 3.

86 **Collis Harvey, J** 2015. *Red: A Natural History of The Redhead.*

87 **Bond, R (ed)** 1902. *The Complete Works of John Lyly: Volume 1,* Clarendon Press, Oxford.

88 **Strong, R** 1969. *Tudor & Jacobean Portraits: Volume 1,* Her Majesty's Stationary Office, London.

89 **Aikin, L** 2010. *Memoirs of the Court of Queen Elizabeth,* Andrews UK Limited, London.

90 **Sherrow, V** 2006. *Encyclopedia of Hair: A Cultural History,* Greenwood Press, London.

Drew-Bear, A 1994. *Painted Faces on the Renaissance Stage: The Moral Significance of Face Painting Conventions,* Bucknell University Press, London and Toronto.

91 **Sherrow, V** 2001. *For Appearance Sake:The Historical Encyclopedia of Good Looks, Beauty, and Grooming,* Oryx Press, Westport.

92 **Fisher, Will** 2001. *'The Renaissance Beard: Masculinity in Early Modern England', Renaissance Quarterly,* Volume 54, Issue 1.

93 **Pitman, J** 2003. *On Blondes.*

94 **De Courtais, G** 2006. *Women's Hats, Headdresses and Hairstyles, With 453 Illustrations: Medieval to Modern,* Dover Publications, Mineola.

Chapter 4

1 **Benson, J** 1882. *A History of England, Political, Military, and Social, from the Earliest Period to the Present,* G. P. Putnam's sons, New York.

2 **Downing, SJ** 2012. *Beauty and Cosmetics: 1550-1950,* Shire Publications, Oxford.

3 **Stone, Lawrence** 1965. *The Crisis of the Aristocracy,* 1558-1641, Clarendon Press, Oxford.

4 **Butler, H (ed)** 2013. *Poucher's Perfumes, Cosmetics and Soaps,* Springer, Heidelberg.

5 **De Courtais, G** 2006. *Women's Hats, Headdresses and Hairstyles, With 453 Illustrations: Medieval to Modern,* Dover Publications, Mineola.

6 **Burke, P** 1994. The Fabrication of Louis XIV, Yale University Press, New Haven and London.

7 **Festa, L** 2005. 'Personal Effects: Wigs and Possessive Individualism in the Long Eighteenth Century', *Eighteenth-Century Life,* Volume 29, Issue 2.

8 While enslaved Africans were commonly transported to the Americas and the Caribbean under terrible circumstances, a small number were brought to England where their legal status was unclear. See **Olusaga, D** 2016. *Black and British,* Macmillan, London.

9 **Festa, L** 2005. 'Personal Effects: Wigs and Possessive Individualism in the Long Eighteenth Century'.

10 **Festa, L** 2005. 'Personal Effects: Wigs and Possessive Individualism in the Long Eighteenth Century'.

11 **Lightfoot, D** 2019. *The Culture and Art of Death in 19th Century America,* McFarland & Company, Jefferson.

12 **Hendricks, N** 2018. Popular Fads and Crazes Through American History, Greenwood, Santa Barbara and Denver.

13 **Festa, L** 2005. 'Personal Effects: Wigs and Possessive Individualism in the Long Eighteenth Century'.

14 **Olsen, K** 1999. *Daily Life in 18th-century England,* Greenwood, Westport and London.

15 **Knight, C** 1845. *Old England, a Pictorial Museum of Regal, Ecclesiastical, Baronial, Municipal, and Popular Antiquities: Volume 2,* Charles Knight and co, London.

16 **Sherrow, V** 2006. *Encyclopedia of Hair: A Cultural History,* Greenwood Press, Westport.

17 See **Gayne, M** 2004. 'Illicit Wigmaking in Eighteenth-Century Paris', *Eighteenth-Century Studies* Volume 38, Issue 1.

18 **Martin, M** 2009. *Selling Beauty: Cosmetics, Commerce and French Society: 1750-1830,* The John Hopkins University Press, Baltimore.

19 See **Martin, M** 2009. *Selling Beauty: Cosmetics, Commerce and French Society: 1750-1830.*

20 **Anderson, J** 2007. *Daily Life During the French Revolution,* Greenwood, Westport and London.

21 **Hosford, D** 2004. 'The Queen's Hair: Marie-Antoinette, Politics, and DNA', *Eighteenth-Century Studies,* Volume 38, Number 1.

22 **Crowston, C** 2013. *Credit, Fashion, Sex, Economies of Regard in Old Regime France,* Duke University Press, Durham and London.

23 **Gayne, M** 2004. 'Illicit Wigmaking in Eighteenth-Century Paris'.

24 **Touchard-Lafosse, G** 1771. *L'oeil-de-boeuf: Chroniques pittoresques et critiques, Gustave Barba, Paris in Martin, M 2009. Selling Beauty: Cosmetics, Commerce and French*

Society: 1750-1830, Johns Hopkins University Press, Baltimore.

25 **Ward, Lock and Co,** 1881. *Sylvia's Book of the Toilet: a Ladies' Guide to Dress and Beauty,* London.

26 **Ziegler, G** 1932. 'The Diuturnal Use of Perfumes and Cosmetics', The Scientific Monthly, Volume 34, Issue 3.

27 **Sherrow, V** 2006. *Encyclopedia of Hair: A Cultural History.*

28 **Festa, L** 2005. 'Personal Effects: Wigs and Possessive Individualism in the Long Eighteenth Century'.

29 **Martin, M** 2009. *Selling Beauty: Cosmetics, Commerce and French Society: 1750-1830.*

30 **Monoghan, T** 2008. *The Slave Trade,* Evans Brothers Limited, London.

31 **Byrd, A et al** 2014. *Hair Story: Untangling the Roots of Black Hair in America,* St Martin's Griffin, New York.

32 **Dabiri, E** 2020. *Don't Touch My Hair,* Penguin, London.

33 **Sobania, N** 2003. *Culture and Customs of Kenya,* Greenwood Publishing Group, Westport and London.

34 **Dabiri, E** 2020. *Don't Touch My Hair.*

35 **Dabiri, E** 2020. *Don't Touch My Hair.*

36 **Byrd, A et al** 2014. *Hair Story: Untangling the Roots of Black Hair in America.*

37 **Byrd, A et al** 2014. *Hair Story: Untangling the Roots of Black Hair in America.*

38 **Kieschnick, J** 2003. *The Impact of Buddhism on Chinese Material Culture,* Princeton University Press, Princeton and Oxford.

39 **Kieschnick, J** 2003. *The Impact of Buddhism on Chinese Material Culture,* Princeton University Press, New Jersey and Woodstock.

40 **Choo, J et al (ed)** 2014. *Early Medieval China: A Sourcebook,* Columbia University Press, New York.

41 **Kyo, C** 2012. *The Search For The Beautiful Woman: A Cultural History of Japanese and Chinese Beauty,* Roman & Littlefield, Lanham and Plymouth.

42 **Hinsch, B** 2019. *Women in Early Medieval China,* Rowman & Littlefield, Lanham and London.

43 **Okakura, Y** 1905. The Japanese Spirit, James Pott & Co, New York in Mizuta, M 2013. '美人 Bijin/Beauty', Review of Japanese Culture and Society, Volume 25.

44 **Andaya, B** 1993. *To Live as Brothers: Southeast Sumatra in the Seventeenth and Eighteenth Centuries,* University of Hawaii Press, Honolulu.

45 **Li, S** 2003. *Chinese Medicinal Herbs: A Modern Edition of a Classic Sixteenth-century Manual,* Dover, Mineola.

46 **Mitsui, T (ed)** 1997. *New Cosmetic Science,* Elsevier Science, Amsterdam.

47 **Chardin, J** 1988. *Sir John Chardin's Travels in Persia,* Dover Publications.

48 **Farmanfarmaian, F** 2000. '"Haft Qalam Ārāyish": Cosmetics in the Iranian World', Iranian Studies, Volume 33, Issues 3-4. See also **Balfour-Paul, J** 2011. *Indigo: Egyptian Mummies to Blue Jeans,* The British Museum Press, London.

49 **Farmanfarmaian, F** 2000. '"Haft Qalam Ārāyish": Cosmetics in the Iranian World'.

50 **Wilson, S** 1895. *Persian Life and Customs: With Scenes and Incidents of Residence and Travel in the Land of the Lion and the Sun,* Fleming H. Revell Company, Chicago.

51 **Edwards, J (ed)** 1884. *The Annals of Hygiene: Volumes 1–2,* University of Pennsylvania Press, Philadelphia.

52 **Meri, J (ed)** 2006. *Medieval Islamic Civilization: An Encyclopedia, Volume 1,* Taylor & Francis Group, New York and Abingdon.

53 **Najmabadi,** *A 2005. Women with Mustaches and Men without Beards: Gender and Sexual Anxieties of Iranian Modernity,* University of California Press, Berkeley and London.

54 **Shoberl, F** 1828. *Persia: Containing a Description of the Country, with an Account of Its Government, Laws, and Religion, and of the Character, Manners and Customs, Arts, Amusements, &c. of Its Inhabitants,* John Grigg, Philadelphia.

55 **Thomas, G** 1834. *Personal Narrative of a Journey from India to England, By Bussorah, Bagdad, the Ruins of Babylon, Curdistan, the Court of Persia, the Western Shore of the Caspian Sea, Astrakhan, Nishney, Novogorod, Moscow, and St. Petersburgh Volume II,* Henry Colburn, London.

56 **Nağmābādī, A et al (ed)** 2003. *Encyclopedia of Women & Islamic Cultures: Family, Body, Sexuality And Health, Volume 3,* Brill, Leiden and Boston.

57 **United States Government Printing Office,** 1881. *Congressional Serial Set: Reports of the United States Commissioners to the Paris Universal Exposition, 1878,* Washington.

58 Isabella Bird writes, "In justice to my sex I must add that the men dye their hair to an equal extent with the women, from the shining blue-black of the Shah's moustache to

the brilliant orange of the beard of Hadji Hussein, by which he forfeits, though not in Persian estimation, the respect due to age." See **Bird, I** 1891. *Journeys In Persia And Kurdistan Including A Summer In The Upper Karun Region and A Visit To The Nestorian Rayahs: Volume I,* John Murray, London.

59 **Bird, I** 1891. *Journeys In Persia And Kurdistan Including A Summer In The Upper Karun Region and A Visit To The Nestorian Rayahs: Volume I.*

60 **McDonough, J et al (ed)** 2002. *The Advertising Age: Encyclopedia of Advertising* , Fitzroy Dearborn Publishers, Chicago and London. See also **Martin, M** 2009. *Selling Beauty: Cosmetics, Commerce and French Society: 1750-1830,* Johns Hopkins University Press, Baltimore.

61 **Martin, M** 2009. *Selling Beauty: Cosmetics, Commerce and French Society: 1750-1830.*

62 **De Courtais, G** 2006. *Women's Hats, Headdresses and Hairstyles, With 453 Illustrations: Medieval to Modern.*

63 **Murphy, D** 2019. *The Young Victoria,* Yale University Press, New Haven and London.

64 **Matthews, M** 2018. *A Victorian Lady's Guide to Fashion and Beauty,* Pen & Sword Books.

65 **Baird, J** 2016. *Victoria: The Queen: An Intimate Biography of the Woman who Ruled an Empire,* Random House, London.

66 **Downing, SJ** 2012. *Beauty and Cosmetics: 1550-1950.*

67 **Byrne, K** 2011. *Tuberculosis and the Victorian Literary Imagination,* Cambridge University Press, Cambridge. See also **Day, C** 2017. *Consumptive Chic: A History of Beauty, Fashion, and Disease,* Bloomsbury Academic, London and New York.

68 **Jalland, P** 1996. *Death in the Victorian Family,* Oxford University Press, Oxford.

69 **Ofek, G** 2016. *Representations of Hair in Victorian Literature and Culture,* Routledge, Abingdon.

70 **Wall, F** 1972. 'Bleaches, Hair Colourings, and Dye Removers' in Balsam, M et al (ed) 1972. *Cosmetics: Science and Technology, Second Edition,* Volume 2, John Wiley & Sons, New York, London, Sydney and Toronto.

71 **Hale, S (ed)** 1831. *Ladies' Magazine and Literary Gazette,* Volume 4, Marsh, Capen and Lyon, Boston.

72 **Montgomery, L** 1994. *Anne of Green Gables,* Wordsworth Editions, Ware.

73 **Sherrow, V** 2006. *Encyclopedia of Hair: A Cultural History.*

74 **Collis Harvey, J** 2015. **Red: A Natural History of The** *Redhead,* Allen & Unwin, London.

75 **Ofek, G** 2016. *Representations of Hair in Victorian Literature and Culture.*

76 **Balfour-Paul, J** 2011. *Indigo: Egyptian Mummies to Blue Jeans.*

77 **Frith, H** 1891. *How to Read Character in Features, Forms, and Faces: A Guide to the General Outlines of Physiognomy,* Ward, Lock, Bowden & Co, London, New York and Melbourne.

78 Queen Victoria was famously adverse to women's emancipation. See **Baird, J** 2016. *Victoria: The Queen: An Intimate Biography of the Woman who Ruled an Empire.*

79 **Ofek, G** 2016. *Representations of Hair in Victorian Literature and Culture.*

80 **Fowler, O** 1859. *The Illustrated Self-Instructor in Phrenology and Physiology,* Fowler and Wells, New York.

81 **Ofek, G** 2016. *Representations of Hair in Victorian Literature and Culture.*

82 **Goodman, R** 2013. *How to be a Victorian,* Penguin Books, London.

83 **Phegley, J** 2012. *Courtship and Marriage in Victorian England,* ABC-CLIO, Santa Barbara.

84 **Jalland, P** 1996. *Death in the Victorian Family.*

85 **Phegley, J** 2012. *Courtship and Marriage in Victorian England.*

86 **Jalland, P** 1996. *Death in the Victorian Family.*

87 **Downing, SJ** 2012. *Beauty and Cosmetics: 1550-1950.*

88 **McDonough, J et al (ed)** 2002. *The Advertising Age: Encyclopedia of Advertising.*

89 **Willett, J (ed)** 2010. *The American Beauty Industry Encyclopedia,* Greenwood.

90 **Wu, K** 2019. 'Archaeologists Find Hair Dye Bottles Used by Self-Conscious Civil War Soldiers Posing for Portraits', *Smithsonian Magazine* <https://www.smithsonianmag.com/smart-news/archaeologists-find-hair-dye-bottles-used-self-conscio us-civil-war-soldiers-posing-portraits-180973696/>.

91 **Hennessy, J** 2015. *The First Battle of Manassas: An End to Innocence: July 18-21, 1861,* Stackpole Books, Mechanicsburg.

84 **Jalland, P** 1996. *Death in the Victorian Family.*

85 **Phegley, J** 2012. *Courtship and Marriage in Victorian England.*

86 **Jalland, P** 1996. *Death in the Victorian Family.*

87 **Downing, SJ** 2012. *Beauty and Cosmetics: 1550-1950.*

88 **McDonough, J et al (ed)** 2002. *The Advertising Age: Encyclopedia of Advertising.*

89 **Willett, J (ed)** 2010. *The American Beauty Industry Encyclopedia,* Greenwood.

90 **Wu, K** 2019. 'Archaeologists Find Hair Dye Bottles Used by Self-Conscious Civil War Soldiers Posing for Portraits'.

91 **Hennessy, J** 2015. *The First Battle of Manassas: An End to Innocence: July 18-21, 1861,* Stackpole Books, Mechanicsburg.

Chapter 5

1 **Wall, F** 1972. 'Bleaches, Hair Colourings, and Dye Removers' in Balsam, M et al (ed) 1972. *Cosmetics: Science and Technology, Second Edition, Volume 2,* John Wiley & Sons, New York, London, Sydney and Toronto.

2 **Redgrove, H et al** 1939. *Hair-Dyes and Hair-Dyeing Chemistry and Technique,* William Heinemann, London.

3 **Adam and Charles Black,** 1842. *The Encyclopaedia Britannica:* Or, Dictionary of Arts, Sciences, and General Literature, Volume 7, Edinburgh.

1735 publication *Dictionarium Polygraphicum* also gave several recipes for dye that involved nutgalls, such as combining these with madder and copper. See **C. Hitch and C. Davis,** 1735. *Dictionarium Polygraphicum: Or, the Whole Body of Arts Regularly Digested: Volume 1,* London.

4 **Wall, F** 1972. 'Bleaches, Hair Colourings, and Dye Removers'.

5 **Wall, F** 1972. 'Bleaches, Hair Colourings, and Dye Removers'.

6 **Zviak, C** 2010. 'Hair Bleaching' in Bouillon, C et al (ed) 2010. *The Science Of Hair Care: Second Edition, Informa Healthcare,* London and New York.

7 **Wall, F** 1972. 'Bleaches, Hair Colourings, and Dye Removers'.

8 **Blaszczyk, R** 2012. *The Color Revolution,* Massachusetts Institute of Technology, Cambridge.

9 **Blaszczyk, R** 2012. *The Color Revolution.*

10 **Garfield, S** 2018. *Mauve: How one man invented a colour that changed the world,* Canongate Books Limited, Edinburgh.

11 **Garfield, S** 2018. *Mauve: How one man invented a colour that changed the world*

12 **Schweitzer, H** 1906. 'The Influence of Sir William Henry Perkin's Discovery Upon Our Science', Science, Volume 24, Issue 616.

13 **Mukkanna, K et al** 2017. 'Para-phenylenediamine allergy: current perspectives on diagnosis and management', *Journal of Asthma and Allergy,* Volume 10.

14 **Guernard, R** 2014. 'How and why we colour hair', Mosaic Science in Canbury Press, 2018. *Bodyology: The Curious Science of Our Bodies,* Kingston upon Thames.

15 **Wall, F** 1972. 'Bleaches, Hair Colourings, and Dye Removers'.

16 **Meyer, A et al** 2015. 'Oxidative transformation processes and products of para-phenylenediamine (PPD) and para-toluenediamine (PTD) - a review', *Environmental Sciences Europe,* Volume 27, Issue 11.

17 **Corbett, J** 1999. 'An historical review of the use of dye precursors in the formulation of commercial oxidation hair dyes', *Dyes and Pigments,* Volume 41.

18 **Wall, F** 1926. *Canitics: The Treatment of Canities Reduced To A Science And Elevated To An Art, Beautician Publications,* New York.

19 **Wall, F** 1972. 'Bleaches, Hair Colourings, and Dye Removers'.

20 **Hamilton, A** 1921. 'Industrial Poisoning in Making Coal-Tar Dyes and Dye Intermediates', *Bulletin of the United States Bureau of Labor Statistics,* Volume 280. See also Wall, F 1926. *Canitics: The Treatment of Canities Reduced To A Science And Elevated To An Art.*

21 **Wall, F** 1926. *Canitics: The Treatment of Canities Reduced To A Science And Elevated To An Art.*

22 **Zdatny, S** 2006. *Fashion, Work, and Politics in Modern France,* Palgrave McMillan, New York and Basingstoke.

23 **Wall, F** 1972. 'Bleaches, Hair Colourings, and Dye Removers'.

24 **Wall, F** 1926. *Canitics: The Treatment of Canities Reduced To A Science And Elevated To An Art.*

25 **Wall, F** 1972. 'Bleaches, Hair Colourings, and Dye Removers'.

26 **Israels, M** 1934. 'Systemic Poisoning by phenylenediamine', *The Lancet,* Volume 223, Issue 5767.

27 **Davison, C** 1943. 'Paraphenylenediamine poisoning with changes in the central nervous system', *Archives of Neurology and Psychiatry,* Volume 49, Issue 2.

28 **Gupta, M et al** 2015. 'Hair dye dermatitis and p-phenylenediamine contact sensitivity: A preliminary

report', *Indian Dermatology Online Journal,* Volume 6, Issue 4.

29 **Marseille, J** 2009. L'Oréal: 1909-2009, Perrin, Paris. See also **Schueller, E.** *De l'innocuité des teintures pour cheveux,* Paris.

30 **Wall, F** 1972. 'Bleaches, Hair Colourings, and Dye Removers'. See also **Redgrove, H et al** 1939. *Hair-Dyes and Hair-Dyeing Chemistry and Technique.*

31 **Turngate, M** 2011. *Branded Beauty: How Marketing Changed the Way We Look,* Kogan Page Limited, London and Philadelphia. See also **Jones, G** 2010. *Beauty Re-imagined, A History of the Global Beauty Industry,* Oxford University Press, Oxford.

32 **Wall, F** 1972. 'Bleaches, Hair Colourings, and Dye Removers'. See also **Wall, F** 1974. 'Historical Development of the Cosmetics Industry' in Balsam, M et al (ed) 1974. *Cosmetics: Science and Technology: Second Edition: Volume III,* John Wiley & Sons, New York, London, Sydney and Toronto.

33 **Schueller, E.** *De l'innocuité des teintures pour cheveux* in Redgrove, H et al 1939. *Hair-Dyes and Hair-Dyeing Chemistry and Technique.*

34 **Wall, F** 1972. 'Bleaches, Hair Colourings, and Dye Removers'.

35 **Wall, F** 1926. *Canitics: The Treatment of Canities Reduced To A Science And Elevated To An Art.*

36 **Wall, F** 1972. 'Bleaches, Hair Colourings, and Dye Removers'.

37 **Wall, F** 1926. *Canitics: The Treatment of Canities Reduced To A Science And Elevated To An Art.*

38 **Wall, F** 1972. 'Bleaches, Hair Colourings, and Dye Removers'.

39 **United States Federal Trade Commission** 1933. *Federal Trade Commission Decisions: Volume 16: Findings, Orders, and Stipulations: December 24, 1931, to July 17,* Washington.

40 **DeForest Lamb, R** 1936. *American Chamber of Horrors: The Truth About Food And Drugs,* J.J. Little And Ives Company, New York.

41 **United States Federal Trade Commission** 1933. *Federal Trade Commission Decisions: Volume 16: Findings, Orders, and Stipulations: December 24,* 1931.

42 **United States Federal Trade Commission** 1933. *Federal Trade Commission Decisions: Volume 16: Findings, Orders, and Stipulations: December 24,* 1931.

43 **Wall, F** 1972. 'Bleaches, Hair Colourings, and Dye Removers'.

44 **Marseille, J** 2009. *L'Oréal: 1909-2009,* Perrin, Paris.

45 **Thain, G et al** 2014. *FMCG: The Power of Fast-Moving Consumer Goods,* First Edition Design Publishing, Sarasota.

46 **Jones, G** 2010. *Beauty Re-imagined, A History of the Global Beauty Industry.*

47 **Draelos, Z** 2005. *Hair Care: An Illustrated Dermatologic Handbook,* Taylor & Francis, London and New York.

54 **Suedfeld, P** 2002. 'Lethal Stereotypes: Hair and Eye Color as Survival Characteristics During the Holocaust', *Journal of Applied Social Psychology,* Volume 32, Issue 11.

55 **Noack, F** 2016. *Veit Harlan: The Life and Work of a Nazi Filmmaker,* University Press of Kentucky, Kentucky.

56 **Pitman, J** 2003. *On Blondes.*

57 **Suedfeld, P** 2002. 'Lethal Stereotypes: Hair and Eye Color as Survival Characteristics During the Holocaust'.

58 **Pitman, J** 2003. *On Blondes.*

59 **Clairol Inc,** 1982. *50 Colourful Years: The Clairol Story.*

60 **Gladwell, M** 2009. 'True Colors: Hair dye and the hidden history of postwar America' in *What the Dog Saw And Other Adventures,* Penguin Books, London.

61 **Gladwell, M** 2009. 'True Colors: Hair dye and the hidden history of postwar America'.

62 From an interview with former Clairol employee Dr Robert Hefford

63 **Kanner, B** 1987. 'To Live and Dye', *New York Magazine,* Volume 20, Issue 8.

64 **Stein, M** 1982. 50 Colourful Years: *The Clairol Story,* Clairol Incorporated.

65 **Jones, G** 2010. *Beauty Re-imagined, A History of the Global Beauty Industry.*

66 **Gladwell, M** 2009. 'True Colors: Hair dye and the hidden history of postwar America'.

67 At her retirement party in 1973, Polykoff mischievously revealed that she had sent this particular letter herself. See **Gladwell, M** 2009. 'True Colors: Hair dye and the hidden history of postwar America'.

68 *International Directory of Company Histories,* Volume 3, St James Press, 1988.

69 **Wall, F** 1974. 'Historical Development of the Cosmetics Industry'.

70 **Bundles, A** 2013, *Madam Walker Theatre Center: An*

Indianapolis Treasure, Arcadia, Mount Pleasant <https://bit.ly/2C9nSOP>.

71 **Walker, S** 2007. *Style and Status: Selling Beauty to African American Women,* 1920-1975, University Press of Kentucky, Kentucky.

72 50 *Colourful Years: The Clairol Story.*

73 *Life Magazine,* Time Inc, 1968, Volume 65, Issue 6.

74 **Jones, G** 2010. *Beauty Re-imagined, A History of the Global Beauty Industry.*

75 **Gladwell, M** 2009. 'True Colors: Hair dye and the hidden history of postwar America'.

76 **Sherrow, V** 2006. *Encyclopedia of Hair: A Cultural History.*

77 **Weitz, R** 2004. *Rapunzel's Daughters, What Women's Hair Tells Us About Women's Lives,* Farrar, Straus and Giroux, New York.

78 **Sherrow, V** 2006. *Encyclopedia of Hair: A Cultural History.*

79 **Sherrow, V** 2006. *Encyclopedia of Hair: A Cultural History.*

80 **U.S. Government Printing Office, 1978.** 'Cancer-causing Chemicals: Safety of Cosmetics and Hair Dyes', *Hearings Before the Subcommittee On Oversight and Investigations Of The Committee On Interstate And Foreign Commerce,* Washington.

81 **Sklar, M** 2013. *Punk Style,* Bloomsbury Academic, London and New York.

82 **Spracklen, K et al** 2018. *The Evolution of Goth Culture: The Origins and Deeds of the New Goths,* Emerald Group Publishing, Bingley.

83 **Matthews, G et al (ed)** 2012. *Japan's Changing Generations: Are Young People Creating a New Society?,* Routledge, London and New York.

84 **Steger, I** 2017. 'A teenager in Japan is suing her school for forcing her to dye her natural brown hair black', *Quartz magazine* <https://qz.com/1113436/a-teenager-in-japan-is-suing-her-school-for-forcing-her-to-dye-her-natural-br own-hair-black/>.

85 **Jiang, S** 2019. 'Gray leap forward: Xi Jinping shows natural hair color in a rare move for Chinese politics', *CNN Style* <https://edition.cnn.com/style/article/xi-jinping-gray-hair/index.html>.

86 **Wall, F** 1926. *Canitics: The Treatment of Canities Reduced To A Science And Elevated To An Art.*

87 **Wahlberg, J et al** 2002. 'Contact allergy to p-phenylenediamine in Sweden: Follow-up after reversed intervention', *Occupational and Environmental Dermatology,* Volume 50.

88 **Lönngren, V** 2012. 'Neutrophilic and Eosinophilic Dermatitis Caused by Contact Allergic Reaction to Paraphenylenediamine in Hair Dye', *Archives of Dermatology,* Volume 148, Issue 11.

89 **Redgrove, H et al** 1939. *Hair-Dyes and Hair-Dyeing Chemistry and Technique.*

90 **Kay, G** 2001. 'Healthy Public Relations: The FDA's 1930s Legislative Campaign', *Bulletin of the History of Medicine,* Volume 75, Issue 3.

91 **Kay, G** 2001. 'Healthy Public Relations: The FDA's 1930s Legislative Campaign'.

92 **Wall, F** 1974. 'Historical Development of the Cosmetics Industry'.

93 **Kay, G** 2001. 'Healthy Public Relations: The FDA's 1930s Legislative Campaign'.

94 **Kay, G** 2005. *Dying to be Beautiful: The Fight for Safe Cosmetics,* Ohio State University, Columbus. See also **Kay, G** 2001. 'Healthy Public Relations: The FDA's 1930s Legislative Campaign'.

95 **Forbes S et al** 1934. 'Fatality Resulting From The Use of Lash-Lure On The Eyebrow and Eyelashes', *American Medical Association,* Volume 103, Number 19.

96 **Kay, G** 2001. 'Healthy Public Relations: The FDA's 1930s Legislative Campaign'.

97 **Ballentine, C** 1981. 'Taste of Raspberries, Taste of Death: The 1937 Elixir Sulfanilamide Incident', FDA Consumer magazine <https://www.fda.gov/files/about%20fda/published/The-Sulfanilamide-Disaster.pdf>.

98 **Harvey, J** 1962. 'The Omnibus Bill', Food, Drug, Cosmetic Law Journal, Volume 17, Issue 9. See also **Zuckerman, S** 1974. 'Colour in Cosmetics' in Balsam, M et al (ed) 1974. *Cosmetics: Science and Technology: Second Edition: Volume III,* John Wiley & Sons, New York, London, Sydney and Toronto.

99 **U.S. Government Printing Office, 1962.** Drug Industry Act of 1962: Hearings Before the Committee on Interstate and Foreign Commerce, House of Representatives, Eighty-seventh Congress, Second Session, Washington.

100 **Mintel,** 2019. 'The hair colour products Gen Z & Millennials want.

101 **Zhang, Y** 2012. 'Hair dye use and risk of human cancer', *Frontiers in Bioscience,* Volume 4, Issue 1.

102 **Mintel** 2011. 'Hair Colourants: Europe'.

103 **Yoon, G** 1995. 'Understanding Aging in Korea', *Korea Journal of Population and Development,* Volume 24, Issue 2.

Jo, S et al 2013. 'The Pattern of Hair Dyeing in Koreans with Gray Hair', *Annals of Dermatology,* Volume 25, Issue 4.

Chandler, A et al 1949. 'The Traditional Chinese Attitude Towards Old Age', *Journal of Gerontology,* Volume 4, Issue 3.

Mintel, 2013. 'Hair colouring is common for Chinese consumers'.

Karasawa, M et al 2011. 'Cultural perspectives on aging and well-being: a comparison of Japan and the United States', *International Journal of Aging & Human Development,* Volume 73, Issue 1.

Mintel 2021. 'Japanese women's haircare needs 'ageing well' messaging'.

104 **Ganapathi, M et al** 2019. 'Indian women are finding a silver lining in their grey hair', *Quartz India* <https://qz.com/india/1560873/not-just-ratna-pathak-many-indian-women-now-flaunt-grey-hair/>

105 **Robinson, C** 2016. 'Grey is a feminist issue' in Legat, N (ed) 2016. *Journal of Urgent Writing: Volume 1,* Massey University Press, Auckland.

106 **Shakespeare, S,** 2015. 'Nicky Clarke claims Kate's greying hair is a disaster!', *Daily Mail* <https://www.dailymail.co.uk/femail/article-3178047/SEBASTIAN-SHAKESPEARE-Nicky-Clarke-claim s-Kate-s-greying-hair-disaster.html>.

107 Professor Beard has even hosted her own BBC Radio 4 podcast on the topic of greying. See **Beard, M** 2016. 'Glad to be Grey', *BBC Radio 4* <https://www.bbc.co.uk/programmes/b071x87c>.

108 **Grose, A** 2013. 'The haters of Mary Beard's grey hair', *The Guardian,* <https://www.theguardian.com/commentisfree/2013/jan/25/mary-beard-long-grey-hair>.

Chapter 6

1 **Corbett, J** 1999. 'An historical review of the use of dye precursors in the formulation of commercial oxidation hair dyes', *Dyes and Pigments,* Volume 41.

2 **Ames, B et al** 1975. 'Hair dyes are mutagenic: identification of a variety of mutagenic ingredients', *Proceedings of the National Academy of Sciences of the United States of America,* Volume 72, Issue 6.

3 **Davies, D et al** 1975. 'The Effect of World War II on Industrial Science', *Proceedings of the Royal Society of London. Series A, Mathematical and Physical Sciences,* Volume 342, Issue 1631.

4 **Carson, R** 2002. *Silent Spring: Fortieth Anniversary Edition,* Mariner Books, Boston and New York.

5 **Carson, R** 2002. *Silent Spring: Fortieth Anniversary Edition.*

6 **Lear, L** 1997. *Rachel Carson: Witness for Nature,* Henry Holt & Co, New York.

7 **Smith, M** 2001. '"Silence, Miss Carson!" Science, Gender, and the Reception of *Silent Spring', Feminist Studies,* Volume 27, Issue 3.

8 **Griswold, E** 2012. 'How Silent Spring Ignited the Environmental Movement', The New York Times Magazine <https://www.nytimes.com/2012/09/23/magazine/how-silent-spring-ignited-the-environmental-moveme nt.html>.

9 **Cancer Research UK,** 2020. 'How Cancer Starts' <https://www.cancerresearchuk.org/about-cancer/what-is-cancer/how-cancer-starts>.

10 **Williams, R** 1972. 'Hepatic metabolism of drugs', *Gut,* Volume 13, Issue 7.

11 **Slack, J** 2014. *Genes: A Very Short Introduction, Oxford University Press, Oxford.*

12 **Venitt, S** 1996. 'Mechanisms of Spontaneous Human Cancers', *Environmental Health Perspectives,* Volume 104.

13 **Griffiths A et al (ed)** 2000. *An Introduction to Genetic Analysis: 7th edition,* W. H. Freeman, New York.

14 See **Mishima, M** 2017. 'Chromosomal aberrations, clastogens vs aneugens', Frontiers in Bioscience, Volume 9. See also **Parry, E et al** 2002. 'Detection and characterization of mechanisms of action of aneugenic chemicals', *Mutagenesis,* Volume 17, Issue 6.

15 **Stoye, E** 2019. 'Why does all life use the same 20 amino acids?', *Chemistry World* <https://www.chemistryworld.com/news/why-does-all-life-use-the-same-20-amino-acids/3010824.articl e>.

16 **Ames, B et al** 1971. 'The Detection of Chemical Mutagens with Enteric Bacteria' in **Hollaender, A (ed)** 1971. *Chemical Mutagens: Principles and Methods for Their Detection: Volume 1,* Plenum Press, New York.

17 **Ames, B et al** 1973. "An Improved Bacterial Test System for the Detection and Classification of Mutagens and Carcinogens', *Proceedings of the National Academy of Sciences of the United States of America,* Volume 70, Issue 3.

18 **Ames, B et al** 1975. 'Methods for Detecting Carcinogens and Mutagens with the Salmonella/Mammalian-Microsome Mutagenicity Test', *Mutation Research,* Volume 31.

19 **Ames, B et al** 1977. 'Flame-Retardant Additives as Possible Cancer Hazards: The main flame retardant in children's pajamas is a mutagen and should not be used.', *Science,* Volume 195.

20 **Ames, B et al** 1975. 'Hair Dyes are Mutagenic: Identification of a variety of Mutagenic Ingredients." *Proceedings of the National Academy of Sciences of the United States of America,* Volume 72, Issue 6.

21 **Hanlon, J** 1978. 'Tint Of Suspicion', *New Scientist,* Volume 78, Issue 1102.

22 **Sherrow, V** 2006. *Encyclopedia of Hair: A Cultural History,* Greenwood Press, Westport.

23 **Venitt, S et al** 1978. 'Chromosomal Damage and Hair Dyes', *The Lancet,* Volume 312, Issue 8081.

24 **International Agency for Research on Cancer,** 1978. *IARC Monographs On The Evaluation of the Carcinogenic Risk of Chemicals To Man: Volume 16: Some Aromatic Amines and Related Nitro Compounds -- Hair Dyes, Colouring Agents and Miscellaneous Industrial Chemicals.*

25 **Maibach, H et al** 1975. 'Percutaneous Penetration Following Use of Hair Dyes', *Archives of Dermatological Research,* Volume 111.

26 **Israels, M** 1934. 'Systemic poisoning by paraphenylene diamine with report of fatal case', Lancet, Issue 508.

27 **International Agency for Research on Cancer,** 2010. *IARC Monographs on the Evaluation of Carcinogenic Risks to Humans: Volume 99: Some Aromatic Amines, Organic Dyes, and Related Exposures.*

28 **Corbett, J** 1999. 'An historical review of the use of dye precursors in the formulation of commercial oxidation hair dyes', *Dyes and Pigments,* Volume 41.

29 **Corbett, J** 1999. 'An historical review of the use of dye precursors in the formulation of commercial oxidation hair dyes',

30 Although tumour incidence was not considered statistically significant, study authors noted the rarity of spontaneous bladder and kidney tumours of this type in laboratory rats. See **Sontag, J** 1981. 'Carcinogenicity of Substituted Benzenediamines (Phenylenediamines) in Rats and Mice', *Journal of the National Cancer Institute,* Volume 66, Issue 3.

31 **U.S. Government Printing Office,** 1978. Cancer-causing Chemicals: Safety of cosmetics and hair dyes, Washington.

32 **U.S. Government Printing Office,** 1978. Cancer-causing Chemicals: Safety of cosmetics and hair dyes

33 On speaking with Professor Ames, he believes the text in the original transcript here, which reads, 'For example, tumours appear with a third of time', was a misquote, and requested that I correct it for accuracy.

34 **U.S. Government Printing Office,** 1978. Cancer-causing Chemicals: Safety of cosmetics and hair dyes

35 **Mary Ann Lieberl Inc,** 1992. 'Final Report on the Safety Assessment of 4-Methoxy-m-Phenylenediamine, 4-Methoxy-rn-Phenylenediamine Sulfate, and 4-Methoxy-m-Phenylenediamine-HCI', *Journal of the American College of Toxicology,* Volume 11, Issue 4.

36 **Estrin, N (ed)** 1984. *The Cosmetic Industry: Scientific and Regulatory Foundations,* Marcel Dekker, New York and Basel.

37 **Venitt, S et al** 1976. 'Mutagenicity and possible carcinogenicity of hair colourants and constituents', *IARC Scientific Publications,* Volume 13.

38 **Doll, R et al** 2002. 'The United Kingdom Childhood Cancer Study: objectives, materials and methods', *British Journal of Cancer,* Volume 82, Issue 5.

39 **McKinney et al** 2008. 'The UK Childhood Cancer Study: Maternal Occupational Exposures and Childhood Leukaemia and Lymphoma', *Radiation Protection Dosimetry,* Volume 132, Issue 2.

40 **McKinney et al** 2008. 'The UK Childhood Cancer Study: Maternal Occupational Exposures and Childhood Leukaemia and Lymphoma'.

41 **Venitt, S et al** 1976. 'Mutagenicity and possible carcinogenicity of hair colourants and constituents'. See also **Venitt, S et al** 1975. 'Proceedings: Mutagenicity of hair colourants in bacteria: possible link with carcinogenicity', *British Journal of Cancer,* Volume 32, Issue 2.

42 **Venitt, S et al** 1984. 'The hair-dye reagent 2-(2',4'-diaminophenoxy)ethanol is mutagenic to Salmonella typhimurium', *Mutation Research,* Volume 135, Issue 1.

43 **European Commission,** 2021 (last updated). *Annex III: List of substances which cosmetic products must not contain except subject to the restrictions laid down* <https://ec.europa.eu/growth/tools-databases/cosing/pdf/COSING_Annex%20III_v2.pdf> and **Scientific Committee on Consumer Safety,** 2010. *Opinion on 2,4-diaminophenoxyethanol dihydrochloride and sulfate.*

44 **'Corbett, J** 1999. 'An historical review of the use of dye precursors in the formulation of commercial oxidation hair dyes'.

45 **Salvador, A et al (ed)** 2018. *Analysis of Cosmetic Products: Second Edition,* Elsevier, Amsterdam, Oxford and Cambridge.

46 **Publications Office of the European Union,** 2006. 'Commission Directive 2006/65/EC of 19 July 2006 amending Council Directive 76/768/EEC, concerning cosmetic products, for the purpose of adapting Annexes II and III thereto to technical progress', Official Journal of the European Union <https://eur-lex.europa.eu/legal-content/EN/TXT/PDF/?uri=CELEX:32006L0065&from=LV>.

47 **Publications Office of the European Union,** 2015. 'Commission Regulation (EU) 2015/1190 of 20 July 2015 amending Annex III to Regulation (EC) No 1223/2009 of the European Parliament and of the Council on cosmetic products', Official Journal of the European Union <https://eur-lex.europa.eu/legal-content/EN/TXT/PDF/?uri=CELEX:32015R1190&from=LV>.

48 **Publications Office of the European Union,** 2019. 'Commission Regulation (EU) 2019/681 of 30 April 2019 amending Annex II to Regulation (EC) No 1223/2009 of the European Parliament and of the Council on cosmetic products', Official Journal of the European Union <https://eur-lex.europa.eu/legal-content/EN/TXT/PDF/?uri=CELEX:32019R0681&from=EN>.

49 **European Commission,** 2021. *Annex III: List of substances which cosmetic products must not contain except subject to the restrictions laid down* <https://ec.europa.eu/growth/tools-databases/cosing/pdf/COSING_Annex%20III_v2.pdf>.

50 **Publications Office of the European Union,** 2009. 'Commission Directive 2009/134/EC of 28 October 2009 amending Council Directive 76/768/EEC concerning cosmetic products for the purposes of adapting Annex III thereto to technical progress', Official Journal of the European Union <https://eur-lex.europa.eu/legal-content/EN/TXT/PDF/?uri=CELEX:32009L0134&from=SK>.

51 **Salvador, A et al (ed),** 2018. *Analysis of Cosmetic Products: Second Edition.*

52 **Salvador, A et al (ed),** 2007. *Analysis of Cosmetic Products: First Edition,* Elsevier, Amsterdam and Oxford.

53 For the current list of member nations, see **Association of Southeast Asian Nations, 2020.** 'ASEAN Member States' <https://asean.org/about-asean/member-states/>.

54 For the current list of member nations, see **MERCOSUR, 2021.** 'MERCOSUR Countries' <https://www.mercosur.int/en/about-mercosur/mercosur-countries/>.

55 **Salvador, A et al (ed)** 2018. *Analysis of Cosmetic Products: Second Edition.*

56 **Barrows, J et al** 2003. 'Color Additives: FDA's Regulatory Process and Historical Perspectives', Food Safety Magazine, reprinted in U.S. Food & Drug Administration, 2017. 'Color Additives History' <https://www.fda.gov/industry/color-additives/color-additives-history#authors>.

57 **U.S. Food & Drug Administration,** 2020. 'Hair Dyes' <https://www.fda.gov/Cosmetics/ProductsIngredients/Products/ucm143066.htm>.

58 **Cosmetic Ingredient Review,** 2007. 'Safety Assessment of p-Phenylenediamine, p-Phenylenediamine HCl, and p-Phenylenediamine Sulfate', Amended Final Report of the Cosmetic Ingredient Review Expert Panel, Washington <http://gov.personalcarecouncil.org/ctfa-static/online/lists/cir-pdfs/FR530.pdf>.

59 **Nelter, T** 2019. 'Lead in hair dye – one company considers it safe', *Environmental Defense Fund* <http://blogs.edf.org/health/2019/01/04/lead-in-hair-dye-company-safe/>.

60 **'Corbett, J** 1999. 'An historical review of the use of dye precursors in the formulation of commercial oxidation hair dyes'.

Chapter 7

1 **Salvador, A et al (ed)** 2018. *Analysis of Cosmetic Products: Second Edition,* Elsevier, Amsterdam, Oxford and Cambridge.

2 **Salvador, A et al (ed)** 2018. *Analysis of Cosmetic Products:*

Second Edition, Elsevier, Amsterdam, Oxford and Cambridge.

3 **European Chemicals Agency,** 2021. 'Animal testing under REACH' <https://echa.europa.eu/animal-testing-under-reach>.

4 **European Commission,** 2013. 'Full EU ban on animal testing for cosmetics enters into force' <https://ec.europa.eu/commission/presscorner/detail/en/IP_13_210>.

5 **European Chemicals Agency,** 2021. 'Animal testing under REACH' <https://echa.europa.eu/animal-testing-under-reach>.

6 **Animal-Free Safety Assessment Collaboration,** 2020. 'Call on EU to uphold cosmetic animal testing ban' <https://www.afsacollaboration.org/cosmetics/uphold-eu-cosmetic-animal-testing-ban/>.

7 **Langley, G et al** 1993. 'A cell suspension agar diffusion test using Neutral Red release to assess the relative irritancy potential of cosmetic ingredients and formulations', *International Journal of Cosmetic Science,* Volume 15, Issue 1.

8 See <https://lushprize.org/>.

9 Para-phenylenediamine had both positive and negative results for mutagenicity in vitro (meaning tests performed in a test tube or culture dish), but was not found to be mutagenic in vivo (live organism) mouse studies. See **European Commission, 2012.** 'Opinion of the Scientific Committee on Consumer Safety on p-phenylenediamine' <https://ec.europa.eu/health/scientific_committees/consumer_safety/docs/sccs_o_094.pdf>.
Para-toluenediamine also showed mutagenic potential in vitro bacteria studies, but not in similar mammal cell in vitro experiments or in vivo mouse studies. See **European Commission, 2012.** 'Scientific Committee on Consumer Safety opinion on Toluene-2,5-diamine and its sulfate' <https://ec.europa.eu/health/scientific_committees/consumer_safety/docs/sccs_o_093.pdf>.
2-methoxymethyl-p-phenylenediamine was mutagenic in all in vitro tests but not in in vivo experiments using animal tissue. See **European Commission, 2012.** 'Scientific Committee on Consumer Safety opinion on 2-methoxy-methyl-p-phenylenediamine and its sulfate salt' <https://ec.europa.eu/health/sites/default/files/scientific_committees/consumer_safety/docs/sccs_o_1 23.pdf>.

10 **European Commission, 2012.** 'Scientific Committee on Consumer Safety opinion on 2-methoxy-methyl-p-phenylenediamine and its sulfate salt'

11 **European Commission,** 2012. 'Opinion of the Scientific Committee on Consumer Safety on p-phenylenediamine'

12 **European Commission,** 2010. 'Scientific Committee on Consumer Safety opinion on reaction products of oxidative hair dye ingredients formed during hair dyeing processes' <https://ec.europa.eu/health/sites/health/files/scientific_committees/consumer_safety/docs/sccs_o_03 7.pdf>.

13 **European Commission,** 2010. 'Scientific Committee on Consumer Safety opinion on reaction products of oxidative hair dye ingredients formed during hair dyeing processes' <https://ec.europa.eu/health/sites/health/files/scientific_committees/consumer_safety/docs/sccs_o_03 7.pdf>.

14 **World Health Organisation,** 2010. 'International Agency for Research on Cancer Monographs on the Evaluation of Carcinogenic Risk to Humans: Volume 99: Some Aromatic Amines, Organic Dyes and Related Exposures', Lyon.

15 **Maiti, S et al** 2016. 'Analysis of cytotoxicity and genotoxicity on E. coli, human blood cells and Allium cepa suggests a greater toxic potential of hair dye', *Ecotoxicology and Environmental Safety,* Volume 124.

16 **Maiti, S et al** 2015. 'Hair Dye-DNA Interaction: Plausible Cause of Mutation', *Cosmetics,* Volume 2.

17 **Czene, K et al** 2003. 'Cancer risks in hairdressers: Assessment of carcinogenicity of hair dyes and gels'.

18 **Pexe, M,** 2019. 'Hairdressers are exposed to high concentrations of formaldehyde during the hair straightening procedure', *Environmental Science and Pollution Research,* Volume 26.

19 **BBC,** 2017. 'Hair dye dangers warning for children' <https://www.bbc.co.uk/news/uk-wales-41796586>.

20 **NHS,** 2021. 'Overview: Bladder Cancer', <https://www.nhs.uk/conditions/bladder-cancer/>.

21 **Cancer Research UK,** 2021. 'Bladder Cancer Research' <https://www.cancerresearchuk.org/health-professional/cancer-statistics/statistics-by-cancer-type/blad der-cancer#heading-Zero>.

22 **World Cancer Research Fund International,** 2018. 'Worldwide Cancer Data' <https://www.wcrf.org/dietandcancer/worldwide-cancer-data/#:~:text=Lung%20and%20breast%20can cers%20

were,million%20new%20cases%20in%202018.>.

23 **Schuttelaar, ML et al** 2016. 'Contact Allergy to Hair Dyes', *Cosmetics,* Volume 3, Issue 3.

24 **Husain, A et al** 2007. 'Identification of N-acetyltransferase 2 (NAT2) transcription start sites and quantitation of NAT2-specific mRNA in human tissues', *Drug Metabolism and Disposition: The Biological Fate of Chemicals,* Volume 35, Issue 5.

25 **Nohynek, G et al** 2015. 'Human systemic exposure to [14C]-paraphenylenediamine-containing oxidative hair dyes: Absorption, kinetics, metabolism, excretion and safety assessment', *Food and Chemical Toxicology,* Volume 81.

26 **Letašiová S et al** 2012. 'Bladder cancer, a review of the environmental risk factors', *Environmental Health,* Volume 11, Issue 1.

27 **Mancini, M et al** 2020. Spotlight on gender-specific disparities in bladder cancer', *Urologia Journal,* Volume 87, Issue 3.

28 **Freedman, N et al** 2011. 'Association between smoking and risk of bladder cancer among men and women', *JAMA,* Volume 306, Issue 7.

29 **NHS,** 2021. 'Causes: Bladder Cancer' <https://www.nhs.uk/conditions/bladder-cancer/causes/>.

30 **Hadkhale, K et al** 2017. 'Occupational variation in incidence of bladder cancer: a comparison of population-representative cohorts from Nordic countries and Canada', *BMJ Open,* Volume 7, Issue 8.

Czene, K et al 2003. 'Cancer risks in hairdressers: Assessment of carcinogenicity of hair dyes and gels', International Journal of Cancer, Volume 105, Issue 1.

31 **Reulen, R et al** 2008. 'A meta-analysis on the association between bladder cancer and occupation', *Scandinavian Journal of Urology and Nephrology,* Volume 42.

Harling, M et al 2010. 'Bladder cancer among hairdressers: a meta-analysis', *Occupational and Environmental Medicine,* Volume 67, Issue 5.

Takkouche, B et al 2009. 'Risk of cancer among hairdressers and related workers: a meta-analysis', *International Journal of Epidemiology,* Volume 38, Issue 6. Could not conclude whether risk had declined.

32 **Takkouche, B et al** 2009. 'Risk of cancer among hairdressers and related workers: a meta-analysis'.

33 **Takkouche, B et al** 2009. 'Risk of cancer among hairdressers and related workers: a meta-analysis'.

34 **Zhang, Y et al** 2012. 'Hair dye use and risk of human cancer', *Frontiers in Bioscience,* Volume 4.

Kim, K et al 2016. 'The use of personal hair dye and its implications for human health', *Environment International,* Volumes 89-90.

Saitta, P et al 2013. 'Is there a true concern regarding the use of hair dye and malignancy development?: a review of the epidemiological evidence relating personal hair dye use to the risk of malignancy', *The Journal of Clinical and Aesthetic Dermatology,* Volume 6, Issue 1.

Gago-Dominguez, M et al 2012. 'Personal hair dye use and the risk of bladder cancer: a case-control study from The Netherlands', *Cancer Causes & Control,* Volume 23, Issue 7.

Takkouche, B et al 2005. 'Personal use of hair dyes and risk of cancer: a meta-analysis', *JAMA,* Volume 293, Issue 20.

35 **Hamann, D et al** 2014. 'p-Phenylenediamine and other allergens in hair dye products in the United States: A consumer exposure study', *Contact Dermatitis,* Volume 70.

Corbett, J 1999. 'An historical review of the use of dye precursors in the formulation of commercial oxidation hair dyes', *Dyes and Pigments,* Volume 41.

Chong, HP et al 2016. 'para-Phenylenediamine Containing Hair Dye: An Overview of Mutagenicity, Carcinogenicity and Toxicity', *Journal of Environmental & Analytical Toxicology,* Volume 6, Issue 5.

36 **Reena, K et al** 2016. 'para-Phenylenediamine Induces Apoptosis Through Activation of Reactive Oxygen Species-Mediated Mitochondrial Pathway, and Inhibition of the NF-jB, mTOR, and Wnt Pathways in Human Urothelial Cells', *Environmental toxicology,* Volume 32, Issue 1.

37 **Espinoza, F et al** 2008. 'Micronuclei assessment in the urothelial cells of women using hair dyes and its modulation by genetic polymorphisms', *Cancer Letters,* Volume 263, Issue 2.

38 **Turesky RJ et al** 2003. 'Identification of aminobiphenyl derivatives in commercial hair dyes', *Chemical Research in Toxicology,* Volume 16, Issue 9.

Johansson G, et al 2015. 'Exposure of hairdressers to ortho- and meta-toluidine in hair dyes', *Occupational and Environmental Medicine,* Volume 72.

Akyüz, M et al 2008. 'Determination of aromatic amines

in hair dye and henna samples by ion-pair extraction and gas chromatography-mass spectrometry', *Journal of Pharmaceutical and Biomedical Analysis,* Volume 47, Issue 1.

39 **Gago-Dominguez, M et al** 2003. 'Permanent hair dyes and bladder cancer: risk modification by cytochrome P4501A2 and N- acetyltransferases 1 and 2', *Carcinogenesis,* Volume 24, Issue 3.

40 **Gago-Dominguez, M et al** 2003. 'Permanent hair dyes and bladder cancer: risk modification by cytochrome P4501A2 and N- acetyltransferases 1 and 2'.

Zhu, Z et al 2015. 'Risks on N-acetyltransferase 2 and bladder cancer: a meta-analysis', *OncoTargets and Therapy,* Volume 8.

Koutros, S et al 2011. 'Hair dye use and risk of bladder cancer in the New England bladder cancer study', *International Journal of Cancer,* Volume 129.

Cascorbi, I. et al 2001. 'Association of NAT1 and NAT2 polymorphisms to urinary bladder cancer: significantly reduced risk in subjects with NAT1*10', *Cancer Research,* Volume 61, Issue 13.

Marcus, P et al 2000. 'NAT2 slow acetylation and bladder cancer risk: a meta-analysis of 22 case-control studies conducted in the general population', *Pharmacogenetics,* Volume 10, Issue 2.

41 **Sabbagh, A et al** 2011. 'Arylamine N-acetyltransferase 2 (NAT2) genetic diversity and traditional subsistence: a worldwide population survey', *PloS One,* Volume 6, Issue 4.

42 Ironically, given their resilience to bladder cancer, some research suggests that hair dyers classed as rapid NAT2 acetylators actually have an increased risk for a type of non-Hodgkin lymphoma called follicular lymphoma if they began dying their hair before 1980. This needs further investigation but reminds us that we are still scratching the surface on just how important genetics is to drug metabolism. See **Zhang, Y** 2009. 'Genetic variations in xenobiotic metabolic pathway genes, personal hair dye use, and risk of non-Hodgkin lymphoma', *American Journal of Epidemiology,* Volume 170, Issue 10 and **Morton, L** 2007. 'Hair dye use, genetic variation in *N*-acetyltransferase 1 (NAT1) and 2 (NAT2), and risk of non-Hodgkin lymphoma', *Carcinogenesis,* Volume 28, Issue 8.

43 **Sabbagh, A et al** 2011. 'Arylamine N-acetyltransferase 2 (NAT2) genetic diversity and traditional subsistence: a worldwide population survey'.

Sabbagh, A et al 2008. 'Worldwide distribution of NAT2 diversity: Implications for NAT2 evolutionary history', BMC Genetics, Volume 9, Issue 21.

44 **Notarianni, L et al** 1996. 'Caffeine as a metabolic probe: NAT2 phenotyping', *British Journal of Clinical Pharmacology,* Volume 41, Issue 3.

45 **Watson, S 2020.** 'What is lymphoma?', WebMD <https://www.webmd.com/cancer/lymphoma/lymphoma-cancer#1>.

46 **Cancer Research UK,** 2021. 'Hodgkin Lymphoma Statistics' <https://www.cancerresearchuk.org/health-professional/cancer-statistics/statistics-by-cancer-type/hod gkin-lymphoma#heading-Zero>.

Cancer Research UK, 2021. 'Non-Hodgkin Lymphoma Statistics' <https://www.cancerresearchuk.org/health-professional/cancer-statistics/statistics-by-cancer-type/non -hodgkin-lymphoma#heading-Zero>.

47 **Cancer Research UK,** 2021. 'Non-Hodgkin Lymphoma Incidence Statistics' <https://www.cancerresearchuk.org/health-professional/cancer-statistics/statistics-by-cancer-type/non -hodgkin-lymphoma/incidence#heading-Zero>.

48 **World Cancer Research Fund International,** 2018. 'Worldwide Cancer Data' <https://www.wcrf.org/dietandcancer/worldwide-cancer-data/#:~:text=Lung%20and%20breast%20can cers%20were,million%20new%20cases%20in%202018.>.GG

49 **Boffetta, P** 1994. 'Employment as hairdresser and risk of ovarian cancer and non-Hodgkin's lymphomas among women', Journal of Occupational Medicine, Volume 36, Issue 1.

Milham, S 1983. Occupational mortality in Washington State: 1950 to 1979, US Department of Health and Human Services, Washington.

Teta, M et al 1984. 'Cancer incidence among cosmetologists', *Journal of the National Cancer Institute,* Volume 72, Issue 5.

Persson, B et al 1989. 'Malignant lymphomas and occupational exposures', *British Journal of Industrial Medicine,* Volume 46.

Skov, T et al 1991. 'Non-Hodgkin's Lymphoma and

Occupation in Denmark', *Scandinavian Journal of Social Medicine,* Volume 19, Issue 3.

Mannetje, A et al 2016. 'Occupation and Risk of Non-Hodgkin Lymphoma and Its Subtypes: A Pooled Analysis from the InterLymph Consortium', *Environmental Health Perspectives,* Volume 124, Issue 4.

Takkouche, B et al 2009. 'Risk of cancer among hairdressers and related workers: a meta-analysis'.

50 **Milham, S** 1983. Occupational mortality in Washington State: 1950 to 1979.

Teta, M et al 1984. 'Cancer incidence among cosmetologists'.

Mannetje, A et al 2016. 'Occupation and Risk of Non-Hodgkin Lymphoma and Its Subtypes: A Pooled Analysis from the InterLymph Consortium'.

51 **Takkouche, B et al** 2009. 'Risk of cancer among hairdressers and related workers: a meta-analysis'.

Mannetje, A et al 2016. 'Occupation and Risk of Non-Hodgkin Lymphoma and Its Subtypes: A Pooled Analysis from the InterLymph Consortium'.

52 **Saitta, P et al** 2013. 'Is there a true concern regarding the use of hair dye and malignancy development?: a review of the epidemiological evidence relating personal hair dye use to the risk of malignancy'.

Zhang, Y et al 2012. 'Hair dye use and risk of human cancer', *Frontiers in Bioscience,* Volume 4.

Qin, L et al 2019. 'A Meta-Analysis on the Relationship Between Hair Dye and the Incidence of Non-Hodgkin's Lymphoma', *Medical Principles and Practice,* Volume 28.

53 **Saitta, P et al** 2013. 'Is there a true concern regarding the use of hair dye and malignancy development?: a review of the epidemiological evidence relating personal hair dye use to the risk of malignancy'.

Qin, L et al 2019. 'A Meta-Analysis on the Relationship Between Hair Dye and the Incidence of Non-Hodgkin's Lymphoma'.

54 **'Saitta, P et al** 2013. 'Is there a true concern regarding the use of hair dye and malignancy development?: a review of the epidemiological evidence relating personal hair dye use to the risk of malignancy'.

55 **Qin, L et al** 2019. 'A Meta-Analysis on the Relationship Between Hair Dye and the Incidence of Non-Hodgkin's Lymphoma'.

Saitta, P et al 2013. 'Is there a true concern regarding the use of hair dye and malignancy development?: a review of the epidemiological evidence relating personal hair dye use to the risk of malignancy'.

56 **Qin, L et al** 2019. 'A Meta-Analysis on the Relationship Between Hair Dye and the Incidence of Non-Hodgkin's Lymphoma'.

57 **Maiti, S et al** 2016. 'Analysis of cytotoxicity and genotoxicity on E. coli, human blood cells and Allium cepa suggests a greater toxic potential of hair dye'.

58 **International Agency for Research on Cancer,** 1993. *IARC Monographs on the Evaluation of Carcinogenic Risks to Humans: Volume 57: Occupational Exposures of Hairdressers and Barbers and Personal Use of Hair Colourants; Some Hair Dyes, Cosmetic Colourants, Industrial Dyestuffs and Aromatic Amines, Lyon.*

59 **Sherrow, V** 2006. *Encyclopedia of Hair: A Cultural History,* Greenwood Press, Westport.

60 **Zhang Y et al** 2020. 'Personal use of permanent hair dyes and cancer risk and mortality in US women: prospective cohort study', *British Medical Journal,* Volume 370.

61 **Blood Cancer UK,** 2021. 'Leukemia' <https://bloodcancer.org.uk/understanding-blood-cancer/leukaemia/>.

WebMD, 2019. 'Leukemia' <https://www.webmd.com/cancer/lymphoma/understanding-leukemia-basics#1>.

62 **WebMD,** 2019. 'Leukemia' <https://www.webmd.com/cancer/lymphoma/understanding-leukemia-basics#1>.

63 **Cancer Research UK,** 2021. 'Leukaemia (all subtypes combined) statistics' <https://www.cancerresearchuk.org/health-professional/cancer-statistics/statistics-by-cancer-type/leuk aemia#heading-Zero>.

64 **Milham, S** 1983. *Occupational mortality in Washington State: 1950 to 1979,* US Department of Health and Human Services, Washington.

Ji, J et al 2005. 'Occurrences of leukemia subtypes by socioeconomic and occupational groups in Sweden', *Journal of Occupational and Environmental Medicine,* Volume 47, Issue 11.

Strom, S et al 2012. 'De novo acute myeloid leukemia risk factors: A Texas case-control study', Cancer, Volume 118, Issue 18.

Tsai, R et al 2014. 'Acute myeloid leukemia risk by industry and occupation', *Leukemia & Lymphoma,* Volume 55, Issue 11.

65 **Takkouche, B et al** 2009. 'Risk of cancer among

hairdressers and related workers: a meta-analysis'.

66 **Mele, A et al** 1994. 'Hair dye use and other risk factors for leukemia and pre-leukemia: a case-control study', *American Journal of Epidemiology,* Volume 139, Issue 6.
Miligi, L et al 1999. 'Occupational, environmental, and life-style factors associated with the risk of hematolymphopoietic malignancies in women', *American Journal of Industrial Medicine,* Volume 36, Issue 1.

67 **Mintel,** 2018. 'A Year of Innovation in Hair Colourants'.

68 **Mintel,** 2020. 'Hair Colourants - Europe - 2020 Databook'.

69 **Mintel,** 2015. 'Category Insights: Hair Colourants 2015'.

70 **Mannetje, A et al** 2016. 'Occupation and Risk of Non-Hodgkin Lymphoma and Its Subtypes: A Pooled Analysis from the InterLymph Consortium'.

71 **Slager, S et al** 2014. 'Medical History, Lifestyle, Family History, and Occupational Risk Factors for Chronic Lymphocytic Leukemia/Small Lymphocytic Lymphoma: The InterLymph Non-Hodgkin Lymphoma Subtypes Project', *JNCI Monographs,* Volume 2014, Issue 48.

72 **Cantor, K et al** 1988. 'Hair Dye Use and Risk of Leukemia and Lymphoma', *American Journal of Public Health,* Volume 78, Issue 5.
Rauscher, G 2004. 'Hair dye use and risk of adult acute leukemia', *American Journal of Epidemiology,* Volume 160, Issue 1.

73 **Rauscher, G** 2004. 'Hair dye use and risk of adult acute leukemia'.

74 **U.S. Government Printing Office,** 1978. Cancer-causing Chemicals: Safety of cosmetics and hair dyes, Washington.

75 **Towle, K et al** 2017. 'Personal use of hair dyes and risk of leukemia: a systematic literature review and meta-analysis', *Cancer Medicine,* Volume 6, Issue 10.

76 **Peters, H et al** 1938. 'Systemic Poisoning due to Synthetic Organic Hair Dye: Fatal Case with Autopsy', *Annals of Internal Medicine.*

77 **Toghill, P et al** 1976. 'Aplastic anaemia and hair dye', *British Medical Journal,* Volume 1.
Hamilton, S 1976. 'Letter: Aplastic anemia and hair dye', *British Medical Journal,* Volume 1.
Hopkins, J et al 1985. 'Severe aplastic anaemia following the use of hair dye: report of two cases and review of literature', *Postgraduate Medical Journal,* Volume 61.

78 **Vitale C et al** 2020. *Aromatic Toxicity, StatPearls Publishing* <https://www.ncbi.nlm.nih.gov/books/NBK532257/>.

79 **El-Amin, E et al** 2014. 'Toxicity Effects of Hair Dye Application on Liver Function in Experimental Animals', *Journal of Clinical Toxicology,* Volume 4, Issue 4.

80 **Chye, S et al** 2008. 'Single strand DNA breaks in human lymphocytes exposed to para-phenylenediamine and its derivatives', *Bulletin of Environmental Contamination and Toxicology,* Volume 80, Issue 1.

81 **Cho, J** 2003. 'Effects of hair dyeing on DNA damage in human lymphocytes', *Journal of Occupational Health,* Volume 45, issue 6.

82 **Peters, H et al** 1938. 'Systemic Poisoning due to Synthetic Organic Hair Dye: Fatal Case with Autopsy'.

83 **Mele, A et al** 1994. 'Hair dye use and other risk factors for leukemia and pre-leukemia: a case-control study'.

84 **Nagata, C et al** 1999. 'Hair dye use and occupational exposure to organic solvents as risk factors for myelodysplastic syndrome', *Leukemia Research,* Volume 23, Issue 1.

85 Confusingly, some types of anaemia such as refractory anaemia, refractory cytopenia and refractory anaemia with excess blasts were renamed as forms of myelodysplasia in 2016. I have chosen to use the terms given in the individual studies. See **NHS** 2021. 'Myelodysplastic syndrome (myelodysplasia)', <https://www.nhs.uk/conditions/myelodysplasia/>.

86 **National Institute of Diabetes and Digestive and Kidney Diseases** 2020. 'Definition & Facts for Aplastic Anemia & Myelodysplastic Syndromes' <https://www.niddk.nih.gov/health-information/blood-diseases/aplastic-anemia-myelodysplastic-syndr omes/definition-facts>.

87 **Lv, L et al** 2010. 'Case–control study of risk factors of myelodysplastic syndromes according to World Health Organization classification in a Chinese population', *American Journal of Hematology,* Volume 86, Issue 2.

88 **Poynter, J** 2016. 'Chemical exposures and risk of acute myeloid leukemia and myelodysplastic syndromes in a population-based study', *International Journal Of Cancer,* Volume 140, Issue 1.

89 **Mintel** 2013. 'Hair colouring is common for Chinese consumers'.

90 **White, B et al (ed)** 2004. Japan's *Changing Generations: Are Young People Creating a New Society?,* Routledge, London.

91 **Mintel** 2014. 'Innovation aims to revive Japan's mature colorants sector'.

92 **WebMD** 2021. 'Multiple Myeloma' <https://www.webmd.com/cancer/multiple-myeloma/multiple-myeloma-symptoms-causes-treatment>.
NHS 2021. 'Overview: Multiple Myeloma' <https://www.nhs.uk/conditions/multiple-myeloma/>.

93 **Cancer Research UK** 2021. 'Myeloma statistics' <https://www.cancerresearchuk.org/health-professional/cancer-statistics/statistics-by-cancer-type/mye loma#heading-Zero>.

94 **Milham, S** 1983. *Occupational mortality in Washington State: 1950 to 1979.*
Spinelli, J et al 1984. 'Multiple Myeloma, Leukemia, and cancer of the ovary in cosmetologists and hairdressers', *American Journal of Industrial Medicine,* Volume 6, Issue 2.
Guidotti, S et al 1982. 'Multiple myeloma in cosmetologists', *American Journal of Industrial Medicine,* Volume 3, Issue 2.

95 **Czene, K et al** 2003. 'Cancer risks in hairdressers: Assessment of carcinogenicity of hair dyes and gels', *International Journal of Cancer,* Volume 105, Issue 1.
Pukkala, E 1992. 'Changing cancer risk pattern among Finnish hairdressers', *International Archives of Occupational and Environmental Health,* Volume 64, Issue 1.

96 **Hamann, D et al** 2014. 'p-Phenylenediamine and other allergens in hair dye products in the United States: A consumer exposure study', *Contact Dermatitis,* Volume 70, Issue 4.

97 **Yazar, K et al** 2009. 'Potent skin sensitizers in oxidative hair dye products on the Swedish market', *Contact Dermatitis,* Volume 61, Issue 5.

98 **Takkouche, B et al** 2009. 'Risk of cancer among hairdressers and related workers: a meta-analysis'.

99 **Zahm, S et al** 1992. 'Use of hair coloring products and the risk of lymphoma, multiple myeloma, and chronic lymphocytic leukemia', *American Journal of Public Health,* Volume 82, Issue 7.
Altekruse, S 1999. 'Deaths from hematopoietic and other cancers in relation to permanent hair dye use in a large prospective study (United States)', *Cancer Causes & Control,* Volume 10, Issue 6.
Thun, M et al 1994. 'Hair dye use and risk of fatal cancers in U.S. women', *Journal of the National Cancer Institute,* Volume 86, Issue 3.

100 **Koutros, S et al** 2009. 'Use of hair colouring products and risk of multiple myeloma among US women', *Occupational and Environmental Medicine,* Volume 66, Issue 1.
Mendelsohn, J et al 2009. 'Personal use of hair dye and cancer risk in a prospective cohort of Chinese women', *Cancer Science,* Volume 100, Issue 6.

101 **Lv, L et al** 2010. 'Case–control study of risk factors of myelodysplastic syndromes according to World Health Organization classification in a Chinese population'.

102 **Mintel** 2016. 'Category Insights: Hair Colourants', and Mintel 2017. 'Home Hair Color US January 2017'.

103 **Huang, W** et al 2019. 'Face masks could raise pollution risks', *Nature,* Volume 574.

104 **Echegaray, F et al** 2018. 'Exploring motivations behind pollution-mask use in a sample of young adults in urban China', *Global Health,* Volume 14.

105 **Correa, A et al** 2000. 'Use of hair dyes, hematopoietic neoplasms, and lymphomas: a literature review. II. Lymphomas and multiple myeloma', *Cancer Investigation,* Volume 18, Issue 4.
Alexander, D et al 2007. 'Multiple myeloma: a review of the epidemiologic literature', *International Journal of Cancer,* Volume 120, Issue 12.

106 **Cancer Research UK** 2021. 'Lung cancer statistics' <https://www.cancerresearchuk.org/health-professional/cancer-statistics/statistics-by-cancer-type/lung -cancer#heading-Zero>.

107 **Cancer Research UK** 2021. 'What is lung cancer?' <https://www.cancerresearchuk.org/about-cancer/lung-cancer/about>.

108 **NHS** 2019. 'Causes: Lung cancer' <https://www.nhs.uk/conditions/lung-cancer/causes/>.

109 **Vedel-Krogh, S et al** 2015. 'Morbidity and Mortality in 7,684 Women According to Personal Hair Dye Use: The Copenhagen City Heart Study followed for 37 Years', *PLoS ONE,* Volume 11, Issue 3.
Mendelsohn, J et al 2009. 'Personal use of hair dye and cancer risk in a prospective cohort of Chinese women'.
Thun, M et al 1994. 'Hair Dye Use and Risk Of Fatal Cancers in US women', *Journal of the National Cancer Institute,* Volume 86, Issue 3.

110 **Menicagli, R et al 2018.** 'The Question on the Potential Cancerous Effects of Hair Dyes: The Monitoring of the

Oxidative Stress Induced by the Hair Dyes with the Dosage of the Salivary Free Radicals', Indian Journal of *Occupational and Environmental Medicine,* Volume 22, Issue 2.

111 **Farhadi, S** 2018. 'Micronucleus Assay of Buccal Mucosal Cells in Hairdressers: The Importance of Occupational Exposure', *Asian Pacific Journal of Cancer Prevention,* Volume 19, Issue 8.

112 **Ramirez-Martinez, A et al** 2016. 'Exposure of hairdressers to the main cosmetics used in hairdressing salons in France: A preliminary study', *Archives of Environmental & Occupational Health* Volume 71.

Hueber-Becker, F et al 2007. 'Occupational exposure of hairdressers to [14C]-para-phenylenediamine-containing oxidative hair dyes: a mass balance study', *Food and Chemical Toxicology,* Volume 45, Issue 1.

Ronda, E et al 2009. 'Airborne exposure to chemical substances in hairdresser salons', *Environmental Monitoring and Assessment,* Volume 153.

De Gennaro, G et al 2014. 'Indoor air quality in hair salons: Screening of volatile organic compounds and indicators based on health risk assessment', *Atmospheric Environment,* Volume 83.

Hadei, Mostafa et al 2018. 'Indoor concentrations of VOCs in beauty salons; association with cosmetic practices and health risk assessment', *Journal of Occupational Medicine and Toxicology,* Volume 13, Issue 30.

113 **Ronda, E et al** 2009. 'Airborne exposure to chemical substances in hairdresser salons'.

Taghi, M et al 2018. 'Evaluating occupational exposure to para-phenylenediamine (PPD) in the inhaled air and environmental factors affecting women hairdressers in Sari', *Iran Occupational Health Journal,* Volume 15, Issue 1.

Hueber-Becker, F et al 2007. 'Occupational exposure of hairdressers to [14C]-para-phenylenediamine-containing oxidative hair dyes: a mass balance study'.

114 **Milham, S** 1983. Occupational mortality in Washington State: 1950 to 1979

Menck, H 1977. 'Lung cancer risk among beauticians and other female workers: brief communication', *Journal of the National Cancer Institute,* Volume 59, Issue 5.

115 **US Centers for Disease Control and Prevention** 2001. 'Women and Smoking: A Report of the Surgeon General's Office on Smoking and Health', Atlanta.

116 **Pukkala, E et al** 1992. 'Changing cancer risk pattern among Finnish hairdressers', *International Archives of Occupational and Environmental Health,* Volume 64, Issue 1.

117 **Ruokolainen, O et al** 2019. 'Thirty-eight-year trends of educational differences in smoking in Finland', *International Journal of Public Health,* Volume 64, Issue 6.

118 **Amos A et al** 2000. 'From social taboo to "torch of freedom": the marketing of cigarettes to women', *Tobacco Control,* Volume 9.

119 **U.S Department of Health and Human Services** 2012. *Preventing Tobacco Use Among Youth and Young Adults: A Report of the Surgeon General*, Washington.

120 **US Centers for Disease Control and Prevention** 2001. 'Women and Smoking: A Report of the Surgeon General's Office on Smoking and Health'.

121 **Toossi, M** 2002. 'A century of change: the U.S. labor force, 1950–2050', *Monthly Labor Review,* Volume 9.

122 **Bureau of Labor Statistics** 1987. *Occupational Outlook Quarterly,* Volume 11, Issue 1.

123 **McCurdy, S et al** 2003. 'Smoking and occupation from the European Community Respiratory Health Survey', *Occupational and Environmental Medicine,* Volume 60.

Czene, K et al 2003. 'Cancer Risks in Hairdressers: Assessment of Carcinogenicity of Hair Dyes and Gels'.

124 **Olsson, A.et al** 2013. 'Lung cancer risk among hairdressers: a pooled analysis of case-control studies conducted between 1985 and 2010', *American Journal of Epidemiology,* Volume 178, Issue 9.

125 **Takkouche, B et al** 2009. 'Risk of cancer among hairdressers and related workers: a meta-analysis'.

126 **Espuga M et al** 2011. 'Prevalence of Possible Occupational Asthma in Hairdressers Working in Hair Salons for Women', *International Archives of Allergy and Immunology,* Volume 155, Issue 4.

Moscato, G et al 2006. 'Asthma and hairdressers', *Current Opinion in Allergy and Clinical Immunology,* Volume 6, Issue 2.

Leino, T. et al 1998. 'Occupational skin and respiratory diseases among hairdressers', Scandinavian Journal of Work, *Environment & Health,* Volume 24, Issue 5.

127 **NHS** 2019. 'Overview: Breast cancer in women' <https://www.nhs.uk/conditions/breast-cancer/>.

128 **Cancer Research UK** 2021. 'Breast cancer statistics' <https://www.cancerresearchuk.org/health-professional/cancer-statistics/statistics-by-cancer-type/bre ast-cancer#heading-Zero>.

129 **Sun, YS et al** 2017. 'Risk Factors and Preventions of Breast Cancer', *International Journal of Biological Sciences,* Volume 13, Issue 11.

130 **Czene, K et al** 2003. 'Cancer risks in hairdressers: Assessment of carcinogenicity of hair dyes and gels'.

Takkouche, B et al 2009. 'Risk of cancer among hairdressers and related workers: a meta-analysis'.

131 **Mokbel, K et al** 2018. 'Does the use of hair dyes increase the risk of developing breast cancer? A Meta-analysis and Review of the Literature', *AntiCancer Research,* Volume 38.

132 **Petro-Nustas, W et al** 2002. 'Risk factors for breast cancer in Jordanian women', *Journal of Nursing Scholarship,* Volume 34, Issue 1.

133 **Heikkinen, S et al** 2015. 'Does Hair Dye Use increase the risk of breast cancer? A population-based case control study of Finnish women', *PLoS ONE,* Volume 10, Issue 8.

134 **Xu, S et al,** 2021. 'Hair chemicals may increase breast cancer risk: A meta-analysis of 210319 subjects from 14 studies', *Plos One,* Volume 16, Issue 2.

135 **Heikkinen, S et al** 2015. 'Does Hair Dye Use increase the risk of breast cancer? A population-based case control study of Finnish women'.

136 **Abdelaziz, S et al** 2018. 'Predictors of Breast Cancer Risk among Hair Dye Users at El-Manial University Hospital', *Malaysian Journal of Nursing,* Volume 9, Issue 3.

137 **Eberle, C et al** 2020. 'Hair dye and chemical straightener use and breast cancer risk in a large US population of black and white women', *International Journal of Cancer,* Volume 147, Issue 2.

138 **Zahm, S et al** 1992. 'Use of hair coloring products and the risk of lymphoma, multiple myeloma, and chronic lymphocytic leukemia'.

139 **Llanos, A et al** 2017. 'Hair Product use and breast cancer risk among African American and White women', *Carcinogenesis,* Volume 38, Issue 9.

140 **Eberle, C et al** 2020. 'Hair dye and chemical straightener use and breast cancer risk in a large US population of black and white women'.

Donovan, M 2007. 'Personal care products that contain estrogens or xenoestrogens may increase breast cancer risk', *Medical Hypotheses,* Volume 68, Issue 4.

141 **Helm, J** 2019. 'Re: Measurement of endocrine disrupting and asthma-associated chemicals in hair products used by Black women', *Environmental Research,* Volume 172.

142 **Stiel L et al** 2016. 'A review of hair product use on breast cancer risk in African American women', *Cancer Medicine,* Volume 5, Issue 3.

143 **Yazar, K et al** 2009. 'Potent skin sensitizers in oxidative hair dye products on the Swedish market'.

144 **Peters, C** 2010. 'Fertility disorders and pregnancy complications in hairdressers - a systematic review', *Journal of Occupational Medicine and Toxicology,* Volume 5, Issue 24.

Rylander, L et al 2002. 'Reproductive outcome among female hairdressers', *Occupational Environmental Medicine,* Volume 59.

Zhu, J 2006. 'Pregnancy outcomes among female hairdressers who participated in the Danish National Birth Cohort', *Scandinavian Journal of Work, Environment & Health,* Volume 32, Issue 1.

Henrotin, J 2015. 'Reproductive disorders in hairdressers and cosmetologists: a meta-analytical approach', *Journal of Occupational Health,* Volume 57, Issue 6.

145 **Jiang, C et al** 2018. 'The effect of pre-pregnancy hair dye exposure on infant birth weight: a nested case-control study', *BMC Pregnancy Childbirth,* Volume 18.

Shishavan, M et al 2021. 'The Association of Hair Coloring During Pregnancy with Pregnancy and Neonate Outcomes: A Cross- Sectional Study', *International Journal of Women's Health and Reproduction Sciences,* Volume 9, Issue 2.

146 **Ziadat , A et al** 2010. 'Disabilities of children in correlation to the usage of hair dye among pregnant women', *International Journal of Pharmacology,* Volume 6, Issue 4.

147 **Bunin, G et al** 1987. Gestational risk factors for Wilm's Tumor: results of a case control study', *Cancer Research,* Volume 47, Issue 11.

McCall, E 2005. 'Maternal hair dye use and risk of neuroblastoma in offspring', *Cancer Causes & Control,* Volume 16, Issue 6.

148 **McCall, E** 2005. 'Maternal hair dye use and risk of neuroblastoma in offspring'.

149 **Chen, Z** 2006. 'Environmental exposure to residential

pesticides, chemicals, dusts, fumes, and metals, and risk of childhood germ cell tumors', *International Journal of Hygiene and Environmental Health,* Volume 209, Issue 1.

150 **Holly, E et al** 2002. 'West Coast study of childhood brain tumours and maternal use of hair-colouring products', *Paediatric and Perinatal Epidemiology,* Volume 16.

151 **Bunin, G et al** 1994. 'Risk Factors for Astrocytic Glioma and Primitive Neuroectodermal Tumor of the Brain in Young Children: A Report from the Children's *Cancer Group', Cancer Epidemiology, Biomarkers & Prevention,* Volume 3.

152 **Efird, J et al** 2005. 'Beauty product-related exposures and childhood brain tumors in seven countries: Results from the SEARCH International Brain Tumor Study', *Journal of Neuro-Oncology,* Volume 72, Issue 2.

153 **Denli, M et al** 2002. 'Effect of long term use of hair dyes on the DNA damage in healthy female subjects', *Kocatepe Tlp Dergisi,* Volume 3, Issue 1.

154 **Ambrosone, C** 2007. 'Hair dye use, meat intake, and tobacco exposure and presence of carcinogen-DNA adducts in exfoliated breast ductal epithelial cells', *Archives of Biochemistry and Biophysics,* Volume 464, Issue 2.

155 **Couto, A et al** 2013. 'Pregnancy, maternal exposure to hair dyes and hair straightening cosmetics, and early age leukemia', *Chemico-Biological Interactions,* Volume 205, Issue 1.

156 **Gao, Z et al** 2018. 'Protective effect of breastfeeding against childhood leukemia in Zhejiang Province, P. R. China: a retrospective case-control study', *The Libyan Journal of Medicine,* Volume 13, Issue 1.

157 **Ezzat, S** 2016. 'Environmental, maternal, and reproductive risk factors for childhood acute lymphoblastic leukemia in Egypt: a case-control study', *BMC Cancer,* Volume 16.

Rafieemehr, H 2019. 'Risk of Acute Lymphoblastic Leukemia: Results of a Case-Control Study', *Asian Pacific Journal of Cancer Prevention,* Volume 20, Issue 8.

McKinney et al 2008. 'The UK Childhood Cancer Study: Maternal Occupational Exposures and Childhood Leukaemia and Lymphoma', *Radiation Protection Dosimetry,* Volume 132, Issue 2.

158 **Mintel,** 2019. 'A year of innovation in hair colourants.'.

159 Publications Office of the European Union 2013. 'Commission Regulation (EU) No 1197/2013 of 25 November 2013 amending Annex III to Regulation (EC) No 1223/2009 of the European Parliament and of the Council on cosmetic products', *Official Journal of the European Union* <https://eur-lex.europa.eu/legal-content/EN/TXT/?uri=CELEX:32013R1197>.

160 **Zanoni, T** 2014. 'Basic Red 51, a permitted semi-permanent hair dye, is cytotoxic to human skin cells: Studies in monolayer and 3D skin model using human keratinocytes (HaCaT)', *Toxicology Letters,* Volume 227, issue 2.

See also **Lademann, J et al** 2008. 'Human percutaneous absorption of a direct hair dye comparing in vitro and in vivo results: Implications for safety assessment and animal testing', *Food and Chemical Toxicology,* Volume 46, Issue 6.

161 **Liu, B et al** 2019. 'The Bio-Safety Concerns of Three Domestic Temporary Hair Dye Molecules: Fuchsin Basic, Victoria Blue B and Basic Red 2', *Molecules,* Volume 24, Issue 9.

162 **Lewis, D et al** 2013. 'A review of aspects of Oxidative hair dye chemistry with special reference to N-Nitrosamine formation', *Materials,* Volume 6, Issue 2.

163 **Turesky RJ et al** 2003. 'Identification of aminobiphenyl derivatives in commercial hair dyes'.

Johansson G, et al 2015. 'Exposure of hairdressers to ortho- and meta-toluidine in hair dyes'.

Akyüz, M et al 2008. 'Determination of aromatic amines in hair dye and henna samples by ion-pair extraction and gas chromatography-mass spectrometry'.

164 **Yazar, K et al** 2009. 'Potent skin sensitizers in oxidative hair dye products on the Swedish market'.

Chapter 8

1 **Weitz, R** 2004. *Rapunzel's Daughters, What Women's Hair Tells Us About Women's Lives, Farrar,* Straus and Giroux, New York.

2 **Jones, R** 2007. *Natural (The Beautiful 'n' Word): Breaking the Psychological Bondage of the American Standard of Beauty,* iUniverse inc, New York, Lincoln and Shanghai.

3 **Mintel** 2018. 'Brits prefer blondes: Blonde is the nation's number one dyed hair colour of choice' <https://www.mintel.com/press-centre/beauty-and-personal-care/brits-

prefer-blondes-blonde-is-the-na tions-number-one-dyed-hair-colour-of-choice>.

4 **Wall, F** 1972. 'Bleaches, Hair Colourings, and Dye Removers' in **Balsam, M et al (ed)** 1972. *Cosmetics: Science and Technology, Second Edition,* Volume 2, John Wiley & Sons, New York, London, Sydney and Toronto.

5 **Singh, S** 2010. *Handbook on Cosmetics (Processes, Formulae with Testing Methods),* Asia Pacific Business Press Inc, Delhi.

6 **PubChem** 2021. 'Compound Summary: Hydrogen peroxide' <https://pubchem.ncbi.nlm.nih.gov/compound/Hydrogen-peroxide>.

7 **ScienceDaily** 2008. 'Hydrogen Peroxide Has A Complex Role In Cell Health' <www.sciencedaily.com/releases/2008/01/080102134129.htm>.

8 **Halliwell, B et al** 2000. 'Hydrogen peroxide in the human body', *FEBS Letters,* Volume 486, Issue 1.

9 **Wittmann, C et al** 2012. 'Hydrogen peroxide in inflammation: messenger, guide, and assassin', *Advances in Hematology,* Volume 2012.

10 **Public Health England** 2009. 'Hydrogen Peroxide Toxicological Overview' <https://assets.publishing.service.gov.uk/government/uploads/system/uploads/attachment_data/file/33 7708/Hydrogen_Peroxide_Toxicological_Overview_phe_v1.pdf>.

11 **Draelos, Z** 2005. *Hair Care: An Illustrated Dermatologic Handbook,* Taylor & Francis, London and New York.

12 **Christie, R** 2015. *Colour Chemistry: 2nd Edition,* The Royal Society of Chemistry, Cambridge.

13 **Stange, M et al (ed)** 2013. *The Multimedia Encyclopedia of Women in Today's World,* SAGE Publications.

14 **Public Health England** 2019. 'General Information: Ammonia' <https://www.gov.uk/government/publications/ammonia-properties-incident-management-and-toxicolo gy/ammonia-general-information>.

15 **Visek, W** 1984. 'Ammonia: its effects on biological systems, metabolic hormones, and reproduction', *Journal of Dairy Science,* Volume 67 and **Padappayil, R** 2021. 'Ammonia Toxicity', *StatPearls* <https://www.ncbi.nlm.nih.gov/books/NBK546677/>

16 **Smith, R** 2017. 'Mechanistic insights into the bleaching of melanin by alkaline hydrogen peroxide', *Free Radical Biology and Medicine,* Volume 108.

17 **Robbins, C** 2012. 'Bleaching and oxidation of human hair' in *Chemical and Physical Behavior of Human Hair,* Springer-Verlag, Berlin and Heidelberg.

18 **Robbins, C** 2012. *Chemical and Physical Behavior of Human Hair.*

19 **Biddle-Perry, G (ed)** 2019. *A Cultural History of Hair in the Modern Age: Volume 6,* Bloomsbury, London.

20 **Robbins, C** 2012. 'Bleaching and oxidation of human hair'.

21 **Tanamachi, H** 2010. '18-MEA and hair appearance', *Journal of Cosmetic Science,* Volume 61.

22 **Habe, T** 2011. 'ToF-SIMS characterization of the lipid layer on the hair surface. I: the damage caused by chemical treatments and UV radiation', *Surface and Interface Analysis,* Volume 43.

23 **Tokunaga, S** 2019. 'Degradation of Hair Surface: Importance of 18-MEA and Epicuticle', *Cosmetics,* Volume 6, Issue 31.

24 **Robbins, C** 2012. 'Bleaching and oxidation of human hair'.

25 **Aguh, C et al (ed)** 2016. *Fundamentals of Ethnic Hair, The Dermatologist's Perspective,* Springer, Cham.

26 **Obukowho, P** 2018. *Hair Relaxers: Science, Design and Application,* Dorrance Publishing, Pittsburgh.

27 **Robbins, C** 2012. 'Bleaching and oxidation of human hair'.

28 **Tokunaga, S** 2019. 'Degradation of Hair Surface: Importance of 18-MEA and Epicuticle'.

29 **Maibach, H et al (ed)** 2014. *Chemical Skin Injury: Mechanisms, Prevention, Decontamination, Treatment,* Springer, Heidelberg, New York.

30 **Biddle-Perry, G (ed)** 2019. *A Cultural History of Hair in the Modern Age: Volume 6.*

31 **Biddle-Perry, G (ed)** 2019. *A Cultural History of Hair in the Modern Age: Volume 6.*

32 **Liljequist, A** 2015. '"Soft, Glossy Tresses": Shampoo Advertisements, White Women's Hair, and the Late and Post World War II Domestic Ideal', *University of Kansas* <https://kuscholarworks.ku.edu/bitstream/handle/1808/19550/Liljequist_ku_0099D_14161_DATA_1.p df?sequence=1&isAllowed=y>.

33 **Clairol Inc** 1982. *50 Colourful Years: The Clairol Story.*

34 **Corbett, J** 1999. 'An historical review of the use of dye precursors in the formulation of commercial oxidation hair dyes', *Dyes and Pigments,* Volume 41.

35 **Corbett, J** 1999. 'An historical review of the use of dye precursors in the formulation of commercial oxidation hair dyes', *Dyes and Pigments,* Volume 41.

36 **Clausen, T et al** 2012. 'Hair Preparations' in **Wiley-VCH Verlag GmbH & Co** 2012. *Ullmann's Encyclopedia of Industrial Chemistry,* Weinheim.

37 **Da França, S** 2015. 'Types of Hair Dye and Their Mechanisms of Action', *Cosmetics,* Volume 2, Issue 2.

38 **Aguh, C et al (ed)** 2016. *Fundamentals of Ethnic Hair, The Dermatologist's Perspective.*

39 **Da França, S** 2015. 'Types of Hair Dye and Their Mechanisms of Action'.

40 **Aguh, C et al (ed)** 2016. *Fundamentals of Ethnic Hair, The Dermatologist's Perspective.*

41 **Ali, N et al** 2018. 'Aqueous MEA and 'Ammonia Sorption-Induced Damage in Keratin Fibers', *American Chemical Society,* Volume 3, Issue 10.

42 **Bailey, A** 2014. 'Comparison of damage to human hair fibers caused by monoethanolamine and ammonia-based hair colorants', *Journal of Cosmetic Science,* Volume 65, Issue 1.

43 **Aguh, C et al (ed)** 2016. *Fundamentals of Ethnic Hair, The Dermatologist's Perspective.*

44 **Da França, S** 2015. 'Types of Hair Dye and Their Mechanisms of Action' and **Clausen, T et al** 2012. 'Hair Preparations'.

45 **Da França, S** 2015. 'Types of Hair Dye and Their Mechanisms of Action'.

46 **Aguh, C et al (ed)** 2016. *Fundamentals of Ethnic Hair, The Dermatologist's Perspective.*

47 **Da França, S** 2015. 'Types of Hair Dye and Their Mechanisms of Action' and **Clausen, T et al** 2012. 'Hair Preparations'.

48 **Aguh, C et al (ed)** 2016. *Fundamentals of Ethnic Hair, The Dermatologist's Perspective.*

49 **Sampathkumar, K et al** 2009. 'Hair dye poisoning and the developing world', *Journal of Emergencies, Trauma, and Shock,* Volume 2, Issue 2.

50 **Da França, S** 2015. 'Types of Hair Dye and Their Mechanisms of Action'.

51 **Evans, J** 2020. 'The post-Covid consumer: is back-to-basics shopping here to stay?', *Financial Times* <https://www.ft.com/content/ce2b0f65-f98a-49cc-b258-7eb8cc257cc4>.

52 **Mintel** 2021. 'Home Hair Color US'.

53 **Mintel** 2021. 'Keep home hair color momentum going post-pandemic'.

54 **Culliney, K** 2020. 'Superdrug sees at-home hair and self-care products surge during lockdown', *Cosmetics Design Europe* <https://www.cosmeticsdesign-europe.com/Article/2020/05/19/Superdrug-hair-dye-skin-care-nails-and-grooming-products-surge-during-coronavirus-lockdown>.

55 **Mintel** 2021. 'Keep home hair color momentum going post-pandemic'.

Chapter 9

1 **Gupta, M et al** 2015. 'Hair dye dermatitis and p-phenylenediamine contact sensitivity: A preliminary report', *Indian Dermatology Online Journal,* Volume 6, Issue 4.

2 **Mintel** 2014. 'Hair colorant users admit to not doing the recommended allergy tests'.

3 **Mintel** 2014. 'Hair colorant users admit to not doing the recommended allergy tests'.

4 **European Commission** 2007. 'Scientific Committee on Consumer Products Opinion on Sensitivity to Hair Dyes - Consumer Self Testing SCCP/1104/07'.

5 **European Commission** 2007. 'Scientific Committee on Consumer Products Opinion on Sensitivity to Hair Dyes - Consumer Self Testing SCCP/1104/07'.

6 **Kirchlechner, S et al** 2016. 'Survey of sensitizing components of oxidative hair dyes (retail and professional products) in Germany', *Journal der Deutschen Dermatologischen Gesellschaft,* Volume 14, Issue 7.

7 **Hamann, D et al** 2014. 'p-Phenylenediamine and other allergens in hair dye products in the United States: a consumer exposure study', *Contact Dermatitis,* Volume 70, Issue 4.

8 **Moro, P et al** 2016. 'Sensitization and Clinically Relevant Allergy to Hair Dyes and Clothes from Black Henna Tattoos: Do People Know the Risk? An Uncommon Serious Case and a Review of the Literature', *Cosmetics,* Volume 3, Issue 3.

9 **Gupta, M et al** 2015. 'Hair dye dermatitis and p-phenylenediamine contact sensitivity: A preliminary report'.

10 **De Groot, A** 2018. *Monographs in Contact Allergy, Volume 1, Non-Fragrance Allergens in Cosmetics (Part 1 and Part 2),* CRC Press, London and New York.

11 **Oakley, A** 2008. 'Baseline series of patch test allergens', DermNet NZ <https://dermnetnz.org/topics/baseline-series-of-patch-test-allergens/>.

12 **Uter, W** 2018. 'Contact Allergy: A Review of Current Problems from a Clinical Perspective', *International Journal of Environmental Research and Public Health,* Volume 15, Issue 6.

13 **Goon, A** 2003. 'High frequency of simultaneous sensitivity to Disperse Orange 3 in patients with positive patch tests to para-phenylenediamine', *Contact Dermatitis,* Volume 48, Issue 5.

14 **Boschnakow, A** 2003. 'Temporary tattooing with henna induces contact allergy to textile dyes', *Journal of the German Society of Dermatology,* Volume 1, Issue 12.

15 **Aeby, P** 2009. 'Skin sensitization to p-phenylenediamine: the diverging roles of oxidation and N-acetylation for dendritic cell activation and the immune response', *The Journal of Investigative Dermatology,* Volume 129, Issue 1.

16 **Schuttelaar, ML et al** 2016. 'Contact Allergy to Hair Dyes', *Cosmetics,* Volume 3, Issue 3.

17 **Aeby, P** 2009. 'Skin sensitization to p-phenylenediamine: the diverging roles of oxidation and N-acetylation for dendritic cell activation and the immune response'.

18 **Rastogi, S** 2006. 'Unconsumed precursors and couplers after formation of oxidative hair dyes', *Contact Dermatitis,* Volume 55, Issue 2.

19 **White, J et al** 2007.'Intermittent exposure to low-concentration paraphenylenediamine can be equivalent to single, higher-dose exposure', *Contact Dermatitis,* Volume 56, Issue 5.

20 **Blömeke, B et al** 2009. 'Para-phenylenediamine and allergic sensitization: risk modification by N-acetyltransferase 1 and 2 genotypes', *British Journal of Dermatology,* Volume 161, Issue 5.

21 **Ninabahen, D et al** 2011. 'Stress and Allergic Diseases', *Immunology and Allergy Clinics of North America,* Volume 31, Issue 1.

22 **Farage, M** 2010. 'The possible relevance of sex hormones on irritant and allergic responses: their importance for skin testing', *Contact Dermatitis,* Volume 62, Issue 2.

23 **Farage, M** 2010.'The possible relevance of sex hormones on irritant and allergic responses: their importance for skin testing'.

24 **Diepgen, T** 2016. 'Prevalence of Contact Allergy to p-Phenylenediamine in the European General Population', *The Journal of Investigative Dermatology,* Volume 136, Issue 2.

25 **Kim, HY et al** 2010. 'Use of Beauty Products among U.S. Adolescents: An Exploration of Media Influence', *Journal of Global Fashion Marketing,* Volume 1, Issue 3.

26 **AlGhamdi, K et al** 2011. 'Knowledge and practices of, and attitudes towards, the use of hair dyes among females visiting a teaching hospital in Riyadh, Saudi Arabia', *Annals of Saudi Medicine,* Volume 31, Issue 6.

27 **Søsted, H et al** 2005. 'Contact dermatitis to hair dyes in a Danish adult population: an interview-based study', *The British Journal of Dermatology,* Volume 153, Issue 1.

28 **Thyssen, J** 2008. 'Epidemiological data on consumer allergy to p-phenylenediamine', *Contact Dermatitis,* Volume 59, Issue 6.

29 **Gupta, M et al** 2015. 'Hair dye dermatitis and p-phenylenediamine contact sensitivity: A preliminary report'.

30 **Patel, S et al** 2007. 'Patch test frequency to p-phenylenediamine: follow up over the last 6 years', *Contact Dermatitis,* Volume 56, Issue 1.

31 5.75% rounded up to 5.8% in the text. See **Pónyai, G et al** 2016. 'para-Phenylenediamine Hypersensitivity: A Report From Budapest, Hungary, 2007-2014', *Dermatitis,* Volume 27, Issue 5.

32 **Schafer, T et al** 2001. 'Epidemiology of contact allergy in adults', *Allergy,* Volume 56 in **Patel, S et al** 2007. 'Patch test frequency to p-phenylenediamine: follow up over the last 6 years'.

33 **Thyssen, J et al** 2011. 'The increase in p-phenylenediamine allergy in Denmark is not explained by an increase in contact allergy to para group chemicals', *Contact Dermatitis,* Volume 64, Issue 3.

34 **Ito, A et al** 2017. 'A multi-institutional joint study of contact dermatitis related to hair colouring and perming agents in Japan', *Contact Dermatitis,* Volume 77, Issue 1.

35 **Thyssen, J et al** 2009. 'p-Phenylenediamine sensitization is more prevalent in central and southern European patch test centres than in Scandinavian: results from a multicentre study', *Contact Dermatitis,* Volume 60, Issue 6.

36 **White, J** 2007. 'A general population from Thailand: incidence of common allergens with emphasis on para-phenylenediamine', *Journal of the British Society for Allergy*

and Clinical Immunology, Volume 37, Issue 12 in **Thyssen, J et al** 2009. 'p-Phenylenediamine sensitization is more prevalent in central and southern European patch test centres than in Scandinavian: results from a multicentre study'.

37 **Dotterud, L et al** 2007. 'Allergic contact sensitization in the general adult population: a population-based study from Northern Norway', *Contact Dermatitis,* Volume 56, Issue 1.

38 **Diepgen, T et al** 2016. 'Prevalence of Contact Allergy to p-Phenylenediamine in the European General Population', *Journal of Investigative Dermatology,* Volume 136, Issue 2.

39 **McFadden, J** 2011. 'Clinical and experimental aspects of allergic contact dermatitis to para-phenylenediamine', *Clinics in Dermatology,* Volume 29, Issue 3.

40 **Schwensen, J et al** 2014. 'p-Phenylenediamine and Risk of Sensitization in Children,' *Current Treatment Options in Allergy,* Volume 1.

41 **Hamza, Y et al** 1992. 'Poisoning from henna dye and para-phenylenediamine mixtures in children in Khartoum', *Annals of Tropical Paediatrics,* Volume 12, Issue 1.

42 **Shashikumar B et al (ed)** 2017. *TATTOO: The Invaluable Compendium for Dermatologists,* Jaypee Brothers Medical Publishers, New Delhi and London.

43 **Gawkrodger, D et al** 2006. 'How safe is patch testing to PPD?', *British Journal of Dermatology,* Volume 154, Issue 6.

44 **Cosmetic Ingredient Review** 2007. *Amended Final Report of the Cosmetic Ingredient Review: Expert Panel Safety Assessment of p-Phenylenediamine, p-Phenylenediamine HC1, and p-Phenylenediamine Sulfate,* Washington.

45 **European Commission** 2021. *Annex III: List of substances which cosmetic products must not contain except subject to the restrictions laid down* <https://ec.europa.eu/growth/tools-databases/cosing/pdf/COSING_Annex%20III_v2.pdf>.

46 **Almeida, P** 2012. 'Quantification of p-phenylenediamine and 2-hydroxy-1,4-naphthoquinone in henna tattoos', *Contact Dermatitis,* Volume 66, Issue 1.

47 **Kligman A et al** 1966. 'The Identification of Contact Allergens by Human Assay: III. The Maximization Test: A Procedure for Screening and Rating Contact Sensitizers', *Journal of Investigative Dermatology,* Volume 47, Issue 5.

48 **De Groot A** 2013. 'Side-effects of henna and semi-permanent "black henna" tattoos: a full review', *Contact Dermatitis,* Volume 69, Issue 1.

49 **Akyüz, M** 2008. 'Determination of aromatic amines in hair dye and henna samples by ion-pair extraction and gas chromatography-mass spectrometry', *Journal of Pharmaceutical and Biomedical Analysis,* Volume 47, Issue 1.

50 **Spornraft-Ragaller, P et al** 2011. 'Extreme patch test reactivity to p-phenylenediamine but not to other allergens in children', *Contact Dermatitis,* Volume 65, Issue 4.

51 **Onder, M** 2008. 'Patch test results in a Turkish paediatric population', *Contact Dermatitis,* Volume 58, Issue 1.

52 **Clayton, T** 2006. 'Allergic contact dermatitis in children: should pattern of dermatitis determine referral? A retrospective study of 500 children tested between 1995 and 2004 in one U.K. centre', *The British Journal of Dermatology,* Volume 154, Issue 1.

53 **De Groot A** 2013. 'Side-effects of henna and semi-permanent "black henna" tattoos: a full review'.

54 **Lorizzo, M et al** 2002. 'Allergic contact dermatitis in hairdressers: Frequency and source of sensitisation', *European Journal of Dermatology,* Volume 12, Issue 2.

55 **Kieć-Swierczyńska, M** 2009. 'Results of patch test in hairdressers examined in the institute of occupational medicine in Łódź', *Medycyna Pracy,* Volume 60.

56 **Gupta, M** 2017. 'Cosmetic contact sensitivity among beauticians and hairdressers: a clinicoepidemiological study'. *Egyptian Journal of Dermatology and Venerology,* Volume 37.

57 Rounded up from 45.5%. See **Tresukosol, P et al** 2012. 'Hand contact dermatitis in hairdressers: clinical and causative allergens', *Asian Pacific Journal of Allergy and Immunology,* Volume 30.

58 23.1% rounded down to 23% and 17.9% rounded up to 18%. See **Søsted, S et al** 2011. 'Hand eczema in hairdressers: A Danish register-based study of the prevalence of hand eczema and its career consequences', *Contact Dermatitis,* Volume 65, Issue 3.

59 **Schaad, J** 1992. 'Te vroeg uit de kappersop-leiding', in **Kanerva, L et al (ed)** 2004. *Condensed Handbook of Occupational Dermatology,* Springer-Verlag, Berlin.

60 **Lind, ML et al** 2007. 'Permeability of Hair Dye Compounds p-Phenylenediamine, Toluene-2,5-Diamine Sulfate and

Resorcinol through Protective Gloves in Hairdressing', *The Annals of Occupational Hygiene,* Volume 51, Issue 5.

61 **Antelmi, A et al** 2015. 'Are gloves sufficiently protective when hairdressers are exposed to permanent hair dyes? An in vivo study', *Contact Dermatitis,* Volume 72, Issue 4.

62 **Havmose, M et al** 2020. 'Use of protective gloves by hairdressers: A review of efficacy and potential adverse effects', *Contact Dermatitis,* Vol 83, Issue 2.

63 **Antelmi, A et al** 2015. 'Are gloves sufficiently protective when hairdressers are exposed to permanent hair dyes? An in vivo study'.

64 **Lind, M et al** 2007. 'Permeability of Hair Dye Compounds p-Phenylenediamine, Toluene-2,5-Diamine Sulfate and Resorcinol through Protective Gloves in Hairdressing'.

65 **Havmose, M et al** 2020. 'Use of protective gloves by hairdressers: A review of efficacy and potential adverse effects'.

66 **Vogel, T** 2016. 'The dark side of p-Phenylenediamine: Biological aspects and prevalence of contact allergy to an extraordinary molecule', *Rijksuniversiteit Groningen* <https://pure.rug.nl/ws/portalfiles/portal/30158342/Chapter_1.pdf>.

67 **Meyer, A et al** 2015. 'Oxidative transformation processes and products of para-phenylenediamine (PPD) and para-toluenediamine (PTD)—a review', *Environmental Sciences Europe,* Volume 27, Issue 11.

68 **Vogel, T** 2017. 'Two decades of p-phenylenediamine and toluene-2,5-diamine patch testing - focus on co-sensitizations in the European baseline series and cross-reactions with chemically related substances', *Contact Dermatitis,* Volume 76, Issue 2.

69 **Schuttelaar, ML et al** 2016. 'Contact Allergy to Hair Dyes'.

70 **Schmidt, J et al** 2014. 'Immune responses to hair dyes containing toluene-2,5-diamine', *The British Journal of Dermatology,* Volume 170, Issue 2.

71 **Meyer, A et al** 2015. 'Oxidative transformation processes and products of para-phenylenediamine (PPD) and para-toluenediamine (PTD)—a review'.

72 **European Commission** 2012. 'Scientific Committee on Consumer Safety opinion on Toluene-2,5-diamine and its sulfate' <https://ec.europa.eu/health/scientific_committees/consumer_safety/docs/sccs_o_093.pdf>.

73 **Lynde, C** 1982. 'Patch test results in 66 hairdressers 1973-81', *Contact Dermatitis,* Volume 8, Issue 5 in **European Commission** 2012. 'Scientific Committee on Consumer Safety opinion on Toluene-2,5-diamine and its sulfate'.

74 **Kirchlechner, S** 2016. 'Survey of sensitizing components of oxidative hair dyes (retail and professional products) in Germany', *Journal of the German Society of Dermatology,* Volume 14, Issue 7.

75 **McDougall, A** 2013. 'P&G announces first permanent hair dye molecule with reduced allergy risk', News & Analysis on Cosmetics Formulation & Packaging in Europe.

76 **Goebel, C** 2014. 'Introduction of a methoxymethyl side chain into p-phenylenediamine attenuates its sensitizing potency and reduces the risk of allergy induction', *Toxicology and Applied Pharmacology,* Volume 274, Issue 3.

77 **Jenkinson, C et al** 2009. 'A Mechanistic Investigation into the Irreversible Protein Binding and Antigenicity of p-Phenylenediamine', *Chemical Research in Toxicology,* Volume 22, Issue 6.

78 **Goebel, C** 2014. 'Introduction of a methoxymethyl side chain into p-phenylenediamine attenuates its sensitizing potency and reduces the risk of allergy induction'.

79 **Kock, M** 2016. 'Continuous usage of a hair dye product containing 2-methoxymethyl-para-phenylenediamine by hair-dye-allergic individuals', *The British Journal of Dermatology,* Volume 174, Issue 5.

80 **Kock, M** 2016. 'Continuous usage of a hair dye product containing 2-methoxymethyl-para-phenylenediamine by hair-dye-allergic individuals'.

81 **Kock, M** 2016. 'Continuous usage of a hair dye product containing 2-methoxymethyl-para-phenylenediamine by hair-dye-allergic individuals'.

82 **Basketter, D et al** 2005. 'Analysis of para-phenylenediamine allergic patients in relation to strength of patch test reaction', *The British Journal of Dermatology,* Volume 153, Issue 2.

Chapter 10

1 **Buse, W** 2017. 'Mediating Nations and Generations: The Yemenite Jewish Marital Henna Ceremony', *Marriage & Family Review,* Volume 53, Issue 8.

2 **Boubaya, A et al** 2013. 'Genetic diversity assessment of Lawsonia inermis germplasm in Tunisian coastal oases by ISSR and RAPD markers', *Dendrobiology,*

Volume 69 and **Semwal, B** 2014. 'Lawsonia inermis L. (henna): ethnobotanical, phytochemical and pharmacological aspects', *Journal of Ethnopharmacology,* Volume 155, Issue 1.

3 **Renaut, L** 2009. 'Ancient Henna Research', *Journal of Near Eastern Studies,* Volume 63, Issue 3.

4 **Aubaile, F** 2012. 'Pathways of diffusion of some plants and animals between Asia and the Mediterranean region', *Revue d'ethnoécologie.*

5 **Zavada, M** 1993. 'The Historical Use of Henna (Lawsone inermis L.) in the Balkans', *Thaiszia Journal of Botany,* Volume 3.

6 **Robertson, W** 1829. *Roostum Zaboolee and Soohrab, from Shah Namuh; or, Book of kings,* Messrs Thacker and co, Calcutta.

7 **Smith, G** 1912. Catalogue General Antiquites Egyptiennes du Musee du Caire: *The Royal Mummies,* Imprimerie de L'institut Francais D'archeologie Orientale, Le Caire.

8 **Fletcher, J** 2002. 'Ancient Egyptian hair and wigs', *The Journal of the Egyptian Study Society,* Volume 13, Issue 2.

9 **Desroches-Noblecourt, C et al** 1985. *La Momie de Ramsès II: Contribution Scientifique à l'Égyptologie,* Editions Recherchesur les Civilisations, Paris.

10 **Newberry, G** 1889. 'On the vegetable remains discovered in the cemetery of **Hawara' in Petrie, W** 1889. *Hawara, Biahmu, and Arsinoe,* Field and Tuer, London.

11 **Rahman, A (ed)** 2012. Studies in Natural Products Chemistry, *Bioactive Natural Products,* Volume 37, Elsevier, Oxford and Amsterdam.

12 See **Fletcher, J** 2002. 'Ancient Egyptian hair and wigs'.

13 Ancient Mesopotamia, the land of the Tigris and Euphrates Rivers, was predominantly situated in modern Iraq and northeastern Syria, together with southeastern Turkey and western Iran. **University of Cambridge** 2021. 'Ancient Mesopotamia - an overview'.

14 **Singer, C et al (ed)** 1954. *A History of Technology,* Volume 1, Oxford University Press, New York.

15 **Scurlock, J** 2007. 'A proposal for the identification of a missing plant: Kamantu', *Wiener Zeitschrift für die Kunde des Morgenlandes,* Volume 97.

Renaut, L 2007. 'A short note on JA Scurlock's recent identification of the kamantu plant with Lawsonia inermis', *Le journal des médecines cunéiformes,* Volume 10.

16 **Renaut, L** 2007. 'A short note on JA Scurlock's recent identification of the kamantu plant with Lawsonia inermis'.

17 **Renaut, L** 2009. 'Ancient Henna Research', and **R, Tatomir** 2016. 'To cause "to make divine" through smoke: ancient Egyptian incense and perfume. An inter- and transdisciplinary re-evaluation of aromatic biotic materials used by the ancient Egyptians' in *Moesica et Christiana,* Muzeul Brăilei "Carol I" - Editura Istros.

18 **Zavada, M** 1993. 'The Historical Use of Henna (Lawsone inermis L.) in the Balkans'.

19 **Renaut, L** 2009. 'Ancient Henna Research'.

20 While already established in the Balkans through its reputation in Classical Greece as a medicine and hair dye, henna usage was later truly popularised under Islamic Ottoman Rule between the 14th and 20th century. There it entered Slavic plantlore as a cure to typhoid fever and later as a ceremonial material during Ramadan and weddings for Slavic Muslims. See **Zavada, M** 1993. 'The Historical Use of Henna (Lawsone inermis L.) in the Balkans'.

21 **Horne, C (ed)** 1917. *The Sacred Books and Early Literature of the East, Volume V, Ancient Arabia,* Parke, Austin, and Lipscomb, New York and London and **Juynboll, G** 1986. 'Dyeing the Hair and Beard in Early Islam: A Hadīth-analytical Study', *Arabica,* Volume 33, Issue 1.

22 **Farmanfarmaian, F** 2000. '"Haft Qalam Ārāyish": Cosmetics in the Iranian World', **Iranian Studies,** Volume 33, Issues 3-4.

23 **Jensen, L** 1963. 'Royal Purple of Tyre', *Journal of Near Eastern Studies,* Volume 22, Issue 2.

24 **Balfour-Paul, J** 2011. *Indigo: Egyptian Mummies to Blue Jeans,* The British Museum Press, London and **Balfour-Paul, J** 2004. *Indigo in the Arab World,* Routledge, Oxon.

25 **Juynboll, G** 1986. 'Dyeing the Hair and Beard in Early Islam: A Hadīth-analytical Study'.

26 **See Deter-Wolf, A et al** 2005. 'The world's oldest tattoos', *Journal of Archaeological Science,* Volume 5.

27 **Saksena, J** 1979. *Art of Rājasthān: Henna and Floor Decorations* in **Jones, C** 2016. 'The History of Henna Hair Dye: Evidence of early cultural henna use in the Arabian Peninsula and along the Arabian Ocean' <http://tapdancinglizard.com/AS_henna_for_hair/chapters/chap2/Arabian_ArabianOcean.pdf>.

28 **Jones, C** 2016. 'The History of Henna Hair Dye: Evidence

of early cultural henna use in the Arabian Peninsula and along the Arabian Ocean'.

29 See **'Renaut, L** 2009. 'Ancient Henna Research'.

30 For further reading see **Gode, P** 1947. 'Studies in the history of Indian Plants: History of Mendi or Henna (between B.C. 2000 and A.D. 1850)', *Annals of the Bhandarkar Oriental Research Institute,* Volume 28, Issues 1 and 2, **Miczak, M** 2001. *Henna's Secret History: The History, Mystery & Folklore of Henna,* Writers Club Press, New York and **Jones, C** 2016. 'The History of Henna Hair Dye: Evidence of early cultural henna use in the Arabian Peninsula and along the Arabian Ocean'.

31 **Topsfield, A** 2012. *Visions of Mughal India: The Collection of Howard Hodgkin,* Ashmolean Museum, Oxford.

32 **Chardin, J** 1988. *Sir John Chardin's Travels in Persia,* Dover Publications.

33 **Sonnini, CNS** 1798. *Voyage dans la haute et basse Egypte: fait par ordre de l'ancien gouvernement et contenant des observations de tous genres,* Volume 3, chez F. Buisson, Paris.

34 **Keene, E** 1911. *My Life Story,* E. Arnold, London.

35 **Farmanfarmaian, F** 2000. '"Haft Qalam Ārāyish": Cosmetics in the Iranian World'.

36 Description from the 19th century translators of **Thonnelier, J et al (ed)** 1881. *Kitabi Kulsum Naneh ou le livre des dames de la Perse,* Ernest Leroux Editeur, Paris.

37 **Rogers, A** 2013. 'Politics, Gender and the Art of Religious Authority in North Africa: Moroccan Women's Henna Practice', *Emory University,* Atlanta.

38 **Flueckiger, J** 2020. *Material Acts in Everyday Hindu Worlds,* State University Of New York Press, New York.

39 **Larsson, G** 2011. 'Islam and tattooing: An old question, a new research topic', *Scripta Instituti Donneriani Aboensis,* Volume 23.

40 **Rogers, M** 1865. *Domestic Life in Palestine,* Poe & Hitchcock.

41 **Westermarck, E** 2014. *Ritual and Belief in Morocco: Volume I,* Macmillan and Co, New York.

42 **Sugathan, P** 1991. 'A new camouflage for vitiligo', Indian Journal of Dermatology, *Venereology and Leprology,* Volume 57, Issue 1.

43 **Abu-Rabia, A** 2005. 'The Evil Eye and Cultural Beliefs among the Bedouin Tribes of the Negev, Middle East', *Folklore,* Volume 116.

44 **Young, K** 1995. *Bodylore,* University of Tennessee Press, Tennessee.

45 **Westermarck, E** 2014. *Ritual and Belief in Morocco: Volume II,* Macmillan and Co, Oxon and New York.

46 **Westermarck, E** 2014. *Ritual and Belief in Morocco: Volume I,* Macmillan and Co, Oxon and New York.

47 **Westermarck, E** 2014. *Ritual and Belief in Morocco: Volume II.*

48 **Jones, C** 2002. 'Henna's Significance in Amazigh Id, Circumcision, and "Night of the Henna" Celebrations' <http://www.tapdancinglizard.com/biblos/significanceofhenna1/sighenna.pdf>.

49 **Bouhdiba, A** 2008. *Sexuality in Islam,* Routledge, Oxon and New York.

50 **Field, H** 1958. *Body Marking in Southwestern Asia,* Papers of the Peabody Museum of Archaeology and Ethnology papers, Volume 45, Issue 1, Peabody Museum, Cambridge.

51 **Buse, W** 2017. 'Mediating Nations and Generations: The Yemenite Jewish Marital Henna Ceremony'.

52 **Westermarck, E** 2014. *Ritual and Belief in Morocco: Volume I.*

53 **Jansen, W** 1987. *Women Without Men: Gender and Marginality in an Algerian Town,* Brill Archive, Leiden.

54 **Makilam** 2007. *The Magical Life of Berber Women in Kabylia,* Peter Lang, New York.

55 **Rogers, A** 2013. 'Politics, Gender and the Art of Religious Authority in North Africa: Moroccan Women's Henna Practice'.

56 **Sharaby, R** 2006. 'The Bride's Henna Ritual: Symbols, Meanings and Changes' Nashim: A Journal of Jewish Women's Studies & Gender Issues, Volume 11 and **Buse, W** 2017. 'Mediating Nations and Generations: The Yemenite Jewish Marital Henna Ceremony'.

57 **Sienna, N** 'Not a Single Memory Left: Jewish henna and the malleability of memory', University of Toronto.

58 **Sienna, N** 'Not a Single Memory Left: Jewish henna and the malleability of memory'.

59 **Redgrove, H et al** 1939. *Hair-Dyes and Hair-Dyeing Chemistry and Technique,* William Heinemann, London.

60 **Studt, L et al** 2012. 'Biosynthesis of Fusarubins Accounts for Pigmentation of Fusarium fujikuroi', *Applied and Environmental Microbiology,* Volume 78, Issue 12.

61 **European Commission** 2013. 'Scientific Committee on Consumer Safety Opinion on Lawsonia inermis (Henna)'.

62 **Gallo, F et al** 2014. 'Henna through the centuries: a quick HPTLC analysis proposal to check henna identity', *Revista Brasileira de Farmacognosia,* Volume 24, Issue 2.

63 **European Commission** 2013. 'Scientific Committee on Consumer Safety Opinion on Lawsonia inermis (Henna)' and **U.S. Food & Drugs Administration** 2020. Temporary Tattoos, Henna/Mehndi, and "Black Henna": Fact Sheet <https://www.fda.gov/cosmetics/cosmetic-products/hair-dyes>.

64 **European Commission** 2004. 'The Scientific Committee on Cosmetic Products and Non-Food Products Intended For Consumers Opinion Concerning Lawsone' <https://ec.europa.eu/health/archive/ph_risk/committees/sccp/documents/out254_en.pdf>.

65 **Babula, P** 2009. 'Naphthoquinones as allelochemical triggers of programmed cell death', *Environmental and Experimental Botany,* Volume 65, Issues 2–3.

66 **Ribeiro, J** 2017. 'Antioxidant and Antifungal Activity of Naphthoquinones Dimeric Derived from Lawsone', *Journal of Biosciences and Medicines,* Volume 5, Issue 2.

67 **Grant, J et al** 2000. 'Role of Reactive Oxygen Intermediates and Cognate Redox Signaling in Disease Resistance', *Plant Physiology,* Volume 124, Issue 1.

68 **Rahal, A et al** 2014. 'Oxidative Stress, Prooxidants, and Antioxidants: The Interplay', *BioMed Research International.*

69 **Szalay, J** 2016. 'What Are Free Radicals?', *Live Science* <https://www.livescience.com/54901-free-radicals.html>.

70 **Lobo, V et al** 2010. 'Free radicals, antioxidants and functional foods: Impact on human health', *Pharmacognosy Reviews,* Volume 4, Issue 8.

71 **Lobo, V et al** 2010. 'Free radicals, antioxidants and functional foods: Impact on human health'.

72 **Szalay, J** 2016. 'What Are Free Radicals?'.

73 **Tognetti, V et al** 2012. 'Stress homeostasis – the redox and auxin perspective', *Plant Cell Environ.*

74 **Calabrese, V et al** 2010. 'Cellular Stress Responses, The Hormesis Paradigm, and Vitagenes: Novel Targets for Therapeutic Intervention in Neurodegenerative Disorders', *Antioxidants & Redox Signaling,* Volume 13, Issue 11.

75 **European Commission** 2004. 'The Scientific Committee on Cosmetic Products and Non-Food Products Intended For Consumers Opinion Concerning Lawsone'.

76 **Fowler, P et al** 2018. 'A review of the genotoxic potential of 1,4-naphthoquinone' *Mutation research Genetic Toxicology and Environmental Mutagenesis,* Volume 834.

77 **Guha, G et al** 2011. 'Antioxidant Activity of Lawsonia inermis Extracts Inhibits Chromium(VI)-Induced Cellular and DNA Toxicity', *Evidence-based Complementary and Alternative medicine.*

78 **Kraeling, M et al** 2007. 'Absorption of lawsone through human skin', *Cutaneous and Ocular Toxicology,* Volume 26, Issue 1.

79 **Murakami, K** 2010. 'Effect of hydroxy substituent on the prooxidant action of naphthoquinone compounds', *Toxicology in Vitro,* Volume 24, Issue 3.

80 **Gopal, V et al** 2015. 'Computational Optimization of Bioanalytical Parameters for the Evaluation of the Toxicity of the Phytomarker 1,4 Naphthoquinone and its Metabolite 1,2,4-trihydroxynapththalene', *Journal of Pharmacopuncture,* Volume 18, Issue 2.

81 **McMillan, D et al** 2004. 'Role of oxidant stress in lawsone-induced hemolytic anemia', *Toxicological Sciences,* Volume 82, Issue 2.

82 Lush's ongoing work with XCellR8 will be written up and submitted to a peer-reviewed journal.

83 **Polat, M** 2009. 'Allergic contact dermatitis to pure henna', *Dermatology Online Journal,* Volume 15, Issue 1.

84 **De Groot, A** 2018. *Monographs in Contact Allergy, Volume 1, Non-Fragrance Allergens in Cosmetics (Part 1 and Part 2),* CRC Press, London and New York.

85 **Van Noorden, C et al** 2009. 'Glucose-6-phosphate dehydrogenase deficiency and malaria: cytochemical detection of heterozygous G6PD deficiency in women', *The Journal of Histochemistry and Cytochemistry,* Volume 57, Issue 11.

86 **Ilkhanipur, H et al** 2013. 'Henna: A cause of life threatening hemolysis in G6PD-deficient patient', *Pakistan Journal of Medical Sciences,* Volume 29, Issue 1.

87 **Katar, S et al** 2020. 'Multiple organ failure after a topical application of henna on a newborn', *Journal of Clinical Neonatology,* Volume 9, Issue 3.

88 **Rushing, J et al** 2011. 'Cesarean versus vaginal delivery: long-term infant outcomes and the hygiene hypothesis', *Clinics in Perinatology,* Volume 38, Issue 2.

89 **Holland, K et al** 2002. 'Cosmetics: what is their influence

on the skin microflora?', *The American Journal of Clinical Dermatology,* Volume 3, Issue 7.

90 **Cordain, L et al** 2002. 'Acne vulgaris: a disease of Western civilization', *Archives of Dermatology,* Volume 138, Issue 12.

91 **Wallen-Russell, C et al** 2019. 'The Role of Every-Day Cosmetics in Altering the Skin Microbiome: A Study Using Biodiversity', *Cosmetics,* Volume 6, Issue 1.

92 **Berenji, F et al** 2010. 'In vitro study of the effects of Henna extracts (Lawsonia inermis) on Malassezia species', *Jundishapur Journal of Microbiology,* Volume 3, Issue 3.

93 **El-Basheir, Z** 2002. 'A preliminary pilot survey on head lice, pediculosis in Sharkia Governorate and treatment of lice with natural plant extracts', *Journal of the Egyptian Society of Parasitology.*

94 **Kathem K et al** 2008. 'Antimicrobial Efficacy of Henna Extracts', *Oman Medical Journal,* Volume 23, Issue 4.

95 **De Groot, A** 2018. *Monographs in Contact Allergy, Volume 1, Non-Fragrance Allergens in Cosmetics.*

96 **Keshavarz, A et al** 2016. 'Efficacy of Traditional Medicine Product Henna and Hydrocortisone on Diaper Dermatitis in Infants', *Iranian Red Crescent Medical Journal,* Volume 18, Issue 5.

97 **Singh, D et al** 2014. 'Lawsonia inermis (L.): A perspective on anticancer potential of Mehndi/Henna', *Biomedical Research and Therapy,* Volume 1.

Chapter 11

1 **Hollins, S** 2020. *A Dark History of Tea, Pen & Sword History, Philadelphia.*

2 **Forbes, A et al** 2011. *China's Ancient Tea Horse Road, Cognoscenti Books.*

3 **Redgrove, H et al** 1939. *Hair-Dyes and Hair-Dyeing Chemistry and Technique,* William Heinemann, London.

Chapter 12

1 **Khosravi, M et al** 2010. 'Evaluation of agriculture soil quality by treated wastewater refuse in arid regions: case study in Sistan and Baluchestan Province, Iran', *International Journal of Sustainable Development and Planning,* Volume 5, Issue 4.

2 **Gallo, F et al** 2014. 'Henna through the centuries: a quick HPTLC analysis proposal to check henna identity', *Revista Brasileira de Farmacognosia,* Volume 24, Issue 2.

3 **Khosravi, M et al** 2010. 'Evaluation of agriculture soil quality by treated wastewater refuse in arid regions: case study in Sistan and Baluchestan Province, Iran'.

4 **BBC** 2015. 'Timeline: Iran and UK relations' <https://www.bbc.co.uk/news/uk-15949285>.

5 Farsi is an Iranian term for the Persian language. Persian is officially used in three mutually intelligible varieties within Iran, Afghanistan and Tajikistan, where it is subject to different regional names, but also spoken wider afield. See **Spooner, B et al** 2012. 'Persian, Farsi, Dari, Tajiki: Language Names and Language Policies', in **Schiffman, H (ed)** 2011. *Language Policy and Language Conflict in Afghanistan and Its Neighbors: The Changing Politics of Language Choice,* Brill, Boston.

6 **United Nations Development Programme.** 'About Iran', <https://www.ir.undp.org/content/iran/en/home/countryinfo.html>.

7 See **Manghebati, G** 2015. 'Almost Iranians: the Forgotten people of Iranian Balochistan Exploring Armed Ethnic Conflict and Terrorism in Iranian Balochistan after the 1979 Islamic Revolution', University of Manitoba, Winnipeg.

8 **Durand-Guédy, D et al (ed)** 2018. 'Cities of Medieval Iran', *Eurasian Studies,* Volume 16, Issue 1-2.

9 **Lambton, A** 1992. 'The Qanāts of Yazd', *Journal of the Royal Asiatic Society,* Third Series, Volume 2, Issue. 1.

10 **Bonine, M et al (ed)** 1981. Modern Iran: *The Dialectics of Continuity and Change,* State University of New York Press, Albany.

11 **Mehr News Agency** 2014. "Mazari,' an old profession still practiced in Yazd'.

12 **Herrmann, G** 1968. 'Lapis Lazuli: The Early Phases of Its Trade', *Iraq,* Volume 30, Issue 1.

13 **Oudbashi, O et al** 2021. 'A "Western" imported technology: An analytical study of the Achaemenid Egyptian blue objects', *Journal of Cultural Heritage,* Volume 47.

14 **Balfour-Paul, J** 2011. *Indigo: Egyptian Mummies to Blue Jeans,* The British Museum Press, London.

15 **Legrand, C** 2012. *Indigo: The Color that Changed the World,* Thames & Hudson, London.

16 **Balfour-Paul, J** 2011. *Indigo: Egyptian Mummies to Blue Jeans.*

17 **Nadri, G** 2016. *The Political Economy of Indigo in India, 1580-1930: A Global Perspective,* Brill, Leiden.
18 **Balfour-Paul, J** 2011. *Indigo: Egyptian Mummies to Blue Jeans.*
19 **Balfour-Paul, J** 2011. *Indigo: Egyptian Mummies to Blue Jeans.*
20 **Farmanfarmaian, F** 2000. '"Haft Qalam Ārāyish": Cosmetics in the Iranian World', Iranian Studies, Volume 33, Issues 3-4.
21 **St Clair, K** 2018. *The Secret Lives of Colour,* John Murray, London.
22 **Edmonds, J** 2006. *The History of Woad and the Medieval Woad Vat,* Lulu Press.
23 **Schneider, J** 1978. 'Peacocks and Penguins: The Political Economy of European Cloth and Colors', *American Ethnologist,* Volume 5, Issue. 3.
24 **Museum of Fine Arts** 2015. *Blue: Cobalt to Cerulean in Art and Culture,* Chronicle Books, Boston.
25 **St Clair, K** 2018. *The Secret Lives of Colour,* John Murray, London.
26 **Museum of Fine Arts** 2015. *Blue: Cobalt to Cerulean in Art and Culture,* Chronicle Books, Boston.
27 **Rodriguez, F** 2017. 'Central American Indigo: Globalization and socioeconomic effects (16th-17th centuries)', *Análise Social,* Volume 224.
28 **Rembert, D** 1979. 'The Indigo of Commerce in Colonial North America', *Economic Botany.*
29 **Nadri, G** 2016. *The Political Economy of Indigo in India, 1580-1930: A Global Perspective.*
30 **Prasad, R** 2018. 'Indigo — The Crop that Created History and then Itself Became History', *Indian Journal of History of Science,* Volume 53, Issue 3.
31 **Asiaticus** 1912. 'The Rise and Fall of the Indigo Industry in India.' *The Economic Journal,* Volume 22, Issue 86.
32 **Prasad, R** 2018. 'Indigo — The Crop that Created History and then Itself Became History'.
33 **Franchi, D et al** 2020. 'Synthesis and Characterization of New Organic Dyes Containing the Indigo Core. *Molecules (Basel, Switzerland),* Volume 25, Issue 15.
34 **St Clair, K** 2018. *The Secret Lives of Colour,* John Murray, London.
35 **Aykuz, M et al** 2008. 'Determination of aromatic amines in hair dye and henna samples by ion-pair extraction and gas chromotography-mass spectrometry', *Journal of Pharmaceutical and Biomedical Analysis,* Volume 47.

Chapter 14

1 **Xu, S et al** 2021. 'Hair chemicals may increase breast cancer risk: A meta-analysis of 210319 subjects from 14 studies', *Plos One,* Volume 16, Issue 2.
2 **U.S. Government Printing Office** 1978. 'Cancer-causing Chemicals: Safety of cosmetics and hair dyes', Washington.
3 Mintel 2021. 'Hair Colourants - UK'.
4 Bessegato, G et al 2018. 'Assessment of several advanced oxidation processes applied in the treatment of environmental concern constituents from a real hair dye wastewater', Journal of Environmental Chemical Engineering, Volume 6.
5 Manjunatha, B et al 2020. 'Herbul black henna (hair dye) causes cardiovascular defects in zebrafish (Danio rerio) embryo model', Environmental Science and Pollution Research, Volume 27.
6 Lellis, B et al 2019. 'Effects of textile dyes on health and the environment and bioremediation potential of living organisms', Biotechnology Research and Innovation, Volume 3, Issue 2.
7 Guerra, E et al 2018. 'Analysis of Dyes in Cosmetics: Challenges and Recent Developments'. Cosmetics, Volume 5, Issue 47.
8 Xu, S et al 2021. 'Hair chemicals may increase breast cancer risk: A meta-analysis of 210319 subjects from 14 studies'.
9 UK Cancer Research 2021. 'Cancer Statistics for the UK'.
10 'Counts reflect laboratory-confirmed cases and deaths, based on WHO case definitions unless stated otherwise, and include both domestic and repatriated cases. Case detection, definitions, testing strategies, reporting practice, and lag times (e.g. time to case notification, and time to reporting of deaths) differ between countries, territories and areas. These factors, amongst others, influence the counts presented with variable under or overestimation of true case and death counts, and variable delays to reflecting these data at a global level.' Data accessed 16th August 2021. See World Health Organisation 2021. 'WHO Coronavirus (COVID-19) Dashboard: United Kingdom' <https://covid19.who.int/region/euro/country/gb>.